Solutions Manual

Intermediate
Counting and Probability

David Patrick
Naoki Sato
Art of Problem Solving

Art of Problem Solving

Books • Online Classes • Videos • Interactive Resources

www.artofproblemsolving.com

Published by: AoPS Incorporated
                 15330 Avenue of Science
                 San Diego, CA 92128
                 (858) 675-4555
                 books@artofproblemsolving.com

ISBN-13: 978-1-934124-07-9

Visit the Art of Problem Solving website at http://www.artofproblemsolving.com

 Scan this code with your mobile device to visit the Art of Problem Solving website, to view our other books, our free videos and interactive resources, our online community, and our online school.

Cover image designed by Vanessa Rusczyk using KaleidoTile software.

Printed in the United States of America.

Printed in 2022.

Contents

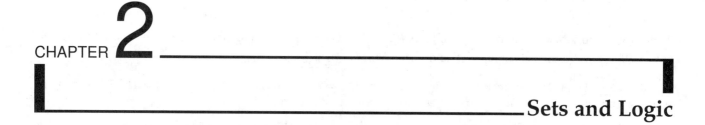

CHAPTER 2

Sets and Logic

Exercises for Section 2.2

2.2.1 $\boxed{\text{No}}$. The set $\emptyset$ is the empty set, and it does not contain any elements. However, the set $\{\emptyset\}$ contains one element, namely the empty set. Hence, the two sets are not equal.

2.2.2

(a) $\boxed{\text{True}}$. The number 3 is an element of $\{1, 3, 5, 9\}$.

(b) $\boxed{\text{True}}$. Neither the order of the elements, nor the fact that an element appears twice in the list, is significant. Elements can be listed in any order, and duplicate elements can be ignored.

(c) $\boxed{\text{False}}$. The set $\{5\}$ is not an element of $\{3, 5, 9\}$. Rather, the set $\{5\}$ is a subset of $\{3, 5, 9\}$, and the number 5 is an element of $\{3, 5, 9\}$.

(d) $\boxed{\text{False}}$. The number 4 is not an element of $\{\{4\}\}$. Rather, the set $\{4\}$ is an element of $\{\{4\}\}$ (in fact, it's the only element).

(e) $\boxed{\text{True}}$. The empty set is a proper subset of $\{1, 2, 9\}$. In fact, $\emptyset$ is a subset of any set, and is a proper subset of any non-empty set.

(f) $\boxed{\text{True}}$. The empty set is an element of $\{\emptyset, \{1\}, 82\}$.

(g) $\boxed{\text{True}}$. The set $\{x \mid x \text{ is an even integer}\}$ is the set of even integers, so it is a subset of the set of integers. Furthermore, not all integers are even, so it is a proper subset.

2.2.3 If x is an element of A, then x is an element of A. In other words, every element of A is in A, so $A \subseteq A$.

2.2.4 If $A \subseteq B$, then every element in A is also in B. And if $B \subseteq A$, then every element in B is also in A. Therefore, the sets A and B must contain the same elements, so $A = B$.

2.2.5 If $A \subseteq B$, then every element in A is an element of B. And if $B \subseteq C$, then every element in B is an element of C. Therefore, every element in A is an element of C, which means that $A \subseteq C$. Hence, the subset relationship is transitive.

If $A \subset B$ and $B \subset C$, then by the same argument as above, $A \subseteq C$. Furthermore, since B is a proper subset of C, there is an element x in C that is not in B, which means that x is not in A either. Therefore, A is a proper subset of C, that is, $A \subset C$. So the proper subset relationship is also transitive.

2.2.6 If $B \subseteq \emptyset$, then every element in B is also an element of the empty set. However, the empty set contains no elements, which means that B also contains no elements, so B must be the empty set.

2.2.7 If $A \subseteq B$, then every element in A is also an element of B, which means that the set B must contain at least as many elements as A, so $\#(A) \leq \#(B)$. In addition, if $\#(A) = \#(B)$, then every element of B must also be an element in A, so the sets A and B are equal, that is, $A = B$.

If $A \subset B$, then every element in A is also an element of B. However, since A is a proper subset of B, there is an element of B that is not in A, so $\#(A) < \#(B)$, or equivalently $\#(A) \leq \#(B) - 1$.

2.2.8   If $A \subset B$ and $B \subset A$, then because the proper subset relationship is transitive, $A \subset A$. However, A is not a proper subset of itself because it is equal to itself, so it is impossible for two sets A and B to simultaneously satisfy $A \subset B$ and $B \subset A$.

2.2.9   By definition, $\mathcal{P}(X)$ is the set of all subsets of X. The empty set has only one subset, namely itself, so $\mathcal{P}(\emptyset) = \{\emptyset\}$. Then the subsets of $\{\emptyset\}$ are $\emptyset$ and $\{\emptyset\}$, so $\mathcal{P}(\mathcal{P}(\emptyset)) = \boxed{\{\emptyset, \{\emptyset\}\}}$.

2.2.10   If S is the empty set, then $\#(S) = \#(\emptyset) = 0$, and $\mathcal{P}(S) = \mathcal{P}(\emptyset) = \{\emptyset\}$, so $\#(\mathcal{P}(S)) = \#(\{\emptyset\}) = 1 = 2^0$. Hence, the result is true when S is the empty set. Otherwise, S contains at least one element.

Let x be an element of S. Then for any subset of S, either x is in the subset, or x is not in the subset. Thus, we can construct a subset of S as follows: For each of element of S, we choose whether to include the element in the subset or not. So for each element, there are two possible choices, and there are n elements. Furthermore, each combination of choices leads to a different subset, so the number of subsets of S is $\#(\mathcal{P}(S)) = 2^n$.

Exercises for Section 2.3

2.3.1   The set $A \cup \emptyset$ is the set of elements that are in either A or the empty set, and the set $A \cap \emptyset$ is the set of elements that are in both A and the empty set. The empty set contains no elements, so $\boxed{A \cup \emptyset = A}$ and $\boxed{A \cap \emptyset = \emptyset}$.

2.3.2   The set $A \cup A$ is the set of elements that are either in either A or A, and the set $A \cap A$ is the set of elements that are in both A and A. The sets A and A contain the same elements, so $A \cap A = A \cup A = A$.

2.3.3   The set $S \cup \{x\}$ is the set of elements that are either in either S or $\{x\}$, and the set $S \cap \{x\}$ is the set of elements that are in both S and $\{x\}$. Since x is an element of S, and x is the only element of $\{x\}$, we conclude that $\boxed{S \cup \{x\} = S}$ and $\boxed{S \cap \{x\} = \{x\}}$.

2.3.4   Let $x \in A \cup (B \cap C)$, so x is in either A or $B \cap C$. If x is in A, then x is in both $A \cup B$ and $A \cup C$, so x is in $(A \cup B) \cap (A \cup C)$. If x is in $B \cap C$, then x is in both B and C, which means that x is in both $A \cup B$ and $A \cup C$, so x is in $(A \cup B) \cap (A \cup C)$. Either way, $x \in (A \cup B) \cap (A \cup C)$.

Now, let $x \in (A \cup B) \cap (A \cup C)$, so x is in both $A \cup B$ and $A \cup C$. If x is in A, then x is in $A \cup (B \cap C)$. If x is not in A, then x must be in B (since $x \in A \cup B$), and x must be in C (since $x \in A \cup C$). Therefore, x is in $B \cap C$, which means that x is in $A \cup (B \cap C)$. Either way, $x \in A \cup (B \cap C)$.

Therefore, $A \cup (B \cap C) = (A \cup B) \cap (A \cup C)$.

2.3.5

(a)   The condition $A \cup B = A$ implies that every element that is in either A or B is in A. Hence, B is a subset of A, or $\boxed{B \subseteq A}$.

(b)   The condition $A \cap B = A$ implies that every element that is in both A and B is in A. Hence, A is a subset of B, or $\boxed{A \subseteq B}$.

2.3.6   Suppose that $A \in \mathcal{P}(S \cap T)$, which means that $A \subseteq (S \cap T)$. Then every element of A is an element of $S \cap T$, which means that every element of A is an element of S and an element of T. This means that $A \subseteq S$ and $A \subseteq T$, which means that $A \in \mathcal{P}(S)$ and $A \in \mathcal{P}(T)$. Therefore, $A \in (\mathcal{P}(S) \cap \mathcal{P}(T))$.

The same argument runs in reverse. Suppose that $A \in (\mathcal{P}(S) \cap \mathcal{P}(T))$. This means that $A \in \mathcal{P}(S)$ and $A \in \mathcal{P}(T)$, which means that $A \subseteq S$ and $A \subseteq T$. But then every element of A is an element of S and an element of T, which means that every element of A is an element of $S \cap T$. Therefore, $A \subseteq (S \cap T)$, which means that $A \in \mathcal{P}(S \cap T)$.

This shows that $\boxed{\mathcal{P}(S \cap T) = \mathcal{P}(S) \cap \mathcal{P}(T)}$.

This might lead you to conjecture that $\mathcal{P}(S \cup T) = \mathcal{P}(S) \cup \mathcal{P}(T)$. However, this is not true; for example, if $S = \{1\}$ and $T = \{2\}$, then $\mathcal{P}(S \cup T) = \{\emptyset, \{1\}, \{2\}, \{1, 2\}\}$, whereas $\mathcal{P}(S) \cup \mathcal{P}(T) = \{\emptyset, \{1\}, \{2\}\}$. It is true that

$$(\mathcal{P}(S) \cup \mathcal{P}(T)) \subseteq \mathcal{P}(S \cup T).$$

We will leave it as an exercise to prove this, and to determine the conditions for them to be equal.

Exercises for Section 2.4

2.4.1

(a) This is a statement. (It is a false statement, but it is a statement.)

(b) This is a statement. (The fact that you probably don't know whether it is true or false doesn't mean that it's not a statement. As it turns out, it is a true statement.)

(c) This is an opinion, not a statement.

(d) This is a a statement.

(e) This is a question, not a statement.

(f) This is a mathematical expression, not a statement.

2.4.2 We construct the following truth table:

p	not p	p or (not p)
T	F	T
F	T	T

We see that the statement p or (not p) is always true.

2.4.3 We construct the following truth table:

p	q	$p \wedge q$	$\neg(p \wedge q)$	$\neg p$	$\neg q$	$(\neg p) \vee (\neg q)$
T	T	T	**F**	**F**	**F**	**F**
T	F	F	**T**	**F**	**T**	**T**
F	T	F	**T**	**T**	**F**	**T**
F	F	F	**T**	**T**	**T**	**T**

Hence, the statements $\neg(p \wedge q)$ and $(\neg p) \vee (\neg q)$ are always either both true or both false.

2.4.4 We construct the following truth table:

p	q	$p \Rightarrow q$	$\neg p$	$(\neg p) \vee q$	$(p \Rightarrow q) \Leftrightarrow ((\neg p) \vee q)$
T	T	T	F	T	T
T	F	F	F	F	T
F	T	T	T	T	T
F	F	T	T	T	T

Hence, the statement $(p \Rightarrow q) \Leftrightarrow ((\neg p) \vee q)$ is true for all statements p and q.

2.4.5

(a) The statement "If $x = 3$, then $x + 2 = 5$" is true. The converse is "If $x + 2 = 5$, then $x = 3$," which is also true, and the contrapositive is "If $x + 2 \neq 5$, then $x \neq 3$," which is true.

(b) The statement "If $y^2 - 3y + 2 = 0$, then $y = 1$" is false, because if $y = 2$, then $y^2 - 3y + 2 = 2^2 - 3 \cdot 2 + 2 = 0$, but y is not equal to 1. The converse is "If $y = 1$, then $y^2 - 3y + 2 = 0$," which is true, and the contrapositive is "If $y \neq 1$, then $y^2 - 3y + 2 \neq 0$," which is false (again, because of the counterexample $y = 2$).

(c) The statement "If $A \subseteq B$, then $A \cap B = A$" is true. If $x \in A \cap B$, then $x \in A$, and if $x \in A$, then $x \in B$ (since $A \subseteq B$), so $x \in A \cap B$. Hence, $A \cap B = A$. The converse is "If $A \cap B = A$, then $A \subseteq B$," which is true (see Exercise 2.3.5(b)), and the contrapositive is "If $A \cap B \neq A$, then $A \not\subseteq B$," which is true.

(d) The statement "If Paris is the capital of France and London is the capital of Japan, then Washington is the capital of the United States" is true. London is not the capital of Japan, so the condition "Paris is the capital of France and London is the capital of Japan" is false, and any statement follows from a false condition.

  The converse is "If Washington is the capital of the United States, then Paris is the capital of France and London is the capital of Japan," which is false, and the contrapositive is "If Washington is not the capital of the United States, then Paris is the not the capital of France or London is not the capital of Japan," which is true.

(e) The statement "If WXY is an equilateral triangle, then $WX = XY = YW$" is true. The converse is "If $WX = XY = YW$, then WXY is an equilateral triangle," which is true, and the contrapositive is "If WX, XY, and YW are not all equal, then WXY is not an equilateral triangle," which is true.

2.4.6

(a) We construct the following truth table:

p	q	r	$q \wedge r$	$p \vee (q \wedge r)$	$p \vee q$	$p \vee r$	$(p \vee q) \wedge (p \vee r)$	$(p \vee (q \wedge r)) \Leftrightarrow ((p \vee q) \wedge (p \vee r))$
T	T	T	T	T	T	T	T	T
T	T	F	F	T	T	T	T	T
T	F	T	F	T	T	T	T	T
T	F	F	F	T	T	T	T	T
F	T	T	T	T	T	T	T	T
F	T	F	F	F	T	F	F	T
F	F	T	F	F	F	T	F	T
F	F	F	F	F	F	F	F	T

Hence, the statement $(p \vee (q \wedge r)) \Leftrightarrow ((p \vee q) \wedge (p \vee r))$ is always true.

(b) We claim that $(p \wedge (q \vee r)) \Leftrightarrow ((p \wedge q) \vee (p \wedge r))$. To prove this, we construct the following truth table:

p	q	r	$q \vee r$	$p \wedge (q \vee r)$	$p \wedge q$	$p \wedge r$	$(p \wedge q) \vee (p \wedge r)$	$(p \wedge (q \vee r)) \Leftrightarrow ((p \wedge q) \vee (p \wedge r))$
T	T	T	T	T	T	T	T	T
T	T	F	T	T	T	F	T	T
T	F	T	T	T	F	T	T	T
T	F	F	F	F	F	F	F	T
F	T	T	T	F	F	F	F	T
F	T	F	T	F	F	F	F	T
F	F	T	T	F	F	F	F	T
F	F	F	F	F	F	F	F	T

Hence, $(p \wedge (q \vee r)) \Leftrightarrow ((p \wedge q) \vee (p \wedge r))$.

2.4.7 We claim that $(p \uparrow p) \uparrow (q \uparrow q)$ is equivalent to $p \vee q$. To prove this, we construct the following truth table:

p	q	$p \uparrow p$	$q \uparrow q$	$(p \uparrow p) \uparrow (q \uparrow q)$
T	T	F	F	T
T	F	F	T	T
F	T	T	F	T
F	F	T	T	F

Hence, $(p \uparrow p) \uparrow (q \uparrow q)$ is equivalent to $p \vee q$.

Exercises for Section 2.5

2.5.1 If $p(x)$ is true for some $x \in S$, then the first statement is true and the second statement is false. Otherwise, $p(x)$ is false for all $x \in S$, which means that the first statement is false and the second statement is true.

2.5.2 One option is to choose a statement $p(x, y)$ that does not depend on y at all. For instance, let $p(x, y)$ denote the statement "$x \geq 0$." Then the first statement from the problem becomes "There exists an integer x such that for all integers y, $x \geq 0$." This statement is seen to be true by taking any integer $x \geq 0$. The second statement from the problem becomes "For all integers x, there exists an integer y such that $x \geq 0$." This statement is seen to be false by taking any integer $x < 0$.

Another option is to choose a statement that can never be true except for a particular value of x. For instance, let $p(x, y)$ denote the statement $(x - 1)(y - 0.5) = 0$. Then the first quantified statement is true, since for $x = 1$, the statement is true for any integer y. On the other hand, the second quantified statement is false, since for an arbitrary integer x with $x \neq 1$, there is no integer y making the product zero.

Review Problems

2.8

(a)

$$D = \boxed{\{9, 19, 29\}},$$

$$P = \boxed{\{2, 3, 5, 7, 11, 13, 17, 19, 23, 29\}},$$

$$U = \boxed{\{1, 5, 9, 13, 17, 21, 25, 29\}},$$

$$V = \boxed{\{3, 7, 11, 15, 19, 23, 27\}},$$

$$W = \boxed{\{2, 6, 10, 14, 18, 22, 26, 30\}},$$

$$D \cap U = \boxed{\{9, 29\}},$$

$$P \cap W = \boxed{\{2\}},$$

$$S \setminus P = \boxed{\{1, 4, 6, 8, 9, 10, 12, 14, 15, 16, 18, 20, 21, 22, 24, 25, 26, 27, 28, 30\}},$$

$$P \setminus (D \cup V) = P \setminus \{3, 7, 9, 11, 15, 19, 23, 27, 29\}$$

$$= \boxed{\{2, 5, 13, 17\}}.$$

(b) We have that $P \cap U = \{5, 13, 17, 29\}$, so $\#(P \cap U) = 4$, and $P \cap V = \{3, 7, 11, 19, 23\}$, so $\#(P \cap V) = 5$. Hence, $\boxed{\#(P \cap V)}$ is greater.

2.9

(a) The set $\{x^2 \mid x \in T\}$ is the set of elements obtained by squaring the elements in T, so

$$\{x^2 \mid x \in T\} = \boxed{\{0, 1, 4, 9, 16, 25\}}.$$

(b) The set $\{x \in \mathbb{Z} \mid x^2 \in T\}$ is the set of integers that, when squared, become an element in T, so

$$\{x \in \mathbb{Z} \mid x^2 \in T\} = \boxed{\{-2, -1, 0, 1, 2\}}.$$

2.10   The answer is $\boxed{\text{no}}$. For example, let $A = \{1, 2\}$, $B = \{3, 4\}$, and $C = \{1, 2\}$. Then $A \cap B = B \cap C = \emptyset$, but $A = C$, so $A \cap C = A = \{1, 2\}$. So it is not necessarily true that $A \cap C = \emptyset$. In fact, we cannot say anything definitive about A and C.

2.11   The answer to both questions is $\boxed{\text{yes}}$:

(a)   The condition $A \cup B = B$ implies that every element that is in either A or B is in B. Hence, A is a subset of B, or $A \subseteq B$. The statement is $\boxed{\text{true}}$.

(b)   The condition $A \cap B = A$ implies that every element that is in both A and B is in A. Hence, A is a subset of B, or $A \subseteq B$. The statement is $\boxed{\text{true}}$.

2.12   The set $A \setminus B$ is obtained by starting with the set A and taking away all the elements that are in both A and B. Hence, if $A \setminus B = A$, then it means that A and B have no elements in common, that is, $A \cap B = \emptyset$.

2.13   Let $n = \#(A \setminus B) = \#(B \setminus A)$, and let $m = \#(A \cap B)$. The set $A \setminus B$ is obtained by starting with the set A and taking away all the elements that are in both A and B, so $n = \#(A) - m$, which implies that $\#(A) = m + n$. Similarly, $\#(B) = m + n$, so $\#(A) = \#(B)$.

2.14   We construct the following truth table:

p	q	r	$p \Rightarrow q$	$q \Rightarrow r$	$(p \Rightarrow q) \wedge (q \Rightarrow r)$	$p \Rightarrow r$	$((p \Rightarrow q) \wedge (q \Rightarrow r)) \Rightarrow (p \Rightarrow r)$
T	T	T	T	T	T	T	T
T	T	F	T	F	F	F	T
T	F	T	F	T	F	T	T
T	F	F	F	T	F	F	T
F	T	T	T	T	T	T	T
F	T	F	T	F	F	T	T
F	F	T	T	T	T	T	T
F	F	F	T	T	T	T	T

Hence, the statement $((p \Rightarrow q) \wedge (q \Rightarrow r)) \Rightarrow (p \Rightarrow r)$ is always true.

2.15   For all of these parts, slightly different phrases are possible.

(a)   Not everyone is a snob. (Note the "$\subset$" notation, as opposed to "$\subseteq$.")

(b)   Every mathematician is a scientist.

(c)   Every mathematician who has been to Mars has drunk a coffee.

(d)   Every person is either a scientist or has drunk a coffee.

(e)   All people who have taken a photo of themselves are snobs.

(f)   Every scientist has taken a photo of someone who has drunk a coffee.

(g)   There is a person who has drunk a coffee, such that every scientist has taken a photo of this person. (Note that this is different from the previous answer, because in this answer, the coffee drinker is the same for all scientists. Thus, the order of the universal quantifier and the existential quantifier makes a difference.)

2.16   For all of these parts, other equivalent answers are possible.

(a) $E \subseteq B$.

(b) $C \setminus B \neq \emptyset$. Another possible answer is $\exists x \in C, \neg(x \in B)$.

(c) $A \cap E \neq \emptyset$. Another possible answer is $\exists x \in A, x \in E$.

(d) $(D = U) \Rightarrow (C \subseteq E)$.

(e) $\forall x \in A, \exists y \in B, p(x, y)$.

(f) $(D \subseteq (B \cup C)) \wedge (D \cap B \cap C = \emptyset)$.

(g) $\forall x \in U, ((\forall y \in E, p(x, y)) \Rightarrow x \in C)$.

2.17

(a) Since the empty set contains no elements, the quantifier $\forall x \in \emptyset$ is not satisfied for any x. Therefore the statement "$\forall x \in \emptyset, p(x)$" is always $\boxed{\text{true}}$, since there is nothing to check (in other words, we don't have to plug x into $p(x)$, since there aren't any).

(b) Since the empty set contains no elements, the quantifier $\exists x \in \emptyset$ can never be satisfied. Therefore the statement "$\exists x \in \emptyset, p(x)$" is always $\boxed{\text{false}}$, since we can never find an x to satisfy $p(x)$.

Challenge Problems

2.18 We can intuitively see what's going on via a Venn Diagram. The top diagram at right shows $(A \cap B) \cup C$, and the bottom diagram shows $A \cap (B \cup C)$. We can see that these are equal if and only if the part of the first diagram that's in C but not in A is empty; that is, if and only if $C \subseteq A$.

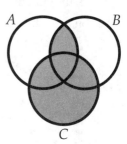

But to prove this formally, we will use a set theory and logic argument. First, we assume that $C \subseteq A$. We want to show that the sets $(A \cap B) \cup C$ and $A \cap (B \cup C)$ are equal.

Let $x \in (A \cap B) \cup C$, so $x \in A \cap B$ or $x \in C$. If $x \in A \cap B$, then $x \in A$ and $x \in B$, so $x \in B \cup C$, and it follows that $x \in A \cap (B \cup C)$. If $x \in C$, then $x \in B \cup C$, and also $x \in A$ (since $C \subseteq A$), so it follows that $x \in A \cap (B \cup C)$. Either way, $x \in A \cap (B \cup C)$.

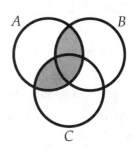

Now, let $x \in A \cap (B \cup C)$, so $x \in A$ and $x \in B \cup C$, which implies that $x \in B$ or $x \in C$. If $x \in B$, then $x \in A \cap B$, so $x \in (A \cap B) \cup C$. If $x \in C$, then $x \in (A \cap B) \cup C$. Either way, $x \in (A \cap B) \cup C$.

We conclude that if $C \subseteq A$, then $(A \cap B) \cup C = A \cap (B \cup C)$.

Now, assume that $(A \cap B) \cup C = A \cap (B \cup C)$. We want to show that $C \subseteq A$.

Let $x \in C$. Then $x \in (A \cap B) \cup C$, so $x \in A \cap (B \cup C)$. It follows that $x \in A$. In other words, every element in C is also in A, so $C \subseteq A$.

2.19

(a) The union of two intervals is not always an interval. For example, the union of the intervals [0,1] and [2,3] is clearly not an interval.

(b) The intersection of two intervals is always an interval. (In particular, the empty set is also an interval, so two intervals that do not intersect still have that their intersection, $\emptyset$, is an interval.)

To prove this, instead of trying to deal with the endpoints, it will be easier to work directly with the definition of an interval. Let I_1 and I_2 be two intervals, and let $I = I_1 \cap I_2$. Let x, y, and z be real numbers, such that $x \le y \le z$ and $x \in I$ and $z \in I$. Since $I = I_1 \cap I_2$, $x \in I_1$ and $x \in I_2$, and $z \in I_1$ and $z \in I_2$. Since I_1 is an interval and $x \le y \le z$, $y \in I_1$. Similarly, I_2 is an interval, so $y \in I_2$. Therefore, $y \in I_1 \cap I_2 = I$, which means that I is also an interval.

2.20

(a)   We construct the following truth table:

p	q	r	$p \oplus q$	$(p \oplus q) \oplus r$	$q \oplus r$	$p \oplus (q \oplus r)$
T	T	T	F	T	F	T
T	T	F	F	F	T	F
T	F	T	T	F	T	F
T	F	F	T	T	F	T
F	T	T	T	F	F	F
F	T	F	T	T	T	T
F	F	T	F	T	T	T
F	F	F	F	F	F	F

Hence, the statements $(p \oplus q) \oplus r$ and $p \oplus (q \oplus r)$ are equivalent.

(b)   We construct the following truth table:

p	q	r	$q \oplus r$	$p \wedge (q \oplus r)$	$p \wedge q$	$p \wedge r$	$(p \wedge q) \oplus (p \wedge r)$
T	T	T	F	F	T	T	F
T	T	F	T	T	T	F	T
T	F	T	T	T	F	T	T
T	F	F	F	F	F	F	F
F	T	T	F	F	F	F	F
F	T	F	T	F	F	F	F
F	F	T	T	F	F	F	F
F	F	F	F	F	F	F	F

Hence, the statements $p \wedge (q \oplus r)$ and $(p \wedge q) \oplus (p \wedge r)$ are equivalent.

2.21   First, to make the problem easier to understand, let's write the statement "$\forall x \in S, \exists y \in T, p(x,y)$" in plain English. This statement becomes "For all $x \in S$, there is a $y \in T$ such that $p(x,y)$."

We want to take the negative of this statement, which is "It is not true that for all $x \in S$, there is a $y \in T$ such that $p(x,y)$." (In general, putting the clause "It is not true that" before a statement is a useful way of taking its negative.) The rest of the problem is unwinding the logic of this statement.

If it is not true that for all $x \in S$, there is a $y \in T$ such that $p(x,y)$, then there exists an $x \in S$ that violates the condition. In other words, there is an $x \in S$ such that it is not true that there is a $y \in T$ such that $p(x,y)$. This is statement (iv).

For this particular $x \in S$, it must be the case that for all $y \in T$, $p(x,y)$ is not true. This is statement (ii).

Hence, statements $\boxed{\text{(ii) and (iv)}}$ are equivalent to the given statement.

2.22

(a)

$$A \ominus B = \{1,3,5,8,9,10\},$$
$$(A \ominus B) \ominus C = \{1,5,6,7,10\},$$
$$B \ominus C = \{2,3,4,5,6,8,10\},$$
$$A \ominus (B \ominus C) = \{1,5,6,7,10\}.$$

(b)   In general, $x \in A \ominus B$ if and only if x is in exactly one of the sets A and B. In other words, x is in A or x is in B, but not both. This is precisely the same way that the "exclusive or" operation works.

For an element x, let $p(x)$ denote the statement "$x \in A$," let $q(x)$ denote the statement "$x \in B$," and let $r(x)$ denote the statement "$x \in C$." Then $x \in A \ominus B$ if and only if the statement $p(x) \oplus q(x)$ is true, and then $x \in (A \ominus B) \ominus C$ if and only if the statement $(p(x) \oplus q(x)) \oplus r(x)$ is true.

Similarly, $x \in B \ominus C$ if and only if the statement $q(x) \oplus r(x)$ is true, and then $x \in A \ominus (B \ominus C)$ if and only if the statement $p(x) \oplus (q(x) \oplus r(x))$ is true.

However, by part (a) of Problem 2.20, the statements $(p(x) \oplus q(x)) \oplus r(x)$ and $p(x) \oplus (q(x) \oplus r(x))$ are equivalent. Hence, $x \in (A \ominus B) \ominus C$ if and only if $x \in A \ominus (B \ominus C)$, which means that $(A \ominus B) \ominus C = A \ominus (B \ominus C)$.

(c) The statement $p(x) \wedge (q(x) \oplus r(x))$ is true if and only if $x \in A \cap (B \ominus C)$, and the statement $(p(x) \wedge q(x)) \oplus (p(x) \wedge r(x))$ is true if and only if $x \in (A \cap B) \ominus (A \cap C)$. Since the statements $p(x) \wedge (q(x) \oplus r(x))$ and $(p(x) \wedge q(x)) \oplus (p(x) \wedge r(x))$ are equivalent, we conclude that $A \cap (B \ominus C) = (A \cap B) \ominus (A \cap C)$ for all sets A, B, and C.

CHAPTER **3**

_____A Piece of PIE

Exercises for Section 3.2

3.2.1 Let x be the number of dogs that are both big and very hairy. Then by PIE, the number of dogs that are either big or very hairy is $30 + 42 - x = 47$, so $x = \boxed{25}$.

3.2.2 First, we count the number of 10-digit binary numbers that start with two ones. The first two digits are determined, and then each of the remaining 8 digits can be 0 or 1, so there are 2^8 such binary numbers.

Next, we count the number of 10-digit binary numbers that end with two ones. The last two digits are determined. The first digit must be a 1, otherwise the number would not have 10 digits. Each of the remaining 7 digits can be 0 or 1, so there are 2^7 such binary numbers.

Finally, we count the number of 10-digit binary numbers that both start with two ones and end with two ones. The first two digits and the last two digits are determined, and then each of the remaining 6 digits can be 0 or 1, so there are 2^6 such binary numbers.

Therefore, by PIE, there are $2^8 + 2^7 - 2^6 = \boxed{320}$ 10-digit binary numbers that either start with two ones or end with two ones.

3.2.3 Let $x\%$ be the percentage of U.S. households that own both a DVD player and a computer. Then the percentage of U.S. households that own a DVD player but not a computer is $(80 - x)\%$, and the percentage of U.S. households that own a computer but not a DVD player is $(70 - x)\%$. Then by PIE, the percentage of U.S. households that own either a DVD player or a computer is $(80 - x)\% + (70 - x)\% + x\% = (150 - x)\%$.

Each of these percentages must be between 0% and 100%, giving us the ranges:

$$
\begin{array}{rcl}
0 \le x \le 100 & \Rightarrow & 0 \le x \le 100 \\
0 \le 80 - x \le 100 & \Rightarrow & -20 \le x \le 80 \\
0 \le 70 - x \le 100 & \Rightarrow & -30 \le x \le 70 \\
0 \le 150 - x \le 100 & \Rightarrow & 50 \le x \le 150
\end{array}
$$

So $50 \le x \le 70$. Therefore, the range of possible percentages of U.S. households that own both a DVD player and a computer is $\boxed{\text{between 50\% and 70\%}}$.

Intuitively, we can see that this answer makes sense. Clearly not more than 70% of households can own both, since only 70% own a computer. If everyone who owns a computer also owns a DVD player, then the 70% of households who own a computer will own both. On the other hand, if the 20% who do not own a DVD player and the 30% who do not own a computer are disjoint sets, then the remaining 50% of people will own both. There is no way fewer people can own both, because there is no way that more people cannot own one or the other.

3.2.4 Since $316^2 = 99,856$ and $317^2 = 100,489$, there are 316 positive integers less than 100,000 that are perfect squares. Since $46^3 = 97,336$ and $47^3 = 103,823$, there are 46 positive integers less than 100,000 that are perfect cubes.

A number is both a perfect square and a perfect cube if and only if it is a perfect sixth power. Since $6^6 = 46,656$ and $7^6 = 117,649$, there are 6 positive integers less than 100,000 that are both a perfect square and a perfect cube.

Therefore, by PIE, there are $316 + 46 - 6 = 356$ positive integers less than 100,000 that are either a perfect square or a perfect cube, which means there are $99,999 - 356 = \boxed{99,643}$ positive integers less than 100,000 that are neither a perfect square nor a perfect cube.

3.2.5   Given that there are 85 teachers and 25 have no children, there are $85 - 25 = 60$ teachers that have a son or a daughter.

Let x be the number of teachers that have both a son and a daughter. Then by PIE, there are $50 + 45 - x = 60$ teachers that have a son or a daughter. Therefore, $x = \boxed{35}$.

3.2.6   The product of two integers is even if and only at least one of the two integers is even. Thus, we seek the number of 9-digit numbers such that either the first digit is even or the last digit is even.

First, we count the number of 9-digit numbers such that the first digit is even. The possible first digits that are even are 2, 4, 6, and 8. (We do not count 0 since 0 cannot be the first digit of a number.) Each of the remaining 8 digits can be 10 possible values, so there are $4 \cdot 10^8$ such numbers.

Next, we count the number of 9-digit numbers such that the last digit is even. The possible last digits that are even are 0, 2, 4, 6, and 8. The first digit has nine possible values (again, we do not count 0), and each of the remaining 7 digits can be 10 possible values, so there are $5 \cdot 9 \cdot 10^7$ such numbers.

Finally, we count the number of 9-digit numbers such that both the first digit and the last digit are even. The possible first digits that are even are 2, 4, 6, and 8, and the possible last digits that are even are 0, 2, 4, 6, and 8. Each of the remaining 7 digits can be 10 possible values, so there are $4 \cdot 5 \cdot 10^7$ such numbers.

Therefore, by PIE, there are $4 \cdot 10^8 + 5 \cdot 9 \cdot 10^7 - 4 \cdot 5 \cdot 10^7 = \boxed{650,000,000}$ 9-digit numbers such that the product of the first digit and last digit is even.

3.2.7   We begin by assigning variables. Let f, s, and x be the number of students in French class, in Spanish Class, and in both classes, respectively. By PIE, there are $f + s - x$ students in either class, which means that there are $100 - (f + s - x) = 100 - f - s + x$ students in neither class.

There are twice as many students in the French class as in the Spanish class, so

$$f = 2s.$$

There are three times as many students in both classes as in neither class, so

$$x = 3(100 - f - s + x).$$

Substituting the first equation into the second, we get $x = 3(100 - 3s + x)$, so

$$s = \frac{2x + 300}{9}.$$

Since the number of students in neither class is less than 10, and x is 3 times the number of students in neither class, we have $x < 3 \cdot 10 = 30$. Checking the range of integers $0 \leq x < 30$, the only values of x that produce an integer value of s are $x = 3, 12$, and 21. Finally, we are given that the number of students in both classes (that is, x) is even, so we must have $x = 12$, and the number of students taking Spanish is $s = (2x + 300)/9 = 324/9 = \boxed{36}$.

Exercises for Section 3.3

3.3.1 Let B, G, and W be the sets of dogs that have won a blue ribbon, green ribbon, and white ribbon, respectively. Then by PIE, the number of dogs that have learned at least one trick is

$$\#(B \cup G \cup W) = \#(B) + \#(G) + \#(W) - \#(B \cap G) - \#(B \cap W) - \#(G \cap W) + \#(B \cap G \cap W)$$
$$= 73 + 39 + 62 - 21 - 41 - 28 + 14$$
$$= 98.$$

Therefore, there are $100 - 98 = \boxed{2}$ dogs that have not learned any tricks.

3.3.2 Let W_1, W_2, and W_3 be the sets of three-letter words, such that the first letter, second letter, and third letter is an A, respectively. Then by PIE, the number of three-letter words that have at least one A is

$$\#(W_1 \cup W_2 \cup W_3) = \#(W_1) + \#(W_2) + \#(W_3) - \#(W_1 \cap W_2) - \#(W_1 \cap W_3) - \#(W_2 \cap W_3) + \#(W_1 \cap W_2 \cap W_3).$$

First we count $\#(W_1)$, the number of three-letter words where the first letter is an A. The second and third letter can be any letters, so $\#(W_1) = 26^2$. Similarly, $\#(W_2) = \#(W_3) = 26^2$.

Next we count $\#(W_1 \cap W_2)$, the number of three-letter words where the first and second letters are A's. The third letter can be any letter, so $\#(W_1 \cap W_2) = 26$. Similarly, $\#(W_1 \cap W_3) = \#(W_2 \cap W_3) = 26$.

Finally, a word is in $W_1 \cap W_2 \cap W_3$ if and only if all three letters are A's, so $\#(W_1 \cap W_2 \cap W_3) = 1$. Therefore, the number of three-letter words that have at least one A is

$$\#(W_1 \cup W_2 \cup W_3) = 3 \cdot 26^2 - 3 \cdot 26 + 1 = \boxed{1951}.$$

Alternatively, we could have found the answer by using complementary counting. If a word does not have at least one A, then it does not have any As. The number of three-letter words that do not have any A's is 25^3, so the number of three-letter words that have at least one A is $26^3 - 25^3 = 1951$.

3.3.3 Let F, B, and L be the sets of seniors who are on the football team, baseball team, and lacrosse team, respectively. Let x be the number of seniors on all three teams. Then the number of students on the lacrosse team is $2x$.

By PIE,
$$\#(F \cup B \cup L) = \#(F) + \#(B) + \#(L) - \#(F \cap B) - \#(F \cap L) - \#(B \cap L) + \#(F \cap B \cap L).$$

Substituting, we get $85 = 74 + 26 + 2x - 18 - 17 - 13 + x$, so $3x = 33$, or $x = \boxed{11}$.

3.3.4 Let A, B, and C be the outcomes in which the first two coins, middle two coins, and last two coins (respectively) come up tails. Note that $\#(A) = \#(B) = \#(C) = 4$, since for each of these outcomes, we have 2 possibilities for the other two flips.

Outcomes in $A \cap B$ have the first three flips come up tails, so there are 2 such outcomes (depending on whether the 4th flip is heads or tails). Similarly, outcomes in $B \cap C$ have the last three flips come up tails, so there are 2 such outcomes. However, outcomes in $A \cap C$ have all four flips come up tails, so there is only 1 such outcome. Lastly, outcomes in $A \cap B \cap C$ also have all four flips tails, so there is only 1 such outcome.

Therefore, by PIE, we have that the number of outcomes in $A \cup B \cup C$ (that is, the number of outcomes in which at least one pair of coins comes up tails) is $4 + 4 + 4 - 2 - 2 - 1 + 1 = 8$. Since there are $2^4 = 16$ total possible outcomes for the four flips, the probability of getting two consecutive tails is $\frac{8}{16} = \boxed{\frac{1}{2}}$.

Note that we can use PIE and symmetry to check our answer. We computed 8 outcomes with two consecutive tails. By symmetry, there should be 8 outcomes with two consecutive heads. We also know that there are 2 outcomes with both consecutive heads and consecutive tails (namely, HHTT and TTHH). So, by PIE, there are $8 + 8 - 2 = 14$ outcomes with consecutive heads or consecutive tails. And, indeed, there are only $16 - 14 = 2$ outcomes with no consecutive heads nor consecutive tails, namely HTHT and THTH.

3.3.5 Let $B, G,$ and W be the sets of dogs that have won a blue ribbon, green ribbon, and white ribbon, respectively. Let $x = \#(B) = \#(G) = \#(W)$ and $y = \#(B \cap G) = \#(B \cap W) = \#(G \cap W)$.

We can use PIE to count the number of dogs with at least one ribbon, which we know to be 180 (since every dog in the school has at least one ribbon). We get that

$$180 = (x + x + x) - (y + y + y) + 15 = 3x - 3y + 15,$$

so $x - y = 55$.

On the other hand, we can also count the number of dogs that have more than one ribbon. Each such dog has two or three ribbons. If we take the sum $\#(B \cap G) + \#(B \cap W) + \#(G \cap W)$, then we have counted each dog with two ribbons exactly once, but we have counted dogs with three ribbons three times, so the number of dogs with more than one ribbon is $y + y + y - 2 \cdot 15 = 3y - 30$.

Since each dog has at least one ribbon, the number of dogs with exactly one ribbon is $180 - (3y - 30) = 210 - 3y$. Therefore, $210 - 3y = 2(3y - 30)$, which means that $y = 30$. Combining this with $x - y = 55$ gives us $x = \boxed{85}$ dogs with any one ribbon, in particular a blue ribbon.

This problem can perhaps be more easily solved using the Venn Diagram shown at right. We can read off of the diagram that the total number of dogs is $3a + 3b + 15 = 180$, and that the relationship between dogs with 1 ribbon and dogs with 2 or more ribbons is $3b = 2(3a + 15)$. This solves to give $a = 15$ and $b = 40$, and the answer is then $b + 2a + 15 = 85$, as before.

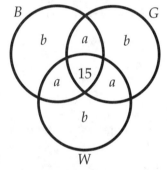

3.3.6 Let $S_1, S_2,$ and S_3 be the sets of 6-digit numbers that do not contain the digits 1, 2, and 3, respectively. Then by PIE, the number of 6-digit numbers that are missing at least one of the digits 1, 2, or 3 is

$$\#(S_1 \cup S_2 \cup S_3) = \#(S_1) + \#(S_2) + \#(S_3) - \#(S_1 \cap S_2) - \#(S_1 \cap S_3) - \#(S_2 \cap S_3) + \#(S_1 \cap S_2 \cap S_3).$$

First we count $\#(S_1)$, the number of 6-digit numbers that do not contain the digit 1. The first digit has 8 possible values (2 through 9), and each of the remaining 5 digits has 9 possible values, so $\#(S_1) = 8 \cdot 9^5$. Similarly, $\#(S_2) = \#(S_3) = 8 \cdot 9^5$.

Next we count $\#(S_1 \cap S_2)$, the number of 6-digit numbers that do not contain the digit 1 or 2. The first digit has 7 possible values (3 through 9), and each of the remaining 5 digits has 8 possible values, so $\#(S_1 \cap S_2) = 7 \cdot 8^5$. Similarly, $\#(S_1 \cap S_3) = \#(S_2 \cap S_3) = 7 \cdot 8^5$.

Finally, we count $\#(S_1 \cap S_2 \cap S_3)$, the number of 6-digit numbers that do not contain the digits 1, 2, or 3. The first digit has 6 possible values (4 through 9), and each of the remaining 5 digits has 7 possible values, so $\#(S_1 \cap S_2 \cap S_3) = 6 \cdot 7^5$.

Therefore, $\#(S_1 \cup S_2 \cup S_3) = 3 \cdot 8 \cdot 9^5 - 3 \cdot 7 \cdot 8^5 + 6 \cdot 7^5 = 829{,}890$. There are a total of $9 \cdot 10^5 = 900{,}000$ 6-digit numbers, so there are $900{,}000 - 829{,}890 = \boxed{70{,}110}$ 6-digit numbers that have at least one 1, one 2, and one 3.

Exercises for Section 3.4

3.4.1 Let W_1 and W_2 be the sets of arrangements of the letters of the word STRATA where the two As are consecutive, and the two Ts are consecutive, respectively. Then by PIE, the number of arrangements where either the two As are consecutive or the two Ts are consecutive is $\#(W_1 \cup W_2) = \#(W_1) + \#(W_2) - \#(W_1 \cap W_2)$.

First we count #(W_1), the number of arrangements where the two As are consecutive. We treat AA as a single block, and the remaining letters are one R, one S, and two Ts, so

$$\#(W_1) = \frac{5!}{2!} = 60.$$

Similarly, #(W_2) = 60.

Next we count #($W_1 \cap W_2$), the number of arrangements where the two As are consecutive and the two Ts are consecutive. We treat both AA and TT as single blocks, and the remaining letters are one R and one S, so #($W_1 \cap W_2$) = 4! = 24. Therefore, #($W_1 \cup W_2$) = 60 + 60 − 24 = 96.

The word STRATA contains two As, one R, one S, and two Ts, so there are a total of

$$\frac{6!}{2!2!} = 180$$

arrangements of the letters. Hence, there are 180 − 96 = $\boxed{84}$ arrangements where the two As are nonconsecutive and the two Ts are nonconsecutive.

3.4.2 First, we factor 126 = $2 \cdot 3^2 \cdot 7$. Thus, a number is relatively prime to 126 if and only if it is not divisible by 2, 3, or 7.

We can now follow the solution to Problem 3.8. There are 210 positive integers less than 211. Then by PIE, the number of positive integers less than or equal to 210 that are divisible by at least one of 2, 3, or 7 is

$$\frac{210}{2} + \frac{210}{3} + \frac{210}{7} - \frac{210}{2 \cdot 3} - \frac{210}{2 \cdot 7} - \frac{210}{3 \cdot 7} + \frac{210}{2 \cdot 3 \cdot 7}$$
$$= 105 + 70 + 30 - 35 - 15 - 10 + 5$$
$$= 150,$$

which means that there are 210 − 150 = $\boxed{60}$ positive integers less than or equal to 210 that are relatively prime to 126.

3.4.3 Since 10 = $2 \cdot 5$ and 12 = $2^2 \cdot 3$, a positive integer is relatively prime to both 10 and 12 if and only if it is not divisible by any of 2, 3, or 5.

In general, for positive integers n and d, the number of positive integers from 1 to n that are multiples of d is $\lfloor n/d \rfloor$. There are 999 positive integers less than 1000. Therefore, by PIE, the number of positive integers from 1 to 999 that are divisible by at least one of 2, 3, or 5 is

$$\left\lfloor \frac{999}{2} \right\rfloor + \left\lfloor \frac{999}{3} \right\rfloor + \left\lfloor \frac{999}{5} \right\rfloor - \left\lfloor \frac{999}{2 \cdot 3} \right\rfloor - \left\lfloor \frac{999}{2 \cdot 5} \right\rfloor - \left\lfloor \frac{999}{3 \cdot 5} \right\rfloor + \left\lfloor \frac{999}{2 \cdot 3 \cdot 5} \right\rfloor$$
$$= 499 + 333 + 199 - 166 - 99 - 66 + 33$$
$$= 733.$$

Hence, there are 999 − 733 = $\boxed{266}$ positive integers from 1 to 999 that are relatively prime to both 10 and 12.

3.4.4 Let the letters A, B, and C denote a fan from Austin High School, Butler High School, and Central High School, respectively. Then we can think of a seating of the nine fans as an arrangement of the nine letters A, A, A, B, B, B, C, C, and C. We want to count the number of arrangements where no three of the same letter appear together.

Let S_A, S_B, and S_C be the sets of arrangements where the three letters A, B, and C appear together, respectively. Then by PIE, the number of arrangements where any of the three letters A, B, or C appear consecutively is

$$\#(S_A \cup S_B \cup S_C) = \#(S_A) + \#(S_B) + \#(S_C) - \#(S_A \cap S_B) - \#(S_A \cap S_C) - \#(S_B \cap S_C) + \#(S_A \cap S_B \cap S_C).$$

First we count $\#(S_A)$, the number of arrangements where the As are consecutive. We consider the three letters A as a single block. Then the number of arrangements of the single block AAA, three letter Bs, and three letter Cs is

$$\frac{7!}{1!3!3!} = 140.$$

Once the positions of the letters have been determined, the fans are distinguishable, so there are 3! ways to seat the fans from each school. Therefore, $\#(S_A) = 140 \cdot 3! \cdot 3! \cdot 3! = 30{,}240$. Similarly, $\#(S_B) = \#(S_C) = 30{,}240$.

Next we count $\#(S_A \cap S_B)$, the number of arrangements where the A's are consecutive and the B's are consecutive. We consider both the three letters A and the three letters B as a single block. Then the number of arrangements of the single block AAA, the single block BBB, and three letter Cs is

$$\frac{5!}{1!1!3!} = 20.$$

As before, there are 3! ways to seat the fans from each school, so $\#(S_A \cap S_B) = 20 \cdot 3! \cdot 3! \cdot 3! = 4{,}320$. Similarly, $\#(S_A \cap S_C) = \#(S_B \cap S_C) = 4{,}320$.

Finally, to count $\#(S_A \cap S_B \cap S_C)$, we consider the three letters A, the three letters B, and the three letters C each as a single block. Then the number of arrangements is 3!, so $\#(S_A \cap S_B \cap S_C) = 3! \cdot 3! \cdot 3! \cdot 3! = 1{,}296$.

Therefore,

$$\#(S_A \cup S_B \cup S_C) = 3 \cdot 30{,}240 - 3 \cdot 4{,}320 + 1{,}296 = 79{,}056.$$

There are a total of $9! = 362{,}880$ ways of seating the nine fans, which means that there are $362{,}880 - 79{,}056 = \boxed{283{,}824}$ ways of seating the nine fans so that no three fans of any high school are seated consecutively.

3.4.5 Let E, P, and S be the sets of enrollments where the economics class, psychology class, and sociology class is empty, respectively. Then by PIE, the number of possible enrollments where at least one of the classes is empty is

$$\#(E \cup P \cup S) = \#(E) + \#(P) + \#(S) - \#(E \cap P) - \#(E \cap S) - \#(P \cap S) + \#(E \cap P \cap S).$$

First we count $\#(E)$, the number of possible enrollments where the economics class is empty. This means each of the 15 students is in psychology or sociology. Hence, $\#(E) = 2^{15}$. Similarly, $\#(P) = \#(S) = 2^{15}$.

Next we count $\#(E \cap P)$, the number of possible enrollments where both the economics class and psychology class is empty. This means all 15 students are in the sociology class. Hence, $\#(E \cap P) = 1$. Similarly, $\#(E \cap S) = \#(P \cap S) = 1$.

Finally, the set $E \cap P \cap S$ is the set of enrollments where all three classes are empty. But every student is in some class, so $\#(E \cap P \cap S) = 0$.

Therefore, $\#(E \cup P \cup S) = 3 \cdot 2^{15} - 3 + 0$. The total number of possible enrollments is 3^{15}, so there are $\boxed{3^{15} - 3 \cdot 2^{15} + 3 = 14{,}250{,}606}$ possible enrollments where no class is empty.

Exercises for Section 3.5

3.5.1 We know that a number is relatively prime to 462 if it has no prime factors in common with 462. Therefore we start by determining the prime factorization of 462, which is $462 = 2 \times 3 \times 7 \times 11$. So we are looking for all of the positive integers less than 529 that do not have any of 2, 3, 7, or 11 as factors.

Thus our PIE expression is:

$$\text{\#'s with a factor of 2, 3, 7, or 11} = \left\lfloor \frac{528}{2} \right\rfloor + \left\lfloor \frac{528}{3} \right\rfloor + \left\lfloor \frac{528}{7} \right\rfloor + \left\lfloor \frac{528}{11} \right\rfloor$$

$$- \left(\left\lfloor \frac{528}{6} \right\rfloor + \left\lfloor \frac{528}{14} \right\rfloor + \left\lfloor \frac{528}{22} \right\rfloor + \left\lfloor \frac{528}{21} \right\rfloor + \left\lfloor \frac{528}{33} \right\rfloor + \left\lfloor \frac{528}{77} \right\rfloor \right)$$

$$+ \left(\left\lfloor \frac{528}{42} \right\rfloor + \left\lfloor \frac{528}{66} \right\rfloor + \left\lfloor \frac{528}{154} \right\rfloor + \left\lfloor \frac{528}{231} \right\rfloor \right)$$

$$- \left\lfloor \frac{528}{462} \right\rfloor$$

$$= (264 + 176 + 75 + 48) - (88 + 37 + 24 + 25 + 16 + 6) + (12 + 8 + 3 + 2) - 1$$

$$= 563 - 196 + 25 - 1 = 391.$$

Thus there are $528 - 391 = \boxed{137}$ positive integers less than 529 that are relatively prime to 462.

3.5.2 Let A_1, A_2, A_3, and A_4 be the sets of deals where the first, second, third, and fourth player receives a pair, respectively. Then by PIE, the number of hands where at least one player receives a pair is

$$\#(A_1 \cup A_2 \cup A_3 \cup A_4) = \#(A_1) + \#(A_2) + \#(A_3) + \#(A_4)$$

$$- \#(A_1 \cap A_2) - \#(A_1 \cap A_3) - \#(A_1 \cap A_4) - \#(A_2 \cap A_3) - \#(A_2 \cap A_4) - \#(A_3 \cap A_4)$$

$$+ \#(A_1 \cap A_2 \cap A_3) + \#(A_1 \cap A_2 \cap A_4) + \#(A_1 \cap A_3 \cap A_4) + \#(A_2 \cap A_3 \cap A_4)$$

$$- \#(A_1 \cap A_2 \cap A_3 \cap A_4).$$

First we count $\#(A_1)$, the number of ways the first player can receive a pair. There are four possible pairs (one for each denomination from 2 through 5), and the number of ways the remaining six cards can be dealt to the remaining three players is $\binom{6}{2}\binom{4}{2} = 90$, because we have $\binom{6}{2}$ choices for cards for the first remaining player, then $\binom{4}{2}$ choices for cards for the next remaining player. Therefore, $\#(A_1) = 4 \cdot 90 = 360$. Similarly, $\#(A_2) = \#(A_3) = \#(A_4) = 360$.

Next we count $\#(A_1 \cap A_2)$, the number of ways both the first player and second player can receive a pair. There are four possible pairs for the first player, then three possible pairs for the second player. Then the number of ways the remaining four cards can be dealt to the remaining two players is $\binom{4}{2} = 6$. Therefore, $\#(A_1 \cap A_2) = 4 \cdot 3 \cdot 6 = 72$. Similarly, $\#(A_1 \cap A_3) = \#(A_1 \cap A_4) = \#(A_2 \cap A_3) = \#(A_2 \cap A_4) = \#(A_3 \cap A_4) = 72$.

Finally, if three players receive a pair, then the fourth remaining player must also receive a pair. This can occur in $4! = 24$ ways. Therefore, $\#(A_1 \cap A_2 \cap A_3) = \#(A_1 \cap A_2 \cap A_4) = \#(A_1 \cap A_3 \cap A_4) = \#(A_2 \cap A_3 \cap A_4) = \#(A_1 \cap A_2 \cap A_3 \cap A_4) = 24$.

So the number of hands where at least one player receives a pair is

$$\#(A_1 \cup A_2 \cup A_3 \cup A_4) = 4 \cdot 360 - 6 \cdot 72 + 4 \cdot 24 - 24 = 1080.$$

The total number of possible hands is

$$\frac{8!}{2!2!2!2!} = 2520.$$

Hence, the probability that no player receives a pair is

$$1 - \frac{1080}{2520} = 1 - \frac{3}{7} = \boxed{\frac{4}{7}}.$$

Seeing a simple answer might make us wonder if there's a more direct solution, and there is. We will present just the highlights of the solution, and let you fill in the details.

We see that player #1 does not get a pair with probability $\frac{6}{7}$ (since for any first card that player #1 receives, 6 of the 7 remaining cards do not match it). Suppose without loss of generality that player #1 receives a 2 and a 3, and that a 4 is dealt to player #2. (Think about why we can make these assumptions.) The other 4 gets dealt to a different player with probability $\frac{4}{5}$, since there are 5 slots remaining for the 5 cards left in the deck. Now the deck is left with a 2, and 3, and the pair of 5's, and the probability that the pair doesn't get dealt to the remaining person is $\frac{5}{6}$. Therefore, the probability of no pair is $\frac{6}{7} \cdot \frac{4}{5} \cdot \frac{5}{6} = \frac{4}{7}$.

3.5.3 Let A, C, S, and R be the sets of seatings where two Americans, Canadians, Spaniards, and Russians sit in the same row, respectively. Then by PIE, the number of seatings where two people from at least one country sit in the same row is

$$\begin{aligned}
\#(A \cup C \cup S \cup R) = {} & \#(A) + \#(C) + \#(S) + \#(R) \\
& - \#(A \cap C) - \#(A \cap S) - \#(A \cap R) - \#(C \cap S) - \#(C \cap R) - \#(S \cap R) \\
& + \#(A \cap C \cap S) + \#(A \cap C \cap R) + \#(A \cap S \cap R) + \#(C \cap S \cap R) \\
& - \#(A \cap C \cap S \cap R).
\end{aligned}$$

We first count $\#(A)$, the number of seatings where two Americans sit in the same row. There are six rows to choose from. Once the row is chosen, there are $3 \cdot 2 = 6$ ways to seat two Americans in that row. There are 10! ways to seat the remaining 10 passengers. Hence, $\#(A) = 6 \cdot 6 \cdot 10! = 130,636,800$. Similarly, $\#(C) = \#(S) = \#(R) = 130,636,800$.

Next, we count $\#(A \cap C)$, the number of seatings where two Americans sit in the same row and two Canadians sit in the same row. Like before, there are six ways to choose the row for the two Americans, and $3 \cdot 2 = 6$ ways to seat two Americans in that row. There are then five ways to choose the row for the two Canadians, and $3 \cdot 2 = 6$ ways to seat the two Canadians in that row. There are 8! ways to seat the remaining 8 passengers. Hence, $\#(A \cap C) = 6 \cdot 6 \cdot 5 \cdot 6 \cdot 8! = 43,545,600$. Similarly, $\#(A \cap S) = \#(A \cap R) = \#(C \cap S) = \#(C \cap R) = \#(S \cap R) = 43,545,600$.

Next, we count $\#(A \cap C \cap S)$, the number of seatings where two Americans, two Canadians, and two Spaniards sit in the same row. There are six ways to choose the row for the two Americans, and $3 \cdot 2 = 6$ ways to seat two Americans in that row. There are then five ways to choose the row for the two Canadians, and $3 \cdot 2 = 6$ ways to seat the two Canadians in that row, and then four ways to choose the row for the Spaniards, and $3 \cdot 2 = 6$ ways to seat the two Spaniards in that row. There are 6! ways to seat the remaining 6 passengers. Hence, $\#(A \cap C \cap S) = 6 \cdot 6 \cdot 5 \cdot 6 \cdot 4 \cdot 6 \cdot 6! = 18,662,400$. Similarly, $\#(A \cap C \cap R) = \#(A \cap S \cap R) = \#(C \cap S \cap R) = 18,662,400$.

Finally, we count $\#(A \cap C \cap S \cap R)$, the number of seatings where two Americans, two Canadians, two Spaniards, and two Russians sit in the same row. Following the same technique as in the previous calculations, we find that $\#(A \cap C \cap S \cap R) = 6 \cdot 6 \cdot 5 \cdot 6 \cdot 4 \cdot 6 \cdot 3 \cdot 6 \cdot 4! = 11,197,440$.

Therefore, the number of seatings where two people from at least one country sit in the same row is

$$\#(A \cup C \cup S \cup R) = \binom{4}{1} \cdot 130,636,800 - \binom{4}{2} \cdot 43,545,600 + \binom{4}{3} \cdot 18,662,400 - 11,197,440 = 324,725,760.$$

The total number of seatings is $12! = 479,001,600$. Hence, the number of seatings where no two people from the same country sit in the same row is $479,001,600 - 324,725,760 = \boxed{154,275,840}$.

3.5.4 There are four 2×2 squares, one for each corner. Let A_1, A_2, A_3, and A_4 be the sets of colorings with a white 2×2 square in the upper-right, upper-left, lower-left, and lower-right corners, respectively. Then by PIE, the number of colorings with a white 2×2 square in some corner is

$$\begin{aligned}
\#(A_1 \cup A_2 \cup A_3 \cup A_4) = {} & \#(A_1) + \#(A_2) + \#(A_3) + \#(A_4) \\
& - \#(A_1 \cap A_2) - \#(A_1 \cap A_3) - \#(A_1 \cap A_4) - \#(A_2 \cap A_3) - \#(A_2 \cap A_4) - \#(A_3 \cap A_4) \\
& + \#(A_1 \cap A_2 \cap A_3) + \#(A_1 \cap A_2 \cap A_4) + \#(A_1 \cap A_3 \cap A_4) + \#(A_2 \cap A_3 \cap A_4) \\
& - \#(A_1 \cap A_2 \cap A_3 \cap A_4).
\end{aligned}$$

First we count $\#(A_1)$, the number of colorings where every square in the upper-right 2×2 square is white. There are four squares that are already white, leaving five squares that can be colored arbitrarily, so $\#(A_1) = 2^5 = 32$. Similarly, $\#(A_2) = \#(A_3) = \#(A_4) = 32$.

Next we count $\#(A_1 \cap A_2)$, the number of colorings where every square in the upper-right and upper-left 2×2 square is white. There are six squares that are already white, leaving three squares that can be colored arbitrarily, so $\#(A_1 \cap A_2) = 2^3 = 8$. Similarly, $\#(A_2 \cap A_3) = \#(A_3 \cap A_4) = \#(A_1 \cap A_4) = 8$.

However, counting $\#(A_1 \cap A_3)$ must be treated differently, as the upper-right and lower-left corners are opposite each other. In each of these colorings, there are seven squares that are already white, leaving two squares that can be colored arbitrarily, so $\#(A_1 \cap A_3) = 2^2 = 4$. Similarly, $\#(A_2 \cap A_4) = 4$.

Next, we count $\#(A_1 \cap A_2 \cap A_3)$, the number of colorings where every square in the upper-right, upper-left, and lower-left 2×2 square is white. For each one of these colorings, there are eight squares that are already white, leaving one square that can be colored arbitrarily, so $\#(A_1 \cap A_2 \cap A_3) = 2$. Similarly, $\#(A_1 \cap A_2 \cap A_4) = \#(A_1 \cap A_3 \cap A_4) = \#(A_2 \cap A_3 \cap A_4) = 2$.

Finally, $\#(A_1 \cap A_2 \cap A_3 \cap A_4) = 1$, because the only coloring in this set is the coloring where every square is white.

Hence,

$$\#(A_1 \cup A_2 \cup A_3 \cup A_4) = 4 \cdot 32 - (4 \cdot 8 + 2 \cdot 4) + 4 \cdot 2 - 1 = 95.$$

This counts the number of colorings that contain a 2×2 white square. There are a total of $2^9 = 512$ colorings. Therefore, the probability that a coloring does not contain a 2×2 white square is

$$1 - \frac{95}{512} = \boxed{\frac{417}{512}}.$$

Exercises for Section 3.6

3.6.1 First, 3150 factors as $2 \cdot 3^2 \cdot 5^2 \cdot 7$. So if n has at least three different prime factors in common with 3150, then n must be a multiple of $2 \cdot 3 \cdot 5 = 30, 2 \cdot 3 \cdot 7 = 42, 2 \cdot 5 \cdot 7 = 70$, or $3 \cdot 5 \cdot 7 = 105$.

There are $3150/30 = 105$ multiples of 30 that are less than or equal to 3150. Similarly, there are $3150/42 = 75$ multiples of 42, $3150/70 = 45$ multiples of 70, and $3150/105 = 30$ multiples of 105 that are less than or equal to 3150. However, every multiple of $2 \cdot 3 \cdot 5 \cdot 7 = 210$ is counted in each of these four numbers, so we must subtract $3 \cdot 3150/210 = 45$.

Therefore, the number of positive integers that are less than or equal to 3150 that have at least three different prime factors in common with 3150 is $105 + 75 + 45 + 30 - 45 = \boxed{210}$.

3.6.2

(a) To count the number of elements that belong to least two of the sets, we begin with the sum

$$\#(A \cap B) + \#(A \cap C) + \#(A \cap D) + \#(B \cap C) + \#(B \cap D) + \#(C \cap D).$$

This sum counts every element that appears in exactly two sets exactly once, but it also counts every element that appears in exactly three sets three times. (For example, if x is in $A \cap B \cap C$, then x is also in $A \cap B$, $A \cap C$, and $B \cap C$.) Hence, we subtract these elements twice to obtain the sum

$$\#(A \cap B) + \#(A \cap C) + \#(A \cap D) + \#(B \cap C) + \#(B \cap D) + \#(C \cap D)$$
$$- 2[\#(A \cap B \cap C) + \#(A \cap B \cap D) + \#(A \cap C \cap D) + \#(B \cap C \cap D)].$$

Now, this sum counts every element that appears in all four sets $6 - 2 \cdot 4 = -2$ times, so we must add these elements three times. Hence, the number of elements that appear in at least two sets is

$$\#(A \cap B) + \#(A \cap C) + \#(A \cap D) + \#(B \cap C) + \#(B \cap D) + \#(C \cap D)$$
$$- 2[\#(A \cap B \cap C) + \#(A \cap B \cap D) + \#(A \cap C \cap D) + \#(B \cap C \cap D)]$$
$$+ 3\#(A \cap B \cap C \cap D)$$
$$= 166 + 100 + 71 + 66 + 47 + 28 - 2(33 + 23 + 14 + 9) + 3 \cdot 4$$
$$= \boxed{332}.$$

(b) To count the number of elements that belong to exactly two of the sets, we again begin with the sum

$$\#(A \cap B) + \#(A \cap C) + \#(A \cap D) + \#(B \cap C) + \#(B \cap D) + \#(C \cap D).$$

As in part (a), this sum counts every element that appears in exactly two sets exactly once, but it also counts every element that appears in exactly three sets three times, so we subtract these elements three times to obtain the sum

$$\#(A \cap B) + \#(A \cap C) + \#(A \cap D) + \#(B \cap C) + \#(B \cap D) + \#(C \cap D)$$
$$- 3[\#(A \cap B \cap C) + \#(A \cap B \cap D) + \#(A \cap C \cap D) + \#(B \cap C \cap D)].$$

Now, this sum counts every element that appears in all four sets $6 - 3 \cdot 4 = -6$ times, so we must add these elements six times. Hence, the number of elements that appear in exactly two sets is

$$\#(A \cap B) + \#(A \cap C) + \#(A \cap D) + \#(B \cap C) + \#(B \cap D) + \#(C \cap D)$$
$$- 3[\#(A \cap B \cap C) + \#(A \cap B \cap D) + \#(A \cap C \cap D) + \#(B \cap C \cap D)]$$
$$+ 6\#(A \cap B \cap C \cap D)$$
$$= 166 + 100 + 71 + 66 + 47 + 28 - 3(33 + 23 + 14 + 9) + 6 \cdot 4$$
$$= \boxed{265}.$$

3.6.3 To slightly simplify the calculations, we'll say that each die has 3 equally-likely outcomes: one outcome is rolling a ⚀ or a ⚁, another outcome is rolling a ⚂ or a ⚃, and the third outcome (the one that we're focused on) is rolling a ⚄ or a ⚅. So there are $3^4 = 81$ equally-likely possible outcomes of rolling the four dice.

(a) There are $\binom{4}{3} = 4$ ways to choose three dice. Once we've chosen the three dice, there are 3 possible outcomes in which these three dice are ⚄ or greater, since the 4th die can be any of our 3 outcomes. This gives us an initial count of $4 \cdot 3 = 12$ successful outcomes. But we have counted the outcome in which all four dice are ⚄ or greater 4 times, once for each choice of three dice. Therefore, we must subtract this outcome 3 times, so that it is only counted once. Thus, there are $12 - 3 = 9$ successful outcomes, and hence the probability is $\frac{9}{81} = \boxed{\frac{1}{9}}.$

(b) The only one of the 9 outcomes from part (a) that we need to exclude is the outcome in which all four dice are ⚄ or greater. Thus, there are 8 successful outcomes, and the probability is $\boxed{\frac{8}{81}}.$

3.6.4 We need to make sure that every element that appears in at least two of the sets is counted exactly once by the large PIE expression. We proceed by cases, based on exactly how many of the sets a particular element is contained in.

Consider an element that appears in exactly two of the five sets, say A and B. This element is counted once in the term $A \cap B$, so it is counted p times in the expression. Hence, $p = 1$.

Now consider an element that appears in exactly three of the five sets, say A, B, and C. This element is also counted once in the terms $A \cap B$, $A \cap C$, $B \cap C$, and $A \cap B \cap C$, so it is counted $3p + q$ times in the expression. Hence, we need $3p + q = 1$, so $q = 1 - 3p = -2$.

Now consider an element that appears in exactly four of the five sets, say $A, B, C,$ and D. This element is also counted once in the terms $A \cap B, A \cap C, A \cap D, B \cap C, B \cap D, C \cap D, A \cap B \cap C, A \cap B \cap D, A \cap C \cap D, B \cap C \cap D,$ and $A \cap B \cap C \cap D$, so it is counted $6p + 4q + r$ times in the expression. Hence, we want $6p + 4q + r = 1$, giving $r = 1 - 6p - 4q = 1 - 6 + 8 = 3$.

Finally, if an element appears in all five sets, then it is counted $10p + 10q + 5r + s$ times in the expression. Then we must have $10p + 10q + 5r + s = 1$, so $s = 1 - 10p - 10q - 5r = 1 - 10 + 20 - 15 = -4$.

Therefore, the constants are $\boxed{p = 1, q = -2, r = 3, \text{ and } s = -4}$.

Exercises for Section 3.7

3.7.1 Label the six children $A, B, C, D, E,$ and F. For a given subset X of children, let S_X denote the set of arrangements where the children in X can be paired off, so that the children in each pair are chasing each other; for example, $S_{\{A,B,C,D\}}$ is the set of all arrangements in which the children A, B, C, D are paired off into two pairs, each of which is two children chasing each other.

Then by PIE, the number of arrangements where some pair of children are chasing each other is equal to:

$$\#(S_{\{A,B\}}) + \#(S_{\{A,C\}}) + \#(S_{\{A,D\}}) + \cdots + \#(S_{\{E,F\}})$$
$$- [\#(S_{\{A,B,C,D\}}) + \#(S_{\{A,B,C,E\}}) + \#(S_{\{A,B,C,F\}}) + \cdots + \#(S_{\{C,D,E,F\}})]$$
$$+ \#(S_{\{A,B,C,D,E,F\}}).$$

First we count $\#(S_{\{A,B\}})$, the number of arrangements where A and B are chasing each other. Each of the other four children have five children they can choose to chase, so $S_{\{A,B\}} = 5^4$. Similarly, $\#(S_{\{A,C\}}) = \#(S_{\{A,D\}}) = \cdots = \#(S_{\{E,F\}}) = 5^4$.

Next we count $\#(S_{\{A,B,C,D\}})$, the number of arrangements where the children $A, B, C,$ and D can be paired off so that the children in each pair are chasing each other. There are $\frac{1}{2!} \cdot \binom{4}{2} = 3$ ways to partition the four children into pairs. Each of the other two children have five children they can choose to chase, so $S_{\{A,B,C,D\}} = 3 \cdot 5^2$.

Finally, we count $\#(S_{\{A,B,C,D,E,F\}})$, the number of arrangements where all six children can be paired off so that the children in every pair are chasing each other. There are $\frac{1}{3!} \cdot \binom{6}{2}\binom{4}{2} = 15$ ways to partition the six children into pairs, so $\#(S_{\{A,B,C,D,E,F\}}) = 15$.

Therefore, the number of arrangements where some pair of children are chasing each other is equal to

$$\binom{6}{2} \cdot 5^4 - \binom{6}{4} \cdot 3 \cdot 5^2 + 15 = 8265.$$

There are a total of $5^6 = 15625$ arrangements. Therefore, the probability that some pair of children are chasing each other is

$$\frac{8265}{15625} = \boxed{\frac{1653}{3125}} \approx 52.9\%.$$

3.7.2 Label the vertices of the shaded square be $C, D, E,$ and F as shown in the diagram on the next page.

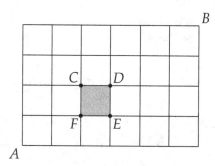

Let P_T, P_R, P_B, and P_L be the sets of paths that include the top edge, right edge, bottom edge, and left edge of the shaded square, respectively. Then by PIE, the number of paths that include an edge of the shaded square is

$$\#(P_T \cup P_R \cup P_B \cup P_L) = \#(P_T) + \#(P_R) + \#(P_B) + \#(P_L) - \#(P_R \cap P_B) - \#(P_T \cap P_L).$$

A path cannot include both the top edge and right edge, so the term $\#(P_T \cap P_R)$ and similar terms are not included in our PIE formula. Also it is not necessary to list the terms that are intersections of 3 or more sets, since no paths can pass through more than 2 of the sides of the shaded square.

First we count $\#(P_T)$. The set P_T can also be described as the set of paths that go from A to C to D to B. Point C is 2 units to the right and 2 units up from A, so there are $\binom{4}{2}$ paths from A to C. Point B is 3 units to the right and 2 units up from D, so there are $\binom{5}{3}$ paths from D to B. Therefore,

$$\#(P_T) = \binom{4}{2}\binom{5}{3} = 60.$$

Similarly,

$$\#(P_R) = \binom{4}{3}\binom{5}{3} = 40, \quad \#(P_B) = \binom{3}{2}\binom{6}{3} = 60, \quad \#(P_L) = \binom{3}{2}\binom{6}{4} = 45.$$

The set $P_R \cap P_B$ can be described as the set of paths that go from A to F to E to D to B. Hence,

$$\#(P_R \cap P_B) = \binom{3}{2}\binom{5}{3} = 30.$$

Similarly,

$$\#(P_T \cap P_L) = \binom{3}{2}\binom{5}{3} = 30.$$

Therefore, the number of paths that include an edge of the shaded square is $60 + 40 + 60 + 45 - 30 - 30 = \boxed{145}$.

Alternative Solution: A path from A to B that includes an edge of the shaded square must pass through exactly one of the points F, G, or H in the diagram below.

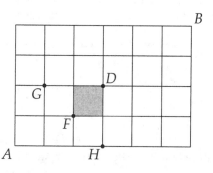

If such a path passes through H, then it must also pass through D. There is only one path from A to D via H, so the number of paths from A to B via H is equal to the number of paths from D to B, which is $\binom{5}{3} = 10$.

Similarly, if a path from A to B passes through G and a side of the shaded square, then it must also pass through D. There are $\binom{3}{1} = 3$ paths from A to G, and $\binom{5}{3} = 10$ paths from D to B, so there are $3 \cdot 10 = 30$ paths from A to B via G.

Finally, every path through F includes a side of the shaded square. There are $\binom{3}{2} = 3$ paths from A to F, and $\binom{7}{4} = 35$ paths from F to B, so there are $3 \cdot 35 = 105$ such paths.

Hence, the total number of paths that include an edge of the shaded square is $10 + 30 + 105 = \boxed{145}$.

3.7.3 First, we constructively count the number of pairs of subsets (A, B) such that B is contained in A. Consider any element $s \in S$. If $B \subseteq A$, then there are three possibilities: (1) s is in both A and B, (2) s is in A but not B, or (3) s is neither in A nor B. This gives us 3 choices for how to deal with s when we are constructing A and B. The same holds for the other five elements. Therefore, the number of pairs (A, B) with $B \subseteq A$ is 3^6.

We can similarly count the number of pairs of subsets (A, B) such that B is contained in $S \setminus A$, or equivalently, $A \cap B = \emptyset$. Again, there are three possible cases for each element $s \in S$: (1) s is in A but not B, (2) s is in B but not A, or (3) s is neither in A nor B. The same holds for the other five elements, so the number of such pairs (A, B) is again 3^6.

However, we must consider pairs (A, B) that appear in both counts. If (A, B) satisfies both $B \subseteq A$ and $B \subseteq (S \setminus A)$, then we also have $B \subseteq (A \cap (S \setminus A))$. But $A \cap (S \setminus A) = \emptyset$, so $B \subseteq \emptyset$. This can only happen if $B = \emptyset$. In this case, A can be any subset of S; hence, the number of pairs (A, B) that appear in both counts is just the number of subsets A of S, which is 2^6.

The total number of pairs of subsets (A, B) is $2^6 \cdot 2^6 = 2^{12}$, so the probability that B is contained in A or $S \setminus A$ is

$$\frac{2 \cdot 3^6 - 2^6}{2^{12}} = \boxed{\frac{697}{2048}}.$$

3.7.4 First, we count the number of pentagons with two particular edges of the n-gon as its sides. If the two edges are adjacent on the n-gon, then we must choose 2 of the remaining $(n-3)$ vertices to be the remaining two vertices of the pentagon. If the two edges are non-adjacent, then we must choose 1 of the remaining $(n-4)$ vertices to be the fifth vertex of the pentagon. There are n ways to choose two adjacent edges, and $\binom{n}{2} - n$ ways to choose two non-adjacent edges, so our initial count is

$$n\binom{n-3}{2} + \left(\binom{n}{2} - n\right)(n-4).$$

After a bit of algebra, this simplifies to $n(n-3)(n-4)$.

Next, we count the number of pentagons with three particular edges on the n-gon as its sides. If all three edges are adjacent, then we must choose 1 of the remaining $(n-4)$ vertices to complete the pentagon. Otherwise, two of the edges must be adjacent, and we must choose one of the remaining $n-4$ non-adjacent edges as the third edge. There are n ways to choose the original adjacent edges in either case, so this gives a total of

$$n(n-4+n-4) = 2n(n-4)$$

such pentagons.

Lastly, there are n pentagons with 4 sides on the n-gon.

Each pentagon with 3 sides on the n-gon is counted 3 times in our original count, so the count of pentagons with 3 edges must be subtracted twice. Each pentagon with 4 sides on the n-gon is counted 6 times in our original count, and then gets subtracted $2 \cdot 4$ times in second count, so it must be added back 3 times. Therefore, the PIE expression is

$$n(n-3)(n-4) - 2(2n(n-4)) + 3n = \boxed{n^3 - 11n^2 + 31n}.$$

As a check, we note that this should equal $\binom{n}{5}$ for all $6 \leq n \leq 8$, and plugging in $n = 6, 7, 8$ we see that it works.

3.7.5 (We use the same notation as in the problem.) Recall that we proved that $B \geq 10$. If no pair overlaps an area more than 1, then every pair of patches overlaps with area exactly 1, meaning that $B = 10$. Therefore, looking at equation (3.7.6) in the text, we see that $D - 2E = 0$, so $D = 2E$. But we also know that $D \geq 5E$, meaning that $2E \geq 5E$. Since $E \geq 0$, the only way that this can happen is if $E = 0$, meaning $D = 0$ as well. But that's what we wanted to prove: recall that D is the area covered by the intersection of sets of 4 patches, and we've shown that this is 0, so there is no point covered by more than 3 patches.

Review Problems

3.25 First we count words starting with a vowel. There are 5 choices for the first letter (since there are 5 vowels), and there are 26 choices for each of the other 3 letters, so there are $5 \cdot 26^3$ words that start with a vowel.

Using the same reasoning, there are $5 \cdot 26^3$ words that end with a vowel, and $5^2 \times 26^2$ words that start and end with a vowel.

Therefore, the number of words that start or end with a vowel is

$$2(5 \cdot 26^3) - (5^2 \cdot 26^2) = (260 - 25) \cdot (26^2) = \boxed{158,860}.$$

3.26 A 3-digit number has the form abc, where a is non-zero and b and c can be any digit.

First, we count the number of numbers where $a = b$. This common digit can be any digit from 1 through 9, and the digit c can be any digit, so there are $9 \cdot 10 = 90$ such numbers. Next, we count the number of numbers where $b = c$. This common digit can be any digit from 0 through 9, and the digit a can be any digit from 1 through 9, so again there are $10 \cdot 9 = 90$ such numbers.

Finally, the number of numbers where all digits are the same is 9. Therefore, by PIE, the number of 3-digit numbers that have two equal consecutive digits is $90 + 90 - 9 = \boxed{171}$.

3.27 From the given data, by PIE, there are $15 + 12 - 6 = 21$ ninth-graders that play either lacrosse or soccer. This is impossible, as there only 20 ninth-graders.

3.28 The probability that I forget my keys or my wallet is $20\% + 30\% - 5\% = 45\%$, so by PIE, the probability that I remember both my keys and my wallet is $100\% - 45\% = \boxed{55\%}$.

3.29

(a) Let S_1, S_2, and S_3 be the sets of four-letter words where the first and second letters, second and third letters, and third and fourth letters are identical, respectively. Then by PIE, the number of four-letter words with at least one pair of identical consecutive letters is

$$\#(S_1 \cup S_2 \cup S_3) = \#(S_1) + \#(S_2) + \#(S_3) - \#(S_1 \cap S_2) - \#(S_1 \cap S_3) - \#(S_2 \cap S_3) + \#(S_1 \cap S_2 \cap S_3).$$

First we count $\#(S_1)$, the number of four-letter words where the first and second letters are identical. There are 26 choices for this common letter. The third and fourth letters can be any letters, so $\#(S_1) = 26^3$. Similarly, $\#(S_2) = \#(S_3) = 26^3$.

Next, we count $\#(S_1 \cap S_2)$, the number of four-letter words where the first, second, and third letters are identical. There are 26 choices for this common letter. Then the fourth letter can be any letter, so $\#(S_1 \cap S_2) = 26^2$. Similarly, $\#(S_2 \cap S_3) = 26^2$.

The number $\#(S_1 \cap S_3)$ is the set of four-letter words where the first and second letters are identical, and the third and fourth letters are identical. There are 26 choices for the first common letter, and 26 choices for the second common letter, so $\#(S_1 \cap S_3) = 26^2$.

Finally, $S_1 \cap S_2 \cap S_3$ is the set of four-letter words where all letters are identical, so $\#(S_1 \cap S_2 \cap S_3) = 26$.

Therefore, the number of four-letter words with at least one pair of identical consecutive letters is

$$\#(S_1 \cup S_2 \cup S_3) = 3 \cdot 26^3 - 3 \cdot 26^2 + 26.$$

The total number of four-letter words is 26^4, so the number of four-letter words that do not contain a pair of identical consecutive letters is

$$26^4 - 3(26^3) + 3(26^2) - 26 = \boxed{406{,}250}.$$

(b) There are 26 choices for the first letter. Once the first letter is chosen, there are 25 choices for the second letter, then 25 choices for the third letter, then 25 choices for the fourth letter. Hence, there are $26 \cdot 25^3 = \boxed{406{,}250}$ such four-letter words.

(c) Factoring out a 26 from both answers, we claim that

$$26^3 - 3(26^2) + 3(26) - 1 = 25^3.$$

The left side of this expression is just the expansion of $(26 - 1)^3$, so clearly they are equal.

3.30 Let X be the set of 10-digit numbers where the first four digits are the same as the next four digits, and let Y be the set of 10-digit numbers where the first four digits are the same as the last four digits.

First we count $\#(X)$. The first four digits can be any number from 1000 to 9999, for a total of 9000 choices. Then the next four digits are determined, and the last two digits can be any digits, so $\#(X) = 9000 \cdot 100 = 900{,}000$. Similarly, $\#(Y) = 900{,}000$.

Next we count $\#(X \cap Y)$. If a 10-digit number is in both X and Y, then it must be of the form *abababab*, where a and b are digits. There are 9 possible values for a and 10 possible values for b, so $\#(X \cap Y) = 90$. Therefore, by PIE, the number of 10-digit numbers that Sam can remember is $\#(X \cup Y) = \#(X) + \#(Y) - \#(X \cap Y) = 900{,}000 + 900{,}000 - 90 = \boxed{1{,}799{,}910}$.

3.31 To count the number of license plates that contain a three-letter palindrome, there are 26 choices for the first letter, 26 choices for the second letter, and then the third letter must be the same as the first letter. There are 10^3 choices for the numbers, so there are $26 \cdot 26 \cdot 10^3$ such license plates.

Similarly, to count the number of license plates that contain a three-digit palindrome, there are 10 choices for the first number, 10 choices for the second number, and then the third number must be the same as the first number. There are 26^3 choices for the letters, so there are $26^3 \cdot 10 \cdot 10$ such license plates.

Finally, using the same constructive counting method, we find that the number of license plates that contain both a three-letter palindrome and a three-digit palindrome is $26 \cdot 26 \cdot 10 \cdot 10$. The total number of license plates is $26^3 \cdot 10^3$. Therefore, by PIE, the probability that a license plate contains a three-letter palindrome or a three-digit palindrome is

$$\frac{26^2 \cdot 10^3 + 26^3 \cdot 10^2 - 26^2 \cdot 10^2}{26^3 \cdot 10^3} = \frac{10 + 26 - 1}{26 \cdot 10} = \frac{35}{260} = \boxed{\frac{7}{52}}.$$

3.32 If k numbers in the permutation $(x_1, x_2, \ldots, x_7)$ are fixed, then the remaining $7 - k$ numbers can be permuted in $(7 - k)!$ ways. Furthermore, there are $\binom{4}{k}$ ways to choose k odd numbers to be fixed. Hence, the PIE expression that counts the number of permutations in which at least one odd number is fixed is:

$$\binom{4}{1} \cdot 6! - \binom{4}{2} \cdot 5! + \binom{4}{3} \cdot 4! - \binom{4}{4} \cdot 3! = \boxed{2250}.$$

3.33 Since all seatings are equally likely, the probability that at least two of the chosen knights had been sitting next to each other is equal to the number of seatings where at least two of the knights had been sitting next to each other divided by the total number of possible seatings.

Let the chosen knights be K_1, K_2, and K_3, and let A, B, and C be the sets of seatings where knights K_1 and K_2, knights K_1 and K_3, and knights K_2 and K_3 sit next to each other, respectively. Then by PIE, the number of seatings where at least two of the knights had been sitting next to each other is

$$\#(A \cup B \cup C) = \#(A) + \#(B) + \#(C) - \#(A \cap B) - \#(A \cap C) - \#(B \cap C) + \#(A \cap B \cap C).$$

First we count $\#(A)$, the number of seatings where knights K_1 and K_2 sit next to each other. We can choose where K_1 sits in 25 possible ways. (We'll ignore the symmetry of the round table here; this is OK to do as long as we also ignore it when counting the total number of possible seatings.) After the seat for K_1 has been chosen, there are two possible spots for K_2, and then 23 possible spots remaining for K_3, so $\#(A) = 25 \cdot 2 \cdot 23$. Similarly, $\#(B) = \#(C) = 25 \cdot 2 \cdot 23$.

Next we count $\#(A \cap B)$, the number of seatings where the knight K_1 sits next to both knights K_2 and K_3. We can choose the seat for K_1 in 25 possible ways. Then knights K_2 and K_3 must sit on either side of K_1, and there are two possible ways. Hence, $\#(A \cap B) = 25 \cdot 2$. Similarly, $\#(A \cap C) = \#(B \cap C) = 25 \cdot 2$. Finally, note that $\#(A \cap B \cap C) = 0$, as it is impossible for all three pairs of knights to be sitting next to each other (one of them has to be the middle, and then the outside two are not next to each other).

Therefore,

$$\#(A \cup B \cup C) = 3 \cdot 25 \cdot 2 \cdot 23 - 3 \cdot 25 \cdot 2 = 3300.$$

The total number of ways of seating the three knights is $25 \cdot 24 \cdot 23 = 13800$ (remember, we are ignoring the symmetry of the round table), so the probability that two of the knights were sitting next to each other is

$$\frac{3300}{13800} = \boxed{\frac{11}{46}}.$$

Alternative solution: First seat all of the knights. There are $25 \cdot 21$ ways to choose 2 adjacent knights and a third non-adjacent knight. There are 25 ways to choose 3 adjacent knights (just choose the middle one). There are $\binom{25}{3}$ ways to choose 3 arbitrary knights. Therefore, the probability that, among 3 randomly-chosen knights, two of them will be adjacent, is:

$$\frac{25 \cdot 21 + 25}{\binom{25}{3}} = \frac{6 \cdot 22}{24 \cdot 23} = \boxed{\frac{11}{46}}.$$

3.34 Let S, H, C, and D be the sets of hands that are void in spades, hearts, clubs, and diamonds, respectively. Then by PIE, the number of hands that are void in at least one suit is

$$\begin{aligned} \#(S \cup H \cup C \cup D) = {} &\#(S) + \#(H) + \#(C) + \#(D) \\ &- \#(S \cap H) - \#(S \cap C) - \#(S \cap D) - \#(H \cap C) - \#(H \cap D) - \#(C \cap D) \\ &+ \#(S \cap H \cap C) + \#(S \cap H \cap D) + \#(S \cap C \cap D) + \#(H \cap C \cap D) \\ &- \#(S \cap H \cap C \cap D). \end{aligned}$$

First, we count $\#(S)$, the number of hands that are void in spades. There are $52 - 13 = 39$ cards to choose from, so $\#(S) = \binom{39}{13}$. Similarly, $\#(H) = \#(C) = \#(D) = \binom{39}{13}$.

Next, we count $\#(S \cap H)$, the number of hands that are void in both spades and hearts. There are $52 - 13 - 13 = 26$ cards to choose from, so $\#(S \cap H) = \binom{26}{13}$. Similarly, $\#(S \cap C) = \#(S \cap D) = \#(H \cap C) = \#(H \cap D) = \#(C \cap D) = \binom{26}{13}$.

Next, we count $\#(S \cap H \cap C)$, the number of hands that are void in spades, hearts, and clubs. The only such hand is the hand consisting of all 13 diamonds, so $\#(S \cap H \cap C) = 1$. Similarly, $\#(S \cap H \cap D) = \#(S \cap C \cap D) = \#(H \cap C \cap D) = 1$.

Finally, $S \cap H \cap C \cap D$ is the set of hands that are void in every suit, so $\#(S \cap H \cap C \cap D) = 0$, since every hand contains cards of some suit!

Therefore, the number of hands that are void in at least one suit is

$$4\binom{39}{13} - 6\binom{26}{13} + 4.$$

The total number of hands is $\binom{52}{13}$, and therefore, the probability that a hand has a void is

$$\boxed{\frac{4\binom{39}{13} - 6\binom{26}{13} + 4}{\binom{52}{13}}} = \frac{1,621,364,909}{31,750,677,980} \approx 5.11\%.$$

3.35 Let's count the number of sequences in which 0 appears at least 3 times. We can then just multiply this count by 10 to get our answer, since there are 10 choices of which digit can appear at least 3 times, and no more than one digit can appear at least 3 times in the same 5-digit sequence (there aren't enough digits).

There are $\binom{5}{3} = 10$ choices for 3 of the 5 digit positions in which a 0 might appear. Once we have chosen the 3 positions, there are $10^2 = 100$ choices for digits in the other 2 positions. This gives an initial count of $10(100) = 1000$ sequences.

However, if a 0 appears in 4 different positions of a sequence, then this sequence is counted 4 times in the above count, and so must be subtracted 3 times. There are $\binom{5}{4} = 5$ possibilities for 4 of the 5 digit positions, and 10 choices for the 5th digit. So there are $5 \times 10 = 50$ sequences that must be subtracted 3 times each, giving a running total of $1000 - 3(50) = 850$.

Finally, the sequence 00000 has been counted 10 times in the first term and subtracted $3(5) = 15$ times in the second term. Thus, it has been counted a net -5 times, and must be added back 6 times.

So the number of sequences with at least 3 0's is $1000 - 150 + 6 = 856$. We multiply this by 10 to get our final answer of $\boxed{8560}$.

Challenge Problems

3.36 We can analyze this by breaking up the event "A or B" into exclusive cases:

$$P(A \text{ or } B) = P(A \text{ and } (\text{not } B)) + P((\text{not } A) \text{ and } B) + P(A \text{ and } B).$$

Also note that

$$P(A \text{ and } (\text{not } B)) = P(A) - P(A \text{ and } B),$$

and similarly

$$P((\text{not } A) \text{ and } B) = P(B) - P(A \text{ and } B).$$

Therefore,

$$\begin{aligned} P(A \text{ or } B) &= P(A \text{ and } (\text{not } B)) + P((\text{not } A) \text{ and } B) + P(A \text{ and } B) \\ &= (P(A) - P(A \text{ and } B)) + (P(B) - P(A \text{ and } B)) + P(A \text{ and } B) \\ &= \boxed{P(A) + P(B) - P(A \text{ and } B)}. \end{aligned}$$

Note the strong similarity to PIE!

3.37 Rewrite the desired inequality as

$$3N \geq 2(S(A) + S(F) + S(J)) - (S(AF) + S(AJ) + S(FJ)).$$

We will think of the right side of this as a PIE-like expression, and count how many times each student is counted by it. The goal is to show that every student is counted 3 times or less, thus proving the inequality.

There are four types of students, namely students who speak exactly zero, one, two, or all three of the languages. We make a table showing how many times each student is counted. Note that the "Total" column is twice the second column, minus the third column, as per the expression above

Languages spoken	Counted in $S(A) + S(F) + S(J)$	Counted in $S(AF) + S(AJ) + S(FJ)$	Total
0	0	0	0
1	1	0	2
2	2	1	3
3	3	3	3

So every student is counted at most 3 times, and thus the inequality holds.

3.38 A set with n elements has 2^n subsets, so we can rewrite the equation $s(X) + s(Y) + s(Z) = s(X \cup Y \cup Z)$ to be:

$$2^{\#(X)} + 2^{\#(Y)} + 2^{\#(Z)} = 2^{\#(X \cup Y \cup Z)}.$$

We are also given that $\#(X) = \#(Y) = 100$, so

$$2^{100} + 2^{100} + 2^{\#(Z)} = 2^{101} + 2^{\#(Z)} = 2^{\#(X \cup Y \cup Z)}.$$

Since $\#(Z)$ and $\#(X \cup Y \cup Z)$ are integers, we must have $\#(Z) = 101$ and $\#(X \cup Y \cup Z) = 102$.

Next, note that PIE gives us

$$\#(X \cup Y) = \#(X) + \#(Y) - \#(X \cap Y) = 200 - \#(X \cap Y),$$

so that $\#(X \cap Y) = 200 - \#(X \cup Y)$. But $X \cup Y$ is at least as large a set as either X or Y, and is no larger than $X \cup Y \cup Z$, therefore $100 \leq \#(X \cup Y) \leq 102$. This means that

$$98 \leq \#(X \cap Y) \leq 100.$$

Similar computations show that $99 \leq \#(X \cap Z) \leq 100$ and $99 \leq \#(Y \cap Z) \leq 100$.

Finally, by PIE, we have that

$$\#(X \cup Y \cup Z) = \#(X) + \#(Y) + \#(Z) - \#(X \cap Y) - \#(X \cap Z) - \#(Y \cap Z) + \#(X \cap Y \cap Z).$$

Filling in the known values $\#(X) = \#(Y) = 100$ and $\#(Z) = 101$, along with $\#(X \cup Y \cup Z) = 102$, and rearranging terms, gives us:

$$\#(X \cap Y \cap Z) = \#(X \cap Y) + \#(X \cap Z) + \#(Y \cap Z) - 199$$
$$\geq 98 + 99 + 99 - 199 = 97.$$

So the lower bound for $\#(X \cap Y \cap Z)$ is $\boxed{97}$. This lower bound is achieved in the following example:

$$X = \{1, 2, 3, \ldots, 97, 98, 99, 100\},$$
$$Y = \{1, 2, 3, \ldots, 97, 98, 101, 102\},$$
$$Z = \{1, 2, 3, \ldots, 97, 99, 100, 101, 102\}.$$

3.39

(a) The form of the expression makes us consider somehow using PIE. The first term, 9^k, counts the number of ways to place k distinguishable items into 9 distinguishable boxes. Using this as our starting point, we can construct a counting argument.

Consider a partition of the numbers $1, 2, \ldots, k$ among the sets $S_1, S_2, \ldots, S_9$. (In other words, we place each number from 1 to k in one of the sets $S_1, S_2, \ldots, S_9$; the sets are our "boxes.") For $1 \le i \le 9$, let A_i be the set of partitions in which S_i is empty. Then the number of partitions where at least one of the sets S_i is empty is $\#(A_1 \cup A_2 \cup \cdots \cup A_9)$. We count the number of such partitions using PIE.

Let $1 \le i \le 9$. Then A_i is the set of partitions where the set S_i is empty. We then distribute the k elements freely among the remaining 8 sets, so $\#(A_i) = 8^k$.

Let $1 \le i < j \le 9$. Then $A_i \cap A_j$ is the set of partitions where both sets S_i and S_j are empty. We can distribute k elements freely among the remaining 7 sets, so $\#(A_i \cap A_j) = 7^k$.

More generally, for any choice of l of the S's, where $1 \le l \le 8$, there are $(9-l)^k$ partitions that leave our chosen l sets empty, since we must then distribute the k elements into the remaining $9-l$ sets. Also note that there are $\binom{9}{l}$ choices for l sets to remain empty.

Therefore, by PIE,

$$\#(A_1 \cup A_2 \cup \cdots \cup A_9) = \binom{9}{1}8^k - \binom{9}{2}7^k + \cdots + \binom{9}{7}2^k - \binom{9}{8}1^k.$$

This is the number of partitions in which at least one of the sets is empty. On the other hand, there are a total of 9^k partitions, so the number of partitions where all of the sets S_i are non-empty is

$$9^k - \binom{9}{1}8^k + \binom{9}{2}7^k - \cdots - \binom{9}{7}2^k + \binom{9}{8}.$$

But if $k < 9$, then there is no way to distribute the numbers $1, 2, \ldots, k$ among the sets $S_1, S_2, \ldots, S_9$ such that each set S_i is non-empty, because we'd need at least 9 objects to place into the sets to make sure that each set gets at least 1 object. Therefore, this number is 0.

(b) By the same reasoning as part (a), we see that the expression counts the number of partitions of $\{1, 2, \ldots, 9\}$ into 9 sets such that none of the sets are empty. But this is the same thing as choosing one element for the first set of the partition, one element for the second set, and so on. In other words, we are choosing a permutation of the 9 elements, and thus there are 9! choices. Therefore,

$$9^9 - \binom{9}{1}8^9 + \binom{9}{2}7^9 - \cdots - \binom{9}{7}2^9 + \binom{9}{8} = 9!.$$

3.40 Let A, B, and C be the set of divisors of 10^{10}, 15^7, and 18^{11}, respectively. Then by PIE, the number of positive integers that divide at least one of these numbers is

$$\#(A \cup B \cup C) = \#(A) + \#(B) + \#(C) - \#(A \cap B) - \#(A \cap C) - \#(B \cap C) + \#(A \cap B \cap C).$$

To count the number of divisors, we first write down the prime factorizations: $10^{10} = 2^{10} \cdot 5^{10}$, $15^7 = 3^7 \cdot 5^7$, and $18^{11} = 2^{11} \cdot 3^{22}$. Every divisor of 10^{10} is of the form $2^a 5^b$, where $0 \le a \le 10$ and $0 \le b \le 10$. Hence, $\#(A) = (10+1)(10+1) = 121$. Similarly, $\#(B) = (7+1)(7+1) = 64$, and $\#(C) = (11+1)(22+1) = 276$.

Next, we count $\#(A \cap B)$, the number of positive integers that divide both 10^{10} and 15^7. A positive integer divides both these numbers if and only if it divides their greatest common divisor, and $\gcd\{10^{10}, 15^7\} = \gcd\{2^{10} \cdot 5^{10}, 3^7 \cdot 5^7\} = 5^7$, so $\#(A \cap B) = 7 + 1 = 8$. Similarly,

$$\gcd\{10^{10}, 18^{11}\} = \gcd\{2^{10} \cdot 5^{10}, 2^{11} \cdot 3^{22}\} = 2^{10},$$

so $\#(A \cap C) = 10 + 1 = 11$, and

$$\gcd\{15^7, 18^{11}\} = \gcd\{3^7 \cdot 5^7, 2^{11} \cdot 3^{22}\} = 3^7,$$

so $\#(B \cap C) = 7 + 1 = 8$.

Finally, we count $\#(A \cap B \cap C)$, the number of positive integers that divide 10^{10}, 15^7, and 18^{11}. Since

$$\gcd\{10^{10}, 15^7, 18^{11}\} = \gcd\{2^{10} \cdot 5^{10}, 3^7 \cdot 5^7, 2^{11} \cdot 3^{22}\} = 1,$$

the only positive integer that divides all three numbers is 1, so $\#(A \cap B \cap C) = 1$.

Therefore, the number of positive integers that divide at least one of 10^{10}, 15^7, and 18^{11} is $121 + 64 + 276 - 8 - 11 - 8 + 1 = \boxed{435}$.

3.41

(a) We rephrase the problem as follows: Let $\pi = (a_1, a_2, \ldots, a_n)$ be a permutation of the numbers $(1, 2, \ldots, n)$. Find the number of such permutations π such that $a_i \neq i$ for all $1 \leq i \leq n$.

For $1 \leq i \leq n$, let A_i be the set of permutations π for which $a_i = i$. Then by PIE, the number of permutations for which $a_i = i$ for some i, $1 \leq i \leq n$, is equal to

$$\begin{aligned}
\#(A_1 \cup A_2 \cup \cdots \cup A_n) = \ &\#(A_1) + \#(A_2) + \cdots + \#(A_n) \\
&- [\#(A_1 \cap A_2) + \#(A_1 \cap A_3) + \cdots + \#(A_{n-1} \cap A_n)] \\
&+ [\#(A_1 \cap A_2 \cap A_3) + \#(A_1 \cap A_2 \cap A_4) + \cdots + \#(A_{n-2} \cap A_{n-1} \cap A_n)] \\
&- \cdots \\
&+ (-1)^{n-1}\#(A_1 \cap A_2 \cap \cdots \cap A_n).
\end{aligned}$$

First we compute $\#(A_1)$, the number of permutations π for which $a_1 = 1$. The $n-1$ numbers $a_2, a_3, \ldots, a_n$ can be any permutation of $2, 3, \ldots, n$, so $\#(A_1) = (n-1)!$. Similarly, $\#(A_i) = (n-1)!$ for $1 \leq i \leq n$.

Next we compute $\#(A_1 \cap A_2)$, the number of permutations π for which $a_1 = 1$ and $a_2 = 2$. The $n-2$ numbers $a_3, a_4, \ldots, a_n$ can be any permutation of $3, 4, \ldots, n$, so $\#(A_1 \cap A_2) = (n-2)!$. Similarly, $\#(A_i \cap A_j) = (n-2)!$ for $1 \leq i < j \leq n$.

More generally, for any distinct indices $i_1, i_2, \ldots, i_k$,

$$\#(A_{i_1} \cap A_{i_2} \cap \cdots \cap A_{i_k}) = (n-k)!.$$

In the PIE formula above, there are $\binom{n}{k}$ terms of the form $A_{i_1} \cap A_{i_2} \cap \cdots \cap A_{i_k}$, so the number of permutations for which $a_i = i$ for some i, $1 \leq i \leq n$, is

$$\begin{aligned}
\#(A_1 \cup A_2 \cup \cdots \cup A_n) &= \binom{n}{1}(n-1)! - \binom{n}{2}(n-2)! + \binom{n}{3}(n-3)! + \cdots + (-1)^{n-1}\binom{n}{n}0! \\
&= \sum_{k=1}^{n}(-1)^{k-1}\binom{n}{k}(n-k)! \\
&= \sum_{k=1}^{n}(-1)^{k-1}\frac{n!}{k!(n-k)!} \cdot (n-k)! \\
&= n!\sum_{k=1}^{n}(-1)^{k-1}\frac{1}{k!}.
\end{aligned}$$

The total number of permutations π is $n!$, so the number of permutations π for which $a_i \neq i$ for all $1 \leq i \leq n$ is

$$D_n = n! - n!\sum_{k=1}^{n}(-1)^{k-1}\frac{1}{k!} = \boxed{n!\sum_{k=0}^{n}(-1)^{k}\frac{1}{k!}}.$$

(b) Let $(a_1, a_2, \ldots, a_n)$ be a permutation of $(1, 2, \ldots, n)$. We say that i is a *fixed point* if $a_i = i$. Let $0 \le k \le n$. We count the number of permutations that have exactly k fixed points.

First, of the values $1, 2, \ldots, n$, we choose k to be fixed. This can be done in $\binom{n}{k}$ ways. Then the remaining $n - k$ values must be permuted in a way that there are no fixed points. This is simply D_{n-k}, so there are $\binom{n}{k} D_{n-k}$ permutations with exactly k fixed points. Since there are a total of $n!$ permutations, and each permutation can have between 0 and n fixed points, we sum over all integers $0 \le k \le n$, and we get

$$\sum_{k=0}^{n} \binom{n}{k} D_{n-k} = n!.$$

3.42 Since every team has an equal chance of winning, every outcome is equally likely. Therefore, the probability that the tournament will produce neither an undefeated team nor a winless team is simply the number of outcomes satisfying this condition divided by the total number of outcomes.

Note that if a tournament does not satisfy the given condition, then there is either a team that wins all of its games, or a team that loses all of its games (or both). To count the number of such tournaments, let W be the set of tournaments in which some team wins all of its games, and let L be the set of tournaments in which some team loses all of its games. Then by PIE, the number of tournaments in which some team wins all of its games or some team loses all of its games is $\#(W \cup L) = \#(W) + \#(L) - \#(W \cap L)$.

The five teams play a total of $5 \cdot 4/2 = 10$ games. Note that if one team wins all of its games, then it can be the only such team. Any of the five teams can be this winning team, and since it plays four games (one against each of the other teams), this leaves $10 - 4 = 6$ games whose outcomes can be any combination of wins and losses. Therefore, $\#(W) = 5 \cdot 2^6 = 320$.

Similarly, if one team loses all of its games, then it can be the only such team. This team plays four games, and the other six games can be any possible combination of wins and losses as well, so $\#(L) = 320$.

Now we count $\#(W \cap L)$. As above, there can only be one team that wins all of its games, and only one team that loses all of its games. There are 5 choices for the winning team, then 4 choices for the losing team. Each team plays four games, but one game is against each other, so this leaves $10 - 4 - 4 + 1 = 3$ games whose outcomes can be any combination of wins and losses. Therefore, $\#(W \cap L) = 5 \cdot 4 \cdot 2^3 = 160$. Hence, $\#(W \cup L) = 320 + 320 - 160 = 480$.

However, this counts the number of tournaments that have the opposite property of what we are interested in. There are a total of $2^{10} = 1024$ possible outcomes. Thus, the probability that the tournament will produce neither an undefeated team nor a winless team is

$$1 - \frac{480}{1024} = 1 - \frac{15}{32} = \boxed{\frac{17}{32}}.$$

3.43

(a) There are n/p_1 positive integers less than or equal to n that are divisible by p_1, and n/p_2 positive integers less than or equal to n that are divisible by p_2. More generally, for $1 \le i \le k$, there are n/p_i positive integers less than or equal to n that are divisible by p_i.

(b) Subtracting all the numbers we found in part (a), we obtain the formula

$$n - \frac{n}{p_1} - \frac{n}{p_2} - \cdots - \frac{n}{p_k}.$$

However, in this count, every positive integer that is divisible by two or more primes gets subtracted more than once. So this count is too small.

(c) For $1 \le i < j \le n$, there are $n/(p_i p_j)$ positive integers less than or equal to n that are divisible by $p_i p_j$, so to account for the positive integers that are divisible by two primes, we add all terms of this form to obtain the formula

$$n - \frac{n}{p_1} - \frac{n}{p_2} - \cdots - \frac{n}{p_k} + \frac{n}{p_1 p_2} + \frac{n}{p_1 p_3} + \cdots + \frac{n}{p_{k-1} p_k}.$$

However, we must now subtract out all positive integers that are divisible by three primes, and so on. Using PIE, this gives us the formula

$$\phi(n) = n - \frac{n}{p_1} - \frac{n}{p_2} - \cdots - \frac{n}{p_k}$$
$$+ \frac{n}{p_1 p_2} + \frac{n}{p_1 p_3} + \cdots + \frac{n}{p_{k-1} p_k}$$
$$- \frac{n}{p_1 p_2 p_3} - \frac{n}{p_1 p_2 p_4} - \cdots - \frac{n}{p_{k-2} p_{k-1} p_k}$$
$$+ \cdots$$
$$+ (-1)^k \frac{n}{p_1 p_2 \cdots p_k}.$$

(d) Suppose that we expand the product

$$n \left(1 - \frac{1}{p_1}\right)\left(1 - \frac{1}{p_2}\right) \cdots \left(1 - \frac{1}{p_k}\right).$$

Then other than n, each term will be a product of n and factors of the form $-1/p_i$. For example, the terms including one factor of $-1/p_i$ are

$$-\frac{n}{p_1}, \quad -\frac{n}{p_2}, \quad \ldots, \quad -\frac{n}{p_k},$$

the terms including two factors of $-1/p_i$ are

$$\frac{n}{p_1 p_2}, \quad \frac{n}{p_1 p_3}, \quad \ldots, \quad \frac{n}{p_{k-1} p_k},$$

and so on. These are the same terms in our formula for $\phi(n)$ above.

We conclude that

$$\phi(n) = n \left(1 - \frac{1}{p_1}\right)\left(1 - \frac{1}{p_2}\right) \cdots \left(1 - \frac{1}{p_k}\right).$$

3.44 To get started on the problem, we draw the two n-pointed stars for $n = 7$.

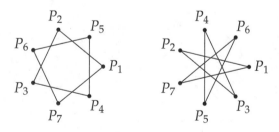

In each figure, the vertices of the pointed star are also the vertices of a regular heptagon. Note that in the first pointed star, P_2 is two vertices away from P_1 (going counterclockwise), and in the second pointed star, P_2 is three vertices away from P_1 (going counterclockwise).

More generally, in an n-pointed star, we let $P_1, P_2, \ldots, P_n$ be the vertices of a regular n-gon (in some order). Suppose that P_2 is a vertices away from P_1 (going counterclockwise). Then P_3 is $2a$ vertices away from P_1, and in general, P_k is $(k-1)a$ vertices away from P_1.

We must have that none of $a, 2a, \ldots, (n-1)a$ are multiples of n, so that our path doesn't prematurely return to P_1. But this means that a must be relatively prime to n; otherwise, if $d = \gcd(a, n) > 1$, then $(n/d)a$ is a multiple of n.

There are some other restrictions on a. For example, a must be less than $n/2$; otherwise, the angles in the path $P_1P_2 \cdots P_nP_1$ would be greater than 180 degrees. Also, a cannot be equal to 1; otherwise, we would obtain a regular n-gon, and so the line segments would intersect each other only at their endpoints. All other values of a, relatively prime to n, lead to a regular n-pointed star.

Thus, the number of non-similar regular 1000-pointed stars is equal to the number of positive integers a, relatively prime to 1000, with $1 < a < 500$. By the previous problem, the number of positive integers less than or equal to 1000 that are relatively prime to 1000 is

$$\phi(1000) = 1000\left(1 - \frac{1}{2}\right)\left(1 - \frac{1}{5}\right) = 1000 \cdot \frac{1}{2} \cdot \frac{4}{5} = 400.$$

Exactly half of these are less than 500, and we must subtract one because a must be greater than 1, so the number of non-similar regular 1000-pointed stars is $\frac{400}{2} - 1 = \boxed{199}$.

CHAPTER 4

Constructive Counting and 1-1 Correspondences

Exercises for Section 4.2

4.2.1 There are a total of $3 + 2 + 3 + 7 = 15$ dots, so there are $\binom{15}{3} = 455$ ways to choose a triple of these dots. We must then subtract the triples where all three points lie on a line. In $\binom{4}{3} = 4$ of these triples, all three points lie on side $\overline{AB}$, so they do not form a triangle. Similarly, there are $\binom{5}{3} = 10$ triples where all three points lie on side $\overline{BC}$, and $\binom{9}{3} = 84$ triples where all three points lie on side $\overline{AC}$. Therefore, the number of triangles is $455 - 4 - 10 - 84 = \boxed{357}$.

4.2.2 Let the three numbers be a, b, and c. Consider the remainders that a, b, and c leave when divided by 3. (In other words, consider a, b, and c modulo 3). If $a + b + c$ is a multiple of 3, then either a, b, and c all leave the same remainder, or else a, b, and c all leave different remainders.

In S, there are 11 numbers congruent to 0 modulo 3, 12 numbers congruent to 1 modulo 3, and 11 numbers congruent to 2 modulo 3. Hence, there are $\binom{11}{3} = 165$ ways of choosing three numbers congruent to 0 modulo 3, $\binom{12}{3} = 220$ ways of choosing three numbers congruent to 1 modulo 3, and $\binom{11}{3} = 165$ ways of choosing three numbers congruent to 2 modulo 3, giving a total of $165 + 220 + 165 = 550$ ways of choosing 3 numbers that all leave the same remainder upon division by 3. Also, there are $11 \cdot 12 \cdot 11 = 1452$ ways of choosing three numbers that are all different modulo 3. Therefore, the total number of ways of choosing a, b, and c is $550 + 1452 = \boxed{2002}$.

4.2.3 The word MISSISSIPPI contains 11 letters, and only one M, so the M must be the middle letter. This leaves 4 I's, 2 P's, and 4 S's. Hence, the first five letters contain 2 I's, 1 P, and 2 S's. Once the first five letters have been ordered, the last five letters are uniquely determined. Therefore, the number of orderings is $\frac{5!}{2!1!2!} = \boxed{30}$.

4.2.4 For a sum of numbers to be odd, there must be an odd number of odd numbers. Since there are five odd numbers from 1 to 9, two players must receive one odd-numbered tile, and the third player must receive three odd-numbered tiles. From here, we present two different solutions.

Solution 1: First, we choose one player to be the one who receives three odd-numbered tiles; this can be done in 3 ways. Then we distribute the odd tiles. Of the five odd-numbered tiles, three go to the chosen player, and one each goes to the other two players. These can be distributed in $\binom{5}{3} \cdot 2 = 20$ ways. Finally, there are four even-numbered tiles remaining, and two each go to the other two players. These can be distributed in $\binom{4}{2} = 6$ ways. Hence, the total numbers of ways to distribute the tiles so that the sum of the numbers for each player is odd is $3 \cdot 20 \cdot 6 = 360$.

The nine tiles themselves can be distributed in $\binom{9}{3}\binom{6}{3} = 1680$ ways. Therefore, the probability that the sum of the numbers for each player is odd is

$$\frac{360}{1680} = \boxed{\frac{3}{14}}.$$

Solution 2: We compute the probability that the first player receives 3 odd tiles. There are 9 tiles total, and 5 of them are odd, so this probability is

$$\frac{\binom{5}{3}}{\binom{9}{3}} = \frac{10}{84} = \frac{5}{42}.$$

We now have 2 odd-numbered tiles and 4 even-numbered tiles remaining to distribute to the other two players. For both players' sums to be odd, we need each remaining player to receive one odd-numbered tile. This occurs with probability $\frac{3}{5}$: think of the first odd tile as being arbitrarily assigned to one of the players, then there are 5 slots left, and we need the other odd tile to go to one of the slots belonging to the other player.

Therefore, the probability that the first player gets 3 odd tiles, and that the other two players also have an odd-numbered sum of their tiles, is $\frac{5}{42} \cdot \frac{3}{5} = \frac{1}{14}$. By symmetry, this is also the probability of this happening with either of the other two players getting 3 odd tiles. Therefore, the overall probability is $3 \cdot \frac{1}{14} = \boxed{\frac{3}{14}}$.

4.2.5 First we consider how the coins may be stacked with respect to being face up or face down. If some coin is face up, then the next coin above must also be face up, which implies that every coin above must be face up. Hence, any possible stacking must consist of a certain number of coins (possibly 0) on the bottom that are all face down, and the rest face up on the top. There are eight coins, and the number of coins that are face down may be any number from 0 to 8, so the number of possible orientations of the coins is 9.

After the orientation has been chosen, we can select four of the eight coins to be gold, which can be done in $\binom{8}{4} = 70$ ways. Hence, the total number of possible stackings is $9 \cdot 70 = \boxed{630}$.

Exercises for Section 4.3

4.3.1 We separately consider the cases where n is even and n is odd.

If n is even, then $n = 2k$ for some positive integer k. A palindrome with $2k$ digits is determined by the first k digits, so there are 2^k palindromes with $2k$ digits. However, since the palindrome must contain at least one 1 and one 2, we must exclude the palindrome that is all 1s and the palindrome that is all 2s, which means there are a total of $2^k - 2$ such palindromes. Since $2^{10} - 2 = 1022$ and $2^{11} - 2 = 2046$, n must be at least $2 \cdot 11 = 22$ if n is even.

If n is odd, then $n = 2k+1$ for some positive integer k. A palindrome with $2k+1$ digits is determined by the first $k+1$ digits, so there are 2^{k+1} palindromes with $2k+1$ digits. However, as above, we must exclude the palindrome that is all 1s and the palindrome that is all 2s, which means that there a total of $2^{k+1} - 2$ such palindromes. Hence, $k+1$ must be at least 11, or k must be at least 10, and so n must be at least $2 \cdot 10 + 1 = 21$ if n is odd.

Thus, the smallest n for which there are at least 2002 such palindromes of length n is $\boxed{21}$.

4.3.2 Let A be the set of even numbers from 1 to 10, and let B be the set of odd numbers from 1 to 10. Then from the given condition, the color of every number in A must differ from the color of every number in B, and these are the only restrictions.

In particular, the numbers in A cannot be represented by three different colors (otherwise, it would be impossible to color any of the numbers in B), so the numbers in A are either represented by one color or two colors.

Suppose the numbers in A are represented by one color. There are three possible choices for this color. Then each element in B can be colored using either of the other two colors, resulting in 2^5 possible colorings. Hence, there are $3 \cdot 2^5 = 96$ possible colorings in this case.

Now suppose the numbers in A are represented by two colors. There are $\binom{3}{2} = 3$ possible ways to choose two colors. Then there are 2^5 ways of coloring the elements in A using these two colors, but we must exclude the 2 colorings where all elements are the same color (because we have already counted these above), so there are $2^5 - 2 = 30$ ways to color the elements in A. Then all elements in B must be the third color. Thus, there are $3 \cdot 30 = 90$ possible colorings in this case.

Hence, the total number of possible colorings is $96 + 90 = \boxed{186}$.

4.3.3 Consider five consecutive positive integers $n, n+1, n+2, n+3$, and $n+4$. Two consecutive integers cannot appear in the subset (since they would differ by 1), so at most three of the five numbers can appear in the subset.

Suppose three of the five numbers appear in the subset; then these three numbers must be $n, n+2$, and $n+4$. But n and $n+4$ differ by 4, so three of the five numbers cannot appear in the subset, which means that at most two of any five consecutive positive integers can appear in the subset.

We can partition S into five subsets of five consecutive positive integers, namely $\{1,2,3,4,5\}, \{6,7,8,9,10\}, \ldots,$ $\{21,22,23,24,25\}$, so at most $5 \cdot 2 = 10$ elements can appear in the subset. The subset $\{1,3,6,8,11,13,16,18,21,23\}$ shows that such a set can contain 10 elements; we have already determined that no two of these elements differ by 1 or 4, and can easily verify that no two of them differ by 9 or 16 as well. So the maximum number of elements is $\boxed{10}$.

4.3.4 First, we factor $21,600 = 2^5 \cdot 3^3 \cdot 5^2$. If 21,600 is the least common multiple of m and n, then in particular both m and n must divide 21,600. Hence, $m = 2^{e_1} 3^{e_2} 5^{e_3}$ and $n = 2^{f_1} 3^{f_2} 5^{f_3}$ for some nonnegative integers $e_1, e_2, e_3, f_1,$ $f_2,$ and f_3. Then

$$\mathrm{lcm}\{m,n\} = 2^{\max\{e_1, f_1\}} 3^{\max\{e_2, f_2\}} 5^{\max\{e_3, f_3\}} = 2^5 \cdot 3^3 \cdot 5^2.$$

Thus, we seek the number of ways to choose nonnegative integers $e_1, e_2, e_3, f_1, f_2,$ and f_3 such that $\max\{e_1, f_1\} = 5$, $\max\{e_2, f_2\} = 3$, and $\max\{e_3, f_3\} = 2$.

If $\max\{e_1, f_1\} = 5$, then one of e_1 and f_1 must be 5. If $e_1 = 5$, then f_1 may be any nonnegative integer from 0 to 5, giving 6 possible values of e_1 and f_1. If $f_1 = 5$, then e_1 may be any nonnegative integer from 0 to 5, giving another 6 possible values of e_1 and f_1. However, the case that both e_1 and f_1 are equal to 5 is counted twice, so we must subtract one, and obtain that the number of possible values of e_1 and f_1 is $2 \cdot 6 - 1 = 11$.

Similarly, the number of possible values of e_2 and f_2 is $2 \cdot 4 - 1 = 7$, and the number of possible values of e_3 and f_3 is $2 \cdot 3 - 1 = 5$. Therefore, the total number of possible pairs (m, n) is $11 \cdot 7 \cdot 5 = \boxed{385}$.

4.3.5 Let $\overline{abcdef}$ be a 6-digit cute number, where each letter stands for one of the digits 1–6.

The number $\overline{abcde}$ is divisible by 5, so $e = 5$.

The numbers $\overline{ab}, \overline{abcd}$, and $\overline{abcd5f}$ are divisible by 2, 4, and 6, respectively, so in particular each of them is even, which means that the digits $b, d,$ and f must be even. But there are only three even digits from 1 through 6, namely 2, 4, and 6, so these must be equal to $b, d,$ and f in some order. This leaves a and c to be 1 and 3 in some order.

Next, the number $\overline{abc}$ is divisible by 3, which means that the sum of its digits must be divisible by 3. Since a and c are 1 and 3 in some order, the sum of its digits are $a + b + c = b + 4$. The only even digit b from 1 through 6 for which $b + 4$ is divisible by 3 is 2, so $b = 2$. This means d and f are equal to 4 and 6 in some order.

As derived above, a and c are 1 and 3 in some order. Suppose $a = 1$ and $c = 3$. Then $\overline{abcd} = \overline{123d}$ must be divisible by 4, which only works for $d = 6$. Then f must be 4, giving the cute number 123654.

Now suppose $a = 3$ and $c = 1$. Then $\overline{abcd} = \overline{321d}$ must be divisible by 4, which again only works for $d = 6$. Then f must again be 4, giving the cute number 321654.

Therefore, there are $\boxed{2}$ cute 6-digit numbers.

4.3.6 Let R be the set of rows that contain an empty desk, and let C be the set of columns that contain an empty desk. Then every empty desk is at the intersection of a row in R and a column in C. Conversely, from the conditions in the problem, the intersection of a row in R and a column in C must be an empty desk, so the set of empty desks is determined by R and C.

There are $2^5 = 32$ possible sets for R. If R is empty, then there are no empty desks, so C must be empty as well.

Otherwise, R is one of the remaining 31 non-empty sets, and for each such set R, there are 31 possible non-empty sets C. Hence, the number of possible arrangements of empty desks is $1 + 31 \cdot 31 = \boxed{962}$.

Exercises for Section 4.4

4.4.1

(a) The sets $\{1, 2, 3, \ldots, 12\}$ and $\{66, 68, 70, \ldots, 88\}$ are in 1-1 correspondence, via the relation $n \leftrightarrow 2n + 64$.

(b) The set $\{3, 6, 9, \ldots, 60\}$ contains 20 elements, and the set $\{4, 9, 14, \ldots, 104\}$ contains 21 elements, so the sets are not in 1-1 correspondence.

(c) Both $\{0, 1, \ldots, 15\}$ and $\mathcal{P}(\{1, 2, 3, 4\})$ contain 16 elements, so the sets are in 1-1 correspondence. We can set up a natural correspondence as follows: For each element $a \in \{0, 1, \ldots, 15\}$, write a as a four-digit number in binary (with leading zeros, if necessary). For example, 5 becomes 0101, and 11 becomes 1011. Then we form a subset of $\{1, 2, 3, 4\}$, where i is in the subset if and only if the ith digit of a is 1. So 0101 corresponds to the subset $\{2, 4\}$, and 1011 corresponds to the subset $\{1, 3, 4\}$. Thus, we have a 1-1 correspondence between $\{0, 1, \ldots, 15\}$ and $\mathcal{P}(\{1, 2, 3, 4\})$. Note that 0 corresponds to $\emptyset$.

(d) The first set contains $\binom{5}{2} = 10$ elements, and the second set also contains 10 elements, so the sets are in 1-1 correspondence. There's not an obvious natural way to make the correspondence, so we can arbitrarily choose it. For instance, if the five items are $\{A, B, C, D, E\}$ and the 10 items are $\{1, 2, \ldots, 10\}$, then one possible correspondence is:

$$
\begin{array}{rclcrcl}
\{A,B\} & \leftrightarrow & 1 & \qquad & \{B,D\} & \leftrightarrow & 6 \\
\{A,C\} & \leftrightarrow & 2 & & \{B,E\} & \leftrightarrow & 7 \\
\{A,D\} & \leftrightarrow & 3 & & \{C,D\} & \leftrightarrow & 8 \\
\{A,E\} & \leftrightarrow & 4 & & \{C,E\} & \leftrightarrow & 9 \\
\{B,C\} & \leftrightarrow & 5 & & \{D,E\} & \leftrightarrow & 10
\end{array}
$$

(e) Let a be a 3-digit number with no 2. Change all the 4's in a to 2's, to obtain a 3-digit number b with no 4. Conversely, we can change all the 2's in b to 4's, which gives back a. Thus, the two sets are in 1-1 correspondence.

(f) Counting digit by digit, the first set contains $8 \cdot 9 = 72$ elements, and the second set contains $9 \cdot 9 = 81$ elements, so the two sets are not in 1-1 correspondence.

4.4.2 Any choice of three different letters gives two possible words in our set (for example, choosing A,B,C gives the words ACB and BCA). Also, any choice of two different letters gives a possible word in our set (for example, choosing D and E gives DED). Therefore, the number of words is

$$
2\binom{26}{3} + \binom{26}{2} = 5200 + 325 = \boxed{5525}.
$$

4.4.3 For a given path, for every change in the x, y, and z coordinate, write down an X, Y, and Z, respectively. This establishes a 1-1 correspondence between the set of paths from (0,0,0) to (4,4,4) and the set of strings of length 12 containing 4 Xs, 4 Ys, and 4 Zs.

The total number of such strings, and hence the total number of such paths, is

$$
\frac{12!}{4!4!4!} = 34{,}650.
$$

We must subtract the number of paths that pass through (2,2,2). The number of paths from (0,0,0) to (2,2,2) is the number of strings of length 6 containing 2 Xs, 2 Ys, and 2 Zs, of which there are

$$
\frac{6!}{2!2!2!} = 90.
$$

The number of paths from (2,2,2) to (4,4,4) is also 90, so the number of paths that pass through (2,2,2) is $90^2 = 8{,}100$. Therefore, the number of paths that do not pass through (2,2,2) is $34{,}650 - 8{,}100 = \boxed{26{,}550}$.

4.4.4 One way to think about this is that A and B must have the same number of elements, and B and C must have the same number of elements, therefore A and C have the same number of elements, and thus are in 1-1 correspondence.

A more formal way to show the correspondence is by examining the bijective functions that exhibit the correspondence. Since A and B are in 1-1 correspondence, there exists a function $f : A \to B$ that is bijective. Similarly, since B and C are in 1-1 correspondence, there exists a function $g : B \to C$ that is bijective. We claim that the composition of the functions, namely the function $g \circ f : A \to C$, is bijective.

To show that $g \circ f$ is bijective, we must show that it is both injective and surjective. Suppose that $(g \circ f)(a) = (g \circ f)(a')$ for some elements $a, a' \in A$. This can be re-written as $g(f(a)) = g(f(a'))$. Since g is injective, $f(a) = f(a')$. Since f is injective, $a = a'$. Thus, $(g \circ f)(a) = (g \circ f)(a')$ implies that $a = a'$, so $g \circ f$ is injective.

Now, let $c \in C$. Since g is surjective, there exists a $b \in B$ such that $g(b) = c$. Since f is surjective, there exists an $a \in A$ such that $f(a) = b$. Hence,

$$(g \circ f)(a) = g(f(a)) = g(b) = c.$$

Thus, for any $c \in C$, there exists an $a \in A$ such that $(g \circ f)(a) = c$, so $g \circ f$ is surjective. Therefore, $g \circ f$ is bijective, and sets A and C are in 1-1 correspondence.

4.4.5 Let $n = \#(A)$, the number of elements in A. Then any proper subset B of A must contain fewer than n elements, so A and B cannot be in 1-1 correspondence.

4.4.6

(a) Note that $42 = 2 \cdot 3 \cdot 7$. The odd divisors of 42 are $\{1, 3, 7, 21\}$, and the even divisors of 42 are $\{2, 6, 14, 42\}$. There are 4 of each, so they are in 1-1 correspondence. Specifically, the correspondence takes an odd divisor to an even divisor by multiplying by 2, and goes back by dividing by 2.

(b) Note that $28 = 2^2 \cdot 7$. The odd divisors of 28 are just 1 and 7, so there are only 2. However, $28 = 2^2 \cdot 7$ has $(2+1)(1+1) = 6$ divisors in all, namely $\{1, 2, 4, 7, 14, 28\}$, so $6 - 2 = 4$ of them are even, namely $\{2, 4, 14, 28\}$. Since there are more even divisors than odd divisors, the set of odd divisors of 28 are not in 1-1 correspondence with the set of even divisors of 28.

(c) Let n be a positive integer for which the set of odd divisors of n and the set of even divisors of n are in 1-1 correspondence. If n is odd, then n has no even divisors, meaning that the set of even divisors is $\emptyset$. But we cannot have $\emptyset$ in 1-1 correspondence with any nonempty set. Thus, n must contain at least one factor of 2. So, let $n = 2^{e_1} p_2^{e_2} p_3^{e_3} \cdots p_k^{e_k}$ be the prime factorization of n.

Then an odd divisor of n must be a divisor of $p_2^{e_2} p_3^{e_3} \cdots p_k^{e_k}$, of which there are

$$(e_2 + 1)(e_3 + 1) \cdots (e_k + 1).$$

The positive integer n has

$$(e_1 + 1)(e_2 + 1)(e_3 + 1) \cdots (e_k + 1)$$

divisors in all, so

$$(e_1 + 1)(e_2 + 1)(e_3 + 1) \cdots (e_k + 1) - (e_2 + 1)(e_3 + 1) \cdots (e_k + 1) = e_1(e_2 + 1)(e_3 + 1) \cdots (e_k + 1)$$

of them are even.

Since the set of odd divisors of n and the set of even divisors of n are in 1-1 correspondence, we must have

$$(e_2 + 1)(e_3 + 1) \cdots (e_k + 1) = e_1(e_2 + 1)(e_3 + 1) \cdots (e_k + 1),$$

which occurs if and only if $e_1 = 1$.

Hence, the set of odd divisors of n and the set of even divisors of n are in 1-1 correspondence if and only if n contains exactly one factor of 2. This is equivalent to saying that n is even but not a multiple of 4.

Exercises for Section 4.5

4.5.1 If Annie and Benny meet, then they must meet after they've each made 6 moves. If they meet at a point P, then following Annie's path from $(0,0)$ to P, combined with following Benny's path backwards from P to $(5,7)$, gives us a 12-step path from $(0,0)$ to $(5,7)$. Conversely, given a 12-step path from $(0,0)$ to $(5,7)$, let point P be the 6th point on the path. Then we get a 6-step path for Annie from $(0,0)$ to P by following the first 6 steps of the 12-step path, and we get a 6-step path for Benny from $(5,7)$ to P by following the last 6 steps, in reverse order, of the 12-step path.

Therefore, we have a 1-1 correspondence:

$$\{\text{Ways in which Annie and Benny can meet}\} \quad \leftrightarrow \quad \{\text{12-step paths from } (0,0) \text{ to } (5,7)\}.$$

There are $\binom{12}{5} = 792$ 12-step paths from $(0,0)$ to $(5,7)$, so there are 792 (equally likely) ways in which Annie and Benny can meet. Annie and Benny each have $2^6 = 64$ equally-likely possible 6-step paths overall. Therefore, the probability that they meet is

$$\frac{792}{(64)(64)} = \frac{792}{4096} = \boxed{\frac{99}{512}}.$$

4.5.2 The sum counts 1 for each 61-tuple $(n_0, n_1, \ldots, n_{60})$ such that $0 \le n_0 \le n_1 \le \cdots \le n_{60} \le 2$. In other words, we have a 1-1 correspondence:

$$\{\text{Terms in the sum}\} \quad \leftrightarrow \quad \{\text{Sequences of integers } 0 \le n_0 \le n_1 \le \cdots \le n_{60} \le 2\}.$$

Hence, the sum is equal to size of the set of sequences shown on the right above, so we must count such sequences. Note that every n_i in the sequence is either 0, 1, or 2. We can informally describe such a sequence as some number of 0's, followed by some number of 1's, followed by some number of 2's.

Case 1 One of the terms in the sequence is a 1.

We can describe such a sequence by choosing the point in the sequence where the first 1 occurs and the point in the sequence where the first 2 occurs. In other words, we must choose $0 \le i < j \le 61$ such that:

$$n_k = \begin{cases} 0 & \text{if } 0 \le k < i, \\ 1 & \text{if } i \le k < j, \\ 2 & \text{if } j \le k \le 60. \end{cases}$$

Note that $i = 0$ gives sequences where $n_0 = 1$ (that is, where there are no 0's), and that $j = 61$ gives sequences where $n_{60} = 1$ (that is, where there are no 2's). So we have a 1-1 correspondence:

$$\left\{ \begin{matrix} \text{Sequences of integers } 0 \le n_0 \le n_1 \le \cdots \le n_{60} \le 2 \\ \text{that contain at least one 1} \end{matrix} \right\} \quad \leftrightarrow \quad \{\text{Integers } (i, j) \text{ such that } 0 \le i < j \le 61\}.$$

But this latter set is easy to count: it is just choices of 2 distinct integers from $\{0, 1, 2, \ldots, 61\}$, which we can do in $\binom{62}{2}$ ways.

Case 2 No 1 occurs in the sequence.

This is the same as Case 1, but where $i = j$. Thus we have the 1-1 correspondence:

$$\left\{ \begin{matrix} \text{Sequences of integers } 0 \le n_0 \le n_1 \le \cdots \le n_{60} \le 2 \\ \text{that do not contain any 1's} \end{matrix} \right\} \quad \leftrightarrow \quad \{\text{Integers } i \text{ such that } 0 \le i \le 61\}.$$

There are 62 elements in the latter set.

Therefore, the sum is $\binom{62}{2} + 62 = 1891 + 62 = \boxed{1953}$.

Note that we could write the count from Case 2 as $\binom{62}{1}$, and then apply Pascal's identity to get the answer:

$$\binom{62}{2} + \binom{62}{1} = \binom{63}{2} = 1953.$$

There is a relatively simple counting explanation for the answer of $\binom{63}{2}$; can you find it?

4.5.3

(a)   There is a 1-1 correspondence

{Rolls with even number of evens} $\leftrightarrow$ {Rolls with odd number of evens},

where the correspondence is given by replacing, on every die, the number n by the number $7 - n$. This correspondence in either direction swaps odd and even numbers. If there are k dice showing even numbers, then after applying the correspondence, there will be $101 - k$ dice showing even numbers. Therefore, each set above consists of exactly half of the rolls, and hence the desired probability is $\boxed{\dfrac{1}{2}}$.

(b)   There is a 1-1 correspondence

{Rolls with sum greater than 353} $\leftrightarrow$ {Rolls with sum less than 354},

again using the correspondence that replaces, on every die, the number n by the number $7 - n$; note that this replaces a roll with sum s with a roll with sum $707 - s$. So the two sets above have an equal number of elements, and in particular each contains exactly half of the possible rolls. Therefore, the probability that the sum of a roll is greater than 353 is exactly $\frac{1}{2}$, and thus the smallest s such that $P(\text{sum of a roll greater than } s) < \frac{1}{2}$ is $\boxed{354}$.

4.5.4   Every such triangle is formed by three chords, as shown, which correspond to six points on the circle. Conversely, any set of six points uniquely determines a triangle: given any six points A, B, C, D, E, F on the circle, in that order, we draw the chords $\overline{AD}$, $\overline{BE}$, and $\overline{CF}$. Since these three chords do not pass through a common point, they must form a triangle, as shown in the picture to the right. No other way of drawing 3 chords using these 6 points will produce a triangle; for example, if we draw $\overline{BF}$, then we will be forced to draw either $\overline{CD}$, $\overline{CE}$, or $\overline{DE}$, and none of these intersect $\overline{BF}$.

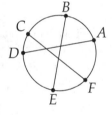

Therefore, we have a 1-1 correspondence

{Triangles formed by portions of chords inside the circle} $\leftrightarrow$ {Sets of 6 points on the circle}.

The latter set is easy to count: there are $\binom{n}{6}$ sets of 6 points on the circle. Therefore, the number of triangles is $\boxed{\binom{n}{6}}$.

Exercises for Section 4.6

4.6.1   The set of legal positions of Chomp on an $m \times n$ board is in 1-1 correspondence with the set of paths from the top-left corner to the bottom right-corner of an $m \times n$ grid (where all the steps are down or to the right), so the number of such positions is $\boxed{\dbinom{m + n}{m}}$.

4.6.2   First, let's look at an example. Consider the partition $24 = 8 + 8 + 4 + 2 + 2$. The Ferrers diagram for this partition is as follows:

If we read this Ferrers diagram by columns instead of rows, then we obtain the partition $24 = 5 + 5 + 3 + 3 + 2 + 2 + 2 + 2$. Note that each part appears an even number of times.

This is true in general. To see why, consider a partition of n into parts of even size, and consider the Ferrers diagram column by column. The number of dots that appear in the first column must be equal to the number of dots in the second column, because otherwise some part (in the original partition) would be equal to 1. Similarly, the number of dots that appear in the third column must be equal to the number of dots that appear in the fourth column (otherwise, some part would be equal to 3), and so on. Thus, each part in the partition generated by the columns appears an even number of times.

Conversely, consider a Ferrers diagram where the columns represent a partition of n into parts that occur an even number of times, and look at the partition corresponding to the rows. No row can end in an odd-numbered column, because if there is a dot in any position in an odd-numbered column, there must also be a dot in the even-numbered column immediately to the right (because those two columns are equal). Therefore, every row must contain an even number of dots, and thus the rows of the diagram give a partition with only even terms.

This establishes a 1-1 correspondence between the set of partitions of n into parts of even size and the set of partitions of n where each part occurs an even number of times, so the number of such partitions are equal.

4.6.3 Let n be the number of problems on the test. Consider the total number of correctly solved problems. We may count this across students, or across problems.

We are given that each problem was solved by 7 students, so the total number of correctly solved problems is $7n$.

The first nine students each solved 4 problems, so the tenth student solved $7n - 36$ problems. Then we must have $7n - 36 \geq 0$, so $n \geq 6$. On the other hand, the tenth student could not have solved more problems than there were on the test, so $7n - 36 \leq n$, meaning that $6n \leq 36$, hence $n \leq 6$. Therefore, $n = 6$, so the tenth student solved $7 \cdot 6 - 36 = \boxed{6}$ problems.

Note that this leads to two partitions of 42, the total number of solved problems on all 10 tests. The first partition, $7 + 7 + 7 + 7 + 7 + 7$, is the sum of the number of correct solutions to each problem. The second partition, $4 + 4 + 4 + 4 + 4 + 4 + 4 + 4 + 4 + 6$, is the sum of the number of problems that each student solved.

4.6.4 Let the vertices of the equilateral triangle be A, B, and C. Each parallelogram must be one of the three different orientations: the sides are parallel to $\overline{AB}$ and $\overline{AC}$, to $\overline{AB}$ and $\overline{BC}$, or to $\overline{AC}$ and $\overline{BC}$. By symmetry, we can count the number of parallelograms whose sides are parallel to $\overline{AB}$ and $\overline{AC}$, and then multiply by three to obtain the total number of parallelograms.

Extend $\overline{AB}$ one unit past B to D, and extend $\overline{AC}$ one unit past C to E, so that triangle ADE is equilateral with side length $n + 1$.

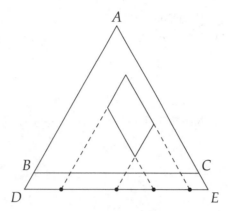

For any parallelogram, extend the sides of the parallelogram to intersect $\overline{DE}$. These extended sides must intersect $\overline{DE}$ at four distinct points. Conversely, any four distinct points on $\overline{DE}$ uniquely determine a parallelogram. (Through the two points closest to D, draw lines parallel to $\overline{AB}$, and through the two points closest to E, draw lines parallel to $\overline{AC}$.) This establishes a 1-1 correspondence between:

$$\left\{\begin{array}{l}\text{parallelograms whose sides are parallel}\\\text{to }\overline{AB}\text{ and }\overline{AC}\end{array}\right\} \quad \leftrightarrow \quad \left\{\begin{array}{l}\text{sets of four distinct (triangular lattice)}\\\text{points on }\overline{DE}\end{array}\right\}.$$

The side $\overline{DE}$ contains $n + 2$ triangular lattice points, so the number of ways of choosing four distinct points on $\overline{DE}$ is $\binom{n+2}{4}$. Therefore, the total number of parallelograms is $\boxed{3\binom{n+2}{4}}$.

4.6.5   First, we look at a small case. Let $n = 25$. Then

$$\left\lfloor \frac{n+1}{2} \right\rfloor + \left\lfloor \frac{n+2}{4} \right\rfloor + \left\lfloor \frac{n+4}{8} \right\rfloor + \left\lfloor \frac{n+8}{16} \right\rfloor + \cdots = \left\lfloor \frac{25+1}{2} \right\rfloor + \left\lfloor \frac{25+2}{4} \right\rfloor + \left\lfloor \frac{25+4}{8} \right\rfloor + \left\lfloor \frac{25+8}{16} \right\rfloor + \left\lfloor \frac{25+16}{32} \right\rfloor + \cdots$$
$$= 13 + 6 + 3 + 2 + 1 + 0 + \cdots$$
$$= 25.$$

Now, we partition the set of positive integers from 1 to 25 according to the number of powers of 2 that divide them. Let S_k be the set of positive integers from 1 to 25 that have exactly k factors of 2. We list the results in the following table:

k	S_k	$\#(S_k)$
0	$\{1, 3, 5, \ldots, 25\}$	13
1	$\{2, 6, 10, \ldots, 22\}$	6
2	$\{4, 12, 20\}$	3
3	$\{8, 24\}$	2
4	$\{16\}$	1

Note that these are the same numbers that appears in the sum above. In general, we claim that the number of positive integers from 1 to n that have exactly k factors of 2 is

$$\left\lfloor \frac{n + 2^k}{2^{k+1}} \right\rfloor.$$

Then the result will follow, because the sum will count every positive integer from 1 to n exactly once.

The sequence of positive integers that have exactly k factors of 2 begins

$$2^k, \quad 3 \cdot 2^k, \quad 5 \cdot 2^k, \quad 7 \cdot 2^k, \quad \ldots.$$

Thus, the ith term of the sequence is $(2i-1)2^k$. Hence, the number of positive integers from 1 to n that have exactly k factors of 2 is given by the positive integer m, where

$$(2m-1)2^k \leq n < [2(m+1)-1]2^k.$$

But

$$(2m-1)2^k \leq n \quad \Leftrightarrow \quad m \leq \frac{n+2^k}{2^{k+1}},$$

and

$$n < [2(m+1)-1]2^k \quad \Leftrightarrow \quad \frac{n+2^k}{2^{k+1}} < m+1.$$

Hence,

$$m \leq \frac{n+2^k}{2^{k+1}} < m+1.$$

Therefore,

$$m = \left\lfloor \frac{n+2^k}{2^{k+1}} \right\rfloor,$$

as desired.

4.6.6 Let's consider the partitions of a smaller number, say 8. There are five partitions of 8 with only even parts: $8, 6+2, 4+4, 4+2+2$, and $2+2+2+2$. For every such partition π with only even parts, we can generate a partition π' with only odd parts by taking every part a and splitting it up as $(a-1)+1$. We list these partitions in a table:

π	π'
8	$7+1$
$6+2$	$5+1+1+1$
$4+4$	$3+3+1+1$
$4+2+2$	$3+1+1+1+1+1$
$2+2+2+2$	$1+1+1+1+1+1+1+1$

Note that in every partition π' generated this way, at least half the parts must be 1s.

We are now ready to generalize to any positive integer n. We claim that for any positive integer n, the number of partitions of n with only odd parts is greater than or equal to the number of partitions of n with only even parts.

If n is odd, then there are clearly no partitions of n with only even parts, so the result holds. Hence, assume that n is even.

For any partition π of n with only even parts, take each part a and split it into $(a-1)+1$, as done above. This generates a partition π' with only odd parts. Furthermore, at least half the parts of π' must be 1s, and there are an even number of parts (because an odd number of odd numbers must sum to an odd number, and n is even).

Conversely, for any partition π' where at least half the parts are 1's, and there are an even number of parts, we can recover the partition π as follows: Pair every part that is not a 1 with a 1, and add them. If there are any 1s left over, pair them and add them to form 2's.

Thus, we have a 1-1 correspondence between the set of partitions of n with only even parts, and the partitions of n with only odd parts, where at least half the parts are 1's.

If $n = 2$ or $n = 4$, then we can check that the number of partitions of n with only even parts is equal to the number of partitions of n with only odd parts. However, for $n \geq 6$, the partition $(n-3)+3$ contains only odd parts, and no 1s, which means that the number of partitions of n with only even parts is less than the number of partitions with only odd parts. In particular, this is true for $n = 2006$.

4.6.7 Often our strategy to prove that a set has an even number of elements is to break the set up into two halves that we can place into 1-1 correspondence with each other. We'll try a modified version of that here.

Let T be a subset of S such that the average of the elements of T is an integer. Then either T contains that average or it does not. Let A be the set of such subsets T that contain the average, and let B be the set of such subsets T that do not contain the average. At this point, we know that $\#(A) + \#(B) = k$.

Let T be a set in A with an average of m, so that $T = \{x_1, x_2, \ldots, x_l, m\}$ for some positive integer l and some distinct elements $x_1, x_2, \ldots, x_l$, none of which are equal to m. Then

$$\frac{x_1 + x_2 + \cdots + x_l + m}{l+1} = m$$
$$\Rightarrow \quad x_1 + x_2 + \cdots + x_l + m = m(l+1)$$
$$\Rightarrow \quad x_1 + x_2 + \cdots + x_l = m(l+1) - m = ml$$
$$\Rightarrow \quad \frac{x_1 + x_2 + \cdots + x_l}{l} = m.$$

Thus, the average of the elements of $\{x_1, x_2, \ldots, x_l\}$ is also m, which means that $\{x_1, x_2, \ldots, x_l\}$ is an element of B.

However, this result assumes that the set $\{x_1, x_2, \ldots, x_l, m\}$ contains more than one element, or in other words that $l \geq 1$. There are also elements of A that contain only one element, namely the singletons $\{1\}, \{2\}, \ldots, \{n\}$.

Conversely, for any element T of B, we can add the average of T to obtain an element of A with at least two elements. This establishes a 1-1 correspondence between B and the sets of A that contain more than one element. Hence, $\#(A) = \#(B) + n$, and

$$n + k = n + \#(A) + \#(B) = n + (n + \#(B)) + \#(B) = 2\#(B) + 2n = 2[\#(B) + n],$$

and hence $n + k$ is even.

Review Problems

4.21 Since 20 has a factor of 5, which is prime, one of a, b, and c must have a factor of 5. There is only one number from 1 to 9 that has a factor of 5, namely 5 itself, so one of a, b, or c must be equal to 5. Then the product of the other two numbers must be divisible by 4, which means either both are even, or one is divisible by 4 and the other is odd.

First, we count the number of triples where one number is 5 and the other two are even. We can choose any of the three numbers to be 5. There are four even numbers from 1 to 9, so there are $3 \cdot 4 \cdot 4 = 48$ such triples.

Next, we count the number of triples where one number is 5, one is divisible by 4, and one is odd. We can choose any one of the three numbers to be divisible by 4, and there are only two numbers from 1 to 9 that are divisible by 4, namely 4 and 8. There are 9 ways to choose the other two numbers so that one is odd and one is 5: we have 2 choices for which number is 5, and then 5 choices for the other odd number, but this counts twice the case where both numbers are 5. So there are $3 \cdot 2 \cdot 9 = 54$ such triples.

Therefore, there are a total of $48 + 54 = \boxed{102}$ triples (a, b, c) such that abc is divisible by 20.

4.22 Let a be the smallest element, so the largest element is $13 - a$. Then we must have $a \leq 13 - a \Rightarrow 2a \leq 13 \Rightarrow a \leq 6$. The set can then contain any combination of elements from $a + 1$ to $12 - a$. There are $12 - 2a$ such elements, thus there are $2^{(12-a)-(a+1)+1} = 2^{12-2a}$ such combinations. Therefore, the total number of subsets that have the given property is

$$\sum_{a=1}^{6} 2^{12-2a} = 1024 + 256 + 64 + 16 + 4 + 1 = \boxed{1365}.$$

4.23 There are 2^6 ways to color the cube, each of which is equally likely. We now need to count the number of these in which we can have four vertical faces of the same color. We divide into cases, based on the number of red faces.

If there are 0 or 1 red faces, then we can always place the cube so that all four vertical faces are blue. There is only 1 way to color to cube to get 0 red faces, and there are 6 ways to color the cube to get 1 red face (we just need to choose which face is red).

If there are 2 red faces, then the cube can be placed so that all four vertical faces are blue if and only if the 2 red faces are on opposite sides of the cube. There are 3 ways to color to cube with 2 opposite red faces (we just need to choose which pairs of opposite faces are red).

If there are 3 red faces, then it is impossible to place the cube with four vertical faces all the same color, since there are only 3 red faces and 3 blue faces.

The situation for 4, 5, and 6 red faces is exactly the same as the situation with 2, 1, and 0 red faces, respectively (with the red faces and blue faces reversed), so the number of cubes in these cases are 3, 6, and 1, respectively.

Therefore, the probability that the cube can be placed with four vertical faces of the same color is

$$\frac{1 + 6 + 3 + 3 + 6 + 1}{2^6} = \frac{20}{64} = \boxed{\frac{5}{16}}.$$

4.24 First, we factor $30^{39} = 2^{39} \cdot 3^{39} \cdot 5^{39}$. Hence, 30^{39} has $(39 + 1)(39 + 1)(39 + 1) = 64{,}000$ divisors.

For a number of the form $2^a 3^b 5^c$ to be a multiple of 30^{29}, we must have $a \geq 29$, $b \geq 29$, and $c \geq 29$. Therefore, to construct a divisor of 30^{39} that is a multiple of 30^{29}, we must choose $29 \leq a \leq 39$, and $29 \leq b \leq 39$, and $29 \leq c \leq 39$. There are 11 choices for each exponent, and thus $11^3 = 1{,}331$ divisors of 30^{39} that are also multiples of 30^{29}. Therefore, the desired probability is $\left(\frac{11}{40}\right)^3 = \boxed{\frac{1{,}331}{64{,}000}}$.

4.25 There are $\binom{40}{4}$ ways of drawing four slips. There are $\binom{10}{2}$ ways of choosing a and b. After a and b have been chosen, there are $\binom{4}{2}$ ways of choosing two slips labeled a, and $\binom{4}{2}$ ways of choosing two slips labeled b. Therefore, the desired probability is

$$\frac{\binom{10}{2}\binom{4}{2}\binom{4}{2}}{\binom{40}{4}} = \frac{1{,}620}{91{,}390} = \boxed{\frac{162}{9139}}.$$

4.26 First, we compute the number of ways to distribute the rolls so that each guest receives a roll of each type. For the first guest, we may choose one of three nut rolls, one of three cheese rolls, and one of three fruit rolls, leaving two rolls of each type. Then for the second guest, we may choose one of two nut rolls, one of two cheese rolls, and one of two fruit rolls, leaving one roll of each type, all of which go to the third guest. Hence, the number of correct distributions is $3^3 \cdot 2^3 = 216$.

Now we compute the total number of ways to distribute the rolls. We must choose 3 of the 9 rolls for the first person, then 3 of the 6 remaining rolls for the second person, and the remaining rolls will go to the third person. Thus, the number of ways to distribute the rolls is $\binom{9}{3}\binom{6}{3} = 1680$.

Therefore, the probability that each guest receives a roll of each type is $\frac{216}{1680} = \boxed{\frac{9}{70}}$.

4.27 If the sides of the square are parallel to the sides of the grid, then the diagonal (from the lower-left to the upper-right corners) of the square must lie along one of the diagonals of the grid, as shown in the picture to the right. Conversely, any choice of a diagonal segment uniquely determines a square. Therefore, there is a 1-1 correspondence:

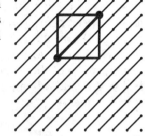

$$\{\text{squares in the grid with sides parallel to the sides of the grid}\}$$
$$\updownarrow$$
$$\{\text{pairs of points on a diagonal segment}\}.$$

There are two diagonal segments each with $2, 3, \ldots, 9$ points, and one central diagonal with 10 points. Therefore the number of pairs of points, and thus the number of squares, is

$$2\left(\binom{2}{2} + \binom{3}{2} + \cdots + \binom{9}{2}\right) + \binom{10}{2} = 2(1 + 3 + 6 + 10 + 15 + 21 + 28 + 36) + 45 = \boxed{285}.$$

4.28 There is a 1-1 correspondence

$$\{\text{Numbers in the sequence}\} \quad \leftrightarrow \quad \{\text{Positive integers written in binary}\}.$$

We simply read the binary integer as an integer in base 4. Since each digit is 0 or 1, the resulting base 4 number will be the sum of distinct powers of 4. Therefore, since 50 is 110010 in base 2, the 50th term of the sequence is the base 4 number $110010 = 4^5 + 4^4 + 4^1 = \boxed{1284}$.

4.29 Choose any element $s \in S$. There is a 1-1 correspondence

$$\{T \subseteq S \text{ with } \#(T) \text{ odd}\} \quad \leftrightarrow \quad \{T \subseteq S \text{ with } \#(T) \text{ even}\},$$

which in both directions is given by the following algorithm: for any subset $T \subseteq S$, if $s \in T$ then the correspondence takes T to $T \setminus \{s\}$, and if $s \notin T$ then the correspondence takes T to $T \cup \{s\}$. This pairs up subsets containing s with subsets that do not contain s. Furthermore, adding or deleting s always changes the parity of $\#(T)$, so every odd subset is mapped to an even subset and vice versa. Therefore, the numbers of even-sized and odd-sized subsets of S are equal.

4.30 By Problem 4.19, for all $1 \leq k \leq n$, the number of partitions of n into exactly k parts is equal to the number of partitions of n in which the largest part is k. Summing over $1 \leq k \leq r$, we get that the number of partitions of n into at most r parts is equal to the number of the partitions of n where the largest part is at most r.

4.31 Every partition of n either contains 1 as a part or it does not.

If a partition of n with k parts contains a 1, then we can remove the 1 to obtain a partition of $n - 1$ with $k - 1$ parts. Conversely, given a partition of $n - 1$ with $k - 1$ parts, we can add a 1 to this partition to get a partition of n with k parts, each of which is at least 2. This establishes a 1-1 correspondence between the set of partitions of n with k parts that contain a 1, and the set of partitions of $n - 1$ with $k - 1$ parts, of which there are $f(n - 1, k - 1)$.

If a partition of n with k parts does not contain a 1, then every part is at least 2. We can then subtract 1 from each part to obtain a partition of $n - k$ with k parts. Conversely, given a partition of $n - k$ with k parts, we can add 1 to each part to get a partition of n with k parts. This establishes a 1-1 correspondence between the set of partitions of n with k parts that do not contain a 1, and the set of partitions of $n - k$ with k parts, of which there are $f(n - k, k)$.

Hence, $f(n, k) = f(n - 1, k - 1) + f(n - k, k)$.

4.32 A path starting at $(0, 0)$ and ending at $(5, 1)$, which passes through all 12 points, corresponds to an ordering of the set of 10 points:

$$\{(1, 0), (2, 0), (3, 0), (4, 0), (5, 0), (0, 1), (1, 1), (2, 1), (3, 1), (4, 1)\}.$$

However, we have the additional condition that the path cannot cross itself. This means that the point $(a, 0)$ must appear before the point $(b, 0)$ for all $1 \le a < b \le 5$, and that the point $(c, 1)$ must appear before the point $(d, 1)$ for all $0 \le c < d \le 4$. In other words, our ordering of the 10 points in the above set must include $(1, 0), (2, 0), (3, 0), (4, 0), (5, 0)$ in order, and also must include $(0, 1), (1, 1), (2, 1), (3, 1), (4, 1)$ in order. This is equivalent to choosing 5 of the 10 points in our list to have y-coordinate 0, and the rest to have y-coordinate 1, as once we assign the y-coordinates, the x-coordinates are determined by the orderings above. Therefore, we have a 1-1 correspondence

$$\{\text{Paths satisfying the condition}\} \quad \leftrightarrow \quad \{\text{Orderings of five 0's and five 1's}\}.$$

The latter set is easy to count, so there are $\boxed{\dbinom{10}{5} = 252}$ such paths.

Challenge Problems

4.33 We claim that it is impossible to place eight knights on the chessboard so that all squares on the chessboard are attacked.

For the sake of contradiction, suppose that there is such a placement. Each knight attacks at most eight squares, and there are eight knights and 64 squares, so for every square to be attacked, each knight must attack eight squares. Consider the square marked A in the chessboard below.

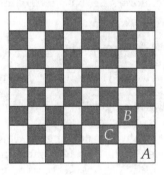

This square can only be attacked by a knight at squares B or C, so we must have one of our knights on either B or C. But a knight at square B or C attacks only six squares, a contradiction of the fact that each knight must attack 8 squares.

Therefore, there is no placement of the knights so that all squares are attacked, so the desired probability is $\boxed{0}$.

4.34 On the test, let a be the number of questions that have an answer of true, leaving $10 - a$ questions that have an answer of false.

First, we look at the case $a \le 5$. Suppose I were to put false for each of the a questions where the answer was actually true. Then the answer to each of the remaining questions is false, and I only write false $5 - a$ more times. So, to ensure that I always get at least four questions correct, we must have $5 - a \ge 4 \Rightarrow a \le 1$.

Conversely, if $a \le 1$, then there is at most one question whose answer is true. Even if I put down false for this question, I still have at least four other questions where I write down false and the correct answer is false, so I always get at least four questions right, and the condition is satisfied.

The case $a \ge 5$ is symmetric, with true and false answers switched, so a test satisfies the condition in the problem if and only if there are 0, 1, 9, or 10 questions where the correct answer is true. Therefore, there are

$$\binom{10}{0} + \binom{10}{1} + \binom{10}{9} + \binom{10}{10} = \boxed{22}$$

such tests.

4.35 First we place the purple balls, row by row. There are four possible places in the first row, then three in the second row, then two in the third row, and then only one in the fourth row, so there are $4 \cdot 3 \cdot 2 \cdot 1 = 24$ possible ways to place the purple balls.

Now choose any purple ball, say in row r_1 and column c_1. There must be a green ball in row r_1, for which there are three possible places. Let this green ball be in column c_2. And there must be another green ball in column c_1, for which there are also three possible places. Let this green ball be in row r_2.

There are now two rows and two columns that do not contain a green ball, which intersect in four places. Let S be the set of these four places. We claim that S contains at least one purple ball.

There is a purple ball (the one we originally chose) at the intersection of row r_1 and column c_1, so no more purple balls can be in row r_1 or column c_1. There is another purple ball in row r_2, and another (potentially the same) purple ball in column c_2, so rows r_1 and r_2 and columns c_1 and c_2 collectively contain at most three (but at least two) purple balls, so S contains either 1 or 2 purple balls.

If S contains one purple ball, then the last two green balls can be placed in only one way. If S contains two purple balls, then they must be in different rows and columns, and so the last two green balls can also be placed in only one way in the remaining two boxes. Thus, the final arrangement is uniquely determined by the placements of the four purple balls and the first two green balls.

Hence, the number of possible arrangements is $24 \cdot 3 \cdot 3 = \boxed{216}$.

4.36 For four numbers to sum to 0, with each equal to 1 or -1, there must be exactly two 1s and two -1s. Thus, the problem is equivalent to finding the number of ways of placing eight 1s in a 4×4 array such that each row and each column contains exactly two 1s.

First, we choose the placement of the two 1s in the first row. There are $\binom{4}{2} = 6$ such choices. Let these 1s be in columns c_1 and c_2. There is a second 1 in column c_1; let this 1 be in row r_1. Similarly, there is a second 1 in column c_2; let this 1 be in row r_2. We have two cases: Either $r_1 = r_2$ or $r_1 \neq r_2$.

Case 1: $r_1 = r_2$. If rows r_1 and r_2 coincide, then we have placed four 1s that take up two rows and two columns, and the other four 1s must be placed at the intersections of the other two rows and other two columns. There are 3 choices for row $r_1 = r_2$, so there are a total of $6 \cdot 3 = 18$ placements in this case.

Case 2: $r_1 \neq r_2$. In this case, we have placed two 1s in the top row, as well as one 1 in row r_1, and one 1 in row r_2. Then the two 1s in the fourth remaining row must go in the two columns other than columns c_1 and c_2, and then the final two 1s can be placed in two different ways. There are $3 \cdot 2 = 6$ ways to choose distinct rows r_1 and r_2, so there are a total of $6 \cdot 6 \cdot 2 = 72$ placements in this case.

Therefore, the number of 4×4 matrices of 1's and -1's where the sum of the entries in each row and in each column is 0 is $18 + 72 = \boxed{90}$.

4.37 We begin by arbitrarily coloring the points in the first row. We have the following cases: either no two adjacent points have the same color, or some two adjacent points have the same color.

Case 1: No two adjacent points have the same color.

If no two adjacent points have the same color, then the colors must alternate, so there are only two such colorings of the first row.

Then we can see that the colors in the next row must also alternate, but either of the two colorings that alternate will work. This holds for every successive row. Since there are two possible colorings for the first row and two colorings for every successive row, the total number of colorings in this case is 2^{11}.

Case 2: Two adjacent points have the same color.

Since there are 2^{11} possible ways to color the first row, and two of them have already been accounted for in

Case 1, there are $2^{11} - 2$ ways to color the first row in this case.

Consider a pair of adjacent points in the first row that have the same color. Then the corresponding points in the second row must have the opposite color. But after the colors of these points have been determined, the colors of all the other points in the second row are uniquely determined. (In fact, the color of each point in the second row is the opposite of the color of the corresponding point in the first row.)

By the same reasoning, the color of every point in every successive row is uniquely determined. Hence, the color of every vertex is uniquely determined by the colors of the first row, so the total number of colorings in this case is $2^{11} - 2$.

Therefore, the total number of possible colorings is $2^{11} + 2^{11} - 2 = 2^{12} - 2 = \boxed{4094}$.

4.38 First, we count the total number of ways of choosing four segments. There are $\binom{10}{2} = 45$ possible line segments, so there are $\binom{45}{4}$ ways of choosing four segments.

Next, we count the number of ways of choosing four segments such that three of them form a triangle. Among the ten points, there are $\binom{10}{3} = 120$ ways of choosing three vertices to form a triangle. There are 45 possible line segments, and we have already chosen three, so there are 42 ways of choosing the fourth segment. Hence, there are $120 \cdot 42 = 5040$ such ways.

Therefore, the probability is $\dfrac{5040}{\binom{45}{4}} = \boxed{\dfrac{16}{473}}$.

4.39 Let T be a subset of S with the given property, and let d be the common difference of the arithmetic sequence formed by the elements of T. Then T is determined uniquely by any element a of the arithmetic sequence, because T must be the intersection of S and the infinite arithmetic sequence

$$\{\ldots, \quad a - 2d, \quad a - d, \quad a, \quad a + d, \quad a + 2d, \quad \ldots\}.$$

If $d < 50$, then for any element a in S, either $a - d$ or $a + d$ is also in S, so T will always have at least two elements. Therefore, we have a 1-1 correspondence

$$\{\text{Subsets } T \text{ with } d < 50\} \quad \leftrightarrow \quad \{\text{Ordered pairs } (d, a) \text{ with } 1 \le d < 50 \text{ and } 1 \le a \le d\}.$$

Hence there are

$$\sum_{d=1}^{49} d = \frac{(50)(49)}{2} = 1225$$

such sequences.

If $d \ge 50$, then T must consist of exactly two elements, and must be one of the sets

$$\{1, d+1\}, \quad \{2, d+2\}, \quad \ldots, \quad \{100 - d, 100\}.$$

Therefore there is a 1-1 correspondence

$$\{\text{Subsets } T \text{ with } d \ge 50\} \quad \leftrightarrow \quad \{\text{Ordered pairs } (d, a) \text{ with } 50 \le d \le 99 \text{ and } 1 \le a \le 100 - d\}.$$

Hence there are

$$\sum_{d=50}^{99} (100 - d) = \sum_{i=1}^{50} i = \frac{(51)(50)}{2} = 1275$$

such sequences.

Therefore, the number of such sets is $1225 + 1275 = \boxed{2500}$.

4.40 We can divide the 2^{10} subsets according to whether they contain the element 10 or not. There are 2^9 subsets that contain the element 10, and 2^9 subsets that do not contain the element 10. If S is a subset of $\{1, 2, 3, \ldots, 10\}$ that does not contain the element 10, then we can form the corresponding set $S \cup \{10\}$, which does contain the element 10; this gives the 1-1 correspondence

$$\{\text{Subsets containing } 10\} \quad \leftrightarrow \quad \{\text{Subsets not containing } 10\}.$$

Let $S = \{x_1, x_2, \ldots, x_n\}$ be a subset of $\{1, 2, 3, \ldots, 10\}$ that does not contain the element 10, where $x_1 < x_2 < \cdots < x_n$. Then the alternating sum of $\{x_1, x_2, \ldots, x_n\}$ is

$$x_n - x_{n-1} + x_{n-2} - \cdots + (-1)^{n-1} x_1,$$

and the alternating sum of the corresponding subset $S \cup \{10\} = \{x_1, x_2, \ldots, x_n, 10\}$ is

$$10 - x_n + x_{n-1} - x_{n-2} + \cdots + (-1)^n x_1.$$

The sum of these two alternating sums is 10. Summing over all 2^9 pairs of corresponding subsets, we find that the sum of all alternating sums is $2^9 \cdot 10 = \boxed{5120}$.

4.41 Color the seats alternately black and white, as shown. Then 18 students are seated in white seats, and 16 students are seated in black seats (since we exclude the middle seat).

All of the students in white seats must move to black seats, but there are only a total of 17 black seats available, so such a reassignment is not possible. In other words, the number of possible reassignments is $\boxed{0}$.

4.42 Suppose that we wish to place k rooks. We must choose k of the 8 rows for the rooks, and independently choose k of the 8 columns for the rooks. Once we have chosen our rows and our columns, then the placement of the rooks is fixed, for as the rows increase from bottom to top, the rooks must be placed in columns from right to left; otherwise, a rook will be below and to the left of another rook. Therefore, there is a 1-1 correspondence

$$\{\text{Placement of } k \text{ rooks subject to the condition}\} \quad \leftrightarrow \quad \{\text{Choices of } k \text{ rows and } k \text{ columns}\}.$$

The latter set has $\binom{8}{k}\binom{8}{k}$ elements, so the total number of ways to place a positive number of rooks is

$$\sum_{k=1}^{8} \binom{8}{k}\binom{8}{k} = \boxed{12869}.$$

Note that the final answer can be computed simply by plugging in the numbers, or by using the identity

$$\sum_{k=0}^{n} \left(\binom{n}{k} \right)^2 = \binom{2n}{n},$$

so that the answer here is $\binom{16}{8} - 1$. (We will prove this identity in Chapter 12, or you can try to prove it now on your own.)

4.43 Note that we have the 1-1 correspondence

$$\{\text{Colorings of the faces of an octahedron}\} \quad \leftrightarrow \quad \{\text{Colorings of the vertices of a cube}\},$$

where we think of the cube as embedded inside the octahedron, so that each vertex of the cube touches a face of the octahedron. This doesn't really change the problem, but it makes it slightly easier to visualize.

Choose one vertex of the cube to be a particular color. Then the other seven vertices can be colored in 7! ways. However, the cube can be rotated by 120° and 240° about the chosen vertex, and these rotations take the cube to itself. This means that each coloring is counted three times. Hence, the total number of colorings (up to rotational symmetry) is 7!/3 = $\boxed{1680}$.

4.44 Let S be a subset of $\{1, 2, \ldots, 3000\}$ with the property that no element in S is double another element in S. Let a be an odd positive integer, and consider the sequence

$$a, \quad 2a, \quad 4a, \quad 8a, \quad 16a, \quad \ldots.$$

Each term in the sequence is half the next term, so no two consecutive terms can appear in S. Thus, the number of elements in S is maximized by taking all the elements of the form $a, 4a, 16a, \ldots$, where a is an odd positive integer; in other words, S is maximized by taking the elements that have an even number of factors of 2.

So the maximal subsets S consists of the following elements:

$$
\begin{array}{cccc}
1, & 4, & 16, & \ldots, \\
3, & 12, & 48, & \ldots, \\
5, & 20, & 80, & \ldots, \\
7, & 28, & 112, & \ldots.
\end{array}
$$

We need to determine $\#(S)$. Instead of counting the number of elements by rows, we can count the number of elements by columns.

We can count the elements in the first column by taking all the numbers from 1 to 3000, and then subtracting the even numbers from 1 to 3000. This is $3000 - \lfloor 3000/2 \rfloor$.

We can then count the elements in the second column by taking all the multiples of 4 from 1 to 3000, and then subtracting the multiples of 8 from 1 to 3000. This is $\lfloor 3000/4 \rfloor - \lfloor 3000/8 \rfloor$.

Similarly, the number of elements in the third column is $\lfloor 3000/16 \rfloor - \lfloor 3000/32 \rfloor$, and so on, so the maximum number of elements in S is

$$
3000 - \left\lfloor \frac{3000}{2} \right\rfloor + \left\lfloor \frac{3000}{4} \right\rfloor - \left\lfloor \frac{3000}{8} \right\rfloor + \left\lfloor \frac{3000}{16} \right\rfloor - \left\lfloor \frac{3000}{32} \right\rfloor + \cdots
$$
$$
= 3000 - 1500 + 750 - 375 + 187 - 93 + 46 - 23 + 11 - 5 + 2 - 1
$$
$$
= 1999.
$$

Hence, S cannot contain 2000 elements.

4.45 We begin with the first row. We may color the first 2006 squares of the first row arbitrarily. Then the color of the last square of the first row is uniquely determined, since the first row must contain an even number of black squares: if we colored an even number of the first 2006 squares black, then we must color the last square white, and if we colored an odd number of the first 2006 squares black, then we must color the last square black.

The same procedure can be applied to any of the first 2006 rows: Color the first 2006 squares arbitrarily, and the color of the last square is uniquely determined. There are 2^{2006} such ways to color each row, so there are a total of $(2^{2006})^{2006} = 2^{2006^2}$ such colorings.

Then the colors of the first 2006 squares of the last row are also uniquely determined, since each column must contain an even number of black squares.

The only square whose color is left to be determined is the last square of the last row. The color of this square must satisfy two conditions: The number of black squares in the last row must be even, and the number of black squares in the last column must be even. Fortunately, these conditions are consistent, because both conditions are equivalent to the total number of black squares being even, and so the color of this last square is uniquely determined.

Therefore, the number of possible colorings is $\boxed{2^{2006^2}}$.

4.46 We may without loss of generality assume that $a_1 < a_2 < a_3$ and $b_1 < b_2 < b_3$. (If this is not the case, then just relabel the numbers.) Then the brick fits inside the box if and only if $a_1 < b_1$ and $a_2 < b_2$ and $a_3 < b_3$.

We find that there are only five ways that all six numbers can be ordered, subject to $a_1 < a_2 < a_3$ and $b_1 < b_2 < b_3$, that satisfy these inequalities:

$$a_1 < a_2 < a_3 < b_1 < b_2 < b_3,$$
$$a_1 < a_2 < b_1 < a_3 < b_2 < b_3,$$
$$a_1 < b_1 < a_2 < a_3 < b_2 < b_3,$$
$$a_1 < a_2 < b_1 < b_2 < a_3 < b_3,$$
$$a_1 < b_1 < a_2 < b_2 < a_3 < b_3.$$

On the other hand, there are $\binom{6}{3} = 20$ possible orderings of the a's and b's, given the condition that $a_1 < a_2 < a_3$ and $b_1 < b_2 < b_3$: we must choose 3 of the 6 slots to be a's, and the rest are b's. All 20 orderings are equally likely over all the possible choices of a's and b's, and as we saw, 5 of them lead to the brick being enclosed in a box.

Therefore, the probability that the brick fits inside the box is $\dfrac{5}{20} = \boxed{\dfrac{1}{4}}$.

Note that the probability is the same if the number 1000 (in the problem) is replaced by any number that is at least 6, as the actual choice of numbers is irrelevant; all that matters is the relative ordering of the numbers that are chosen.

4.47 For convenience, let $\mathbb{N}$ denote the set $\{1, 2, 3, \ldots\}$ of positive integers. (These are sometimes called *natural numbers*, hence the notation $\mathbb{N}$.)

(a) Let $f : \mathbb{N} \to \mathbb{Z}$ be defined as

$$f(n) = \begin{cases} \frac{n}{2} & \text{if } n \text{ is even,} \\ -\frac{n-1}{2} & \text{if } n \text{ is odd.} \end{cases}$$

Note that all of the even integers in $\mathbb{N}$ map to the positive integers, and all of the odd integers in $\mathbb{N}$ map to the negative integers. Also note that every integer is in the range of $\mathbb{Z}$. So f establishes a 1-1 correspondence $\mathbb{N} \to \mathbb{Z}$.

(b) First, note that every rational number can be represented in lowest terms as m/n, where m is an integer, n is a positive integer, and $(m, n) = 1$. Let T be the subset of ordered pairs (m, n) of integers where $n > 0$ and $(m, n) = 1$; then $\mathbb{Q}$ is in 1-1 correspondence with T.

We can list all of the elements of T by constructing a spiral on the Cartesian plane starting at the origin and extending outwards in a counterclockwise direction, as shown in the picture at right. Note that not all of the lattice points are elements of T, but we can skip those that are not. (The lattice points that are members of T are circled in the diagram.) In other words, we are making a correspondence between $\mathbb{N}$ and T, where 1 corresponds to the first element of T in the spiral (namely, $(1,1)$, which corresponds to the rational number $\frac{1}{1}$), 2 corresponds to the second element of T in the spiral (namely, $(0,1)$, which corresponds to the rational number $\frac{0}{1}$), 3 corresponds to the third element of T in the spiral (namely, $(-1,1)$, which corresponds to the rational number $\frac{-1}{1}$), 4 corresponds to the fourth element of T in the spiral (namely, $(2,1)$, which corresponds to the rational number $\frac{2}{1}$), and so on. Every element of T will occur in the list, so T is in 1-1 correspondence with $\mathbb{N}$, and hence $\mathbb{Q}$ is also in 1-1 correspondence with $\mathbb{N}$.

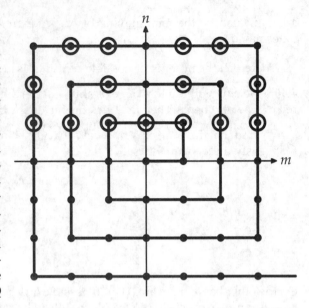

(c) Let $[0,1] = \{r \in \mathbb{R} \mid 0 \leq r \leq 1\}$. We can make a 1-1 correspondence $[0,1] \leftrightarrow \mathcal{P}(\mathbb{N})$ as follows. Write every such r as a binary decimal: $r = .r_1 r_2 r_3 \ldots$, where each digit r_i is either 0 or 1. This corresponds to a subset N_r of $\mathbb{N}$, where $i \in N_r$ if and only if $r_i = 1$ in the binary decimal expansion. Thus, $[0,1]$ cannot be in 1-1 correspondence with $\mathbb{N}$, and hence neither is the larger set $\mathbb{R}$. So $\mathbb{R}$ is uncountable.

CHAPTER 5

The Pigeonhole Principle

Exercises for Section 5.2

5.2.1 We argue by contradiction. Suppose that each of the boxes contains at most one ball. If we add up the total of all of the balls in all of the boxes, then this total must be at most k, since there is at most 1 ball in each box. But we already know that this total is n, since there are n balls. Therefore, we must have $n \leq k$. But this is a contradiction, as we are given that $n > k$. Therefore, at least one box contains more than one ball.

5.2.2 Imagine placing each coin in a box called "heads" or a box called "tails," depending on its result. By the Pigeonhole Principle, since I have 3 coins, at least one of the boxes must contain at least 2 coins.

5.2.3 If we draw 13 cards, all with different rank, then there will be no pairs, so 13 cards will not suffice. On the other hand, if we draw 14 cards, then by the Pigeonhole Principle, there must be two cards of the same rank, which means there must be a pair. Therefore, we must draw at least $\boxed{14}$ cards.

Exercises for Section 5.3

5.3.1 There are only 10 different units digits an integer can have, namely 0, 1, 2, ..., 9. Therefore, by the Pigeonhole Principle, among any 11 integers, there must be two with the same units digit.

5.3.2

(a) Since there are 8 rows and 8 columns, we can place at most 8 rooks on the chessboard so that no two rooks lie in the same row or same column. If we tried to place 9 or more rooks, then by the Pigeonhole Principle, there would have to be at least 2 rooks in some row, which is not allowed. But if we place 8 rooks on a diagonal of the chessboard as shown at right, then no two rooks lie in the same row or same column. So the maximum number of rooks we can place is $\boxed{8}$.

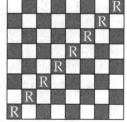

(b) We can divide the black squares into 7 diagonals, as shown in the diagram on the left below (on the next page). Each diagonal can contain at most one bishop, so the number of bishops that are on black squares can be at most 7. Similarly, the number of bishops that are on white squares can be at most 7, so there can be at most 14 bishops on the chessboard such that no two lie in the same diagonal. It is indeed possible to place $\boxed{14}$ bishops such that no two lie in the same diagonal, as shown in the diagram on the right below (on the next page).

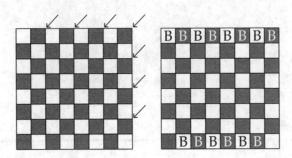

5.3.3 The possible groups that can sum to 4 are: 4, 3 + 1, 2 + 2, 2 + 1 + 1, and 1 + 1 + 1 + 1. If we have at least four 1's in our sum, then we're done, so assume that we have three or fewer 1's. If we have two or three 1's, then we must have at least one 2, 3, or 4, because otherwise the other five or six elements would all be at least 5, which would make the total too large. In any of these cases, we can pair a 2, 3, or 4 with the appropriate number of 1's to get a group that sums to 4.

If we have only one 1, then we must have either at least two 2's or a 3 or a 4; if we have only one 2 and every other of the six remaining elements is 5 or greater, then the total is too big.

Finally, if we have no 1's, then we must show that we will either have two 2's or a 4. In fact, we must have two 2's: if we have only one 2 and the other seven elements are all at least 3, then the total is at least $2 + 7(3) = 23 > 20$, so this cannot happen.

So, in any case, we must have a group that sums to 4.

Note: while this solution did not explicitly invoke the Pigeonhole Principle, the type of reasoning that we used is definitely of the same flavor as the Pigeonhole Principle.

5.3.4 If x is an element in S, then no other element in S can be congruent to $7 - x$ modulo 7. Hence, we count the number of elements in $\{1, 2, 3, \ldots, 50\}$ that are congruent to $0, 1, \ldots, 6$ modulo 7, respectively. We find that there are 7 numbers congruent to 0, 2, 3, 4, 5, and 6 modulo 7, and 8 numbers congruent to 1 modulo 7.

Then to maximize the number of elements in S, we take the 8 numbers that are congruent to 1 modulo 7, the 7 numbers that are congruent to 2 modulo 7 (or 5 modulo 7), and the 7 numbers that are congruent to 3 modulo 7 (or 4 modulo 7). We can add one number (but only one) that is congruent to 0 modulo 7, so that S contains a maximum of $8 + 7 + 7 + 1 = \boxed{23}$ elements.

5.3.5 Divide each of the $n + 1$ numbers by n, and consider their remainders. There are n possible remainders, namely $0, 1, \ldots, n - 1$. Since there are $n + 1$ numbers, by the Pigeonhole Principle, some two numbers leave the same remainder when divided by n. The difference between these two numbers is then divisible by n.

5.3.6 If two numbers from 1 to 100 sum to 125, then they must be one of the following pairs: $\{25, 100\}$, $\{26, 99\}$, $\{27, 98\}, \ldots, \{62, 63\}$. There are 38 such pairs, and B can contain at most one element from each such pair. The subset B can also contain any combination of the remaining elements $1, 2, 3, \ldots, 24$, so B can contain a maximum of $38 + 24 = \boxed{62}$ elements.

Exercises for Section 5.4

5.4.1 We have 13 cards, each of which must be one of four suits. Hence, by the Pigeonhole Principle, at least $\lfloor (13 - 1)/4 \rfloor + 1 = 4$ cards must be in the same suit. (Another way to think of this is that if we had at most 3 cards of each suit, then we'd only have at most $4 \times 3 = 12$ cards in our hand, but we know that we have 13 cards.)

5.4.2 Each integer has remainder 0, 1, 2, 3, or 4 upon division by 5. There are 17 numbers and 5 possible remainders. If there are 5 numbers all with different remainders, then we can add these five numbers together: the remainders will add to $0 + 1 + 2 + 3 + 4 = 10$, and thus the sum will be a multiple of 5.

On the other hand, if one of the possible remainders is not a remainder of any of the 17 numbers, then the 17 numbers only have 4 possible remainders, and thus, by the Pigeonhole Principle, there must be at least 5 numbers with the same remainder. When we add these 5 numbers together, the result will be a multiple of 5.

5.4.3 There are a total of $\binom{11}{3} = 165$ triangles. By the Pigeonhole Principle, we know that at least $\lfloor (165-1)/4 \rfloor + 1 = 42$ triangles must have the same color. Furthermore, we can color 41 of the triangles amber, 41 burgundy, 41 chartreuse, and 42 dark green, which means it is not always true that at least 43 triangles have the same color. Hence, the largest number N for which at least N triangles have the same color, for any coloring, is $\boxed{42}$.

5.4.4

(a) There are $12 \times 6 = 72$ letters sent in August, but there are only $\binom{12}{2} = 66$ pairs of members of the club. Therefore, by the Pigeonhole Principle, there must be some pair of people that has more than 1 letter between them; that is, there must be a pair of people who send letters to each other.

(b) In September, only $12 \times 5 = 60$ letters are sent, so we cannot invoke the Pigeonhole Principle as we did in part (a). But this does not prove that the conclusion for part (a) does not hold – we still need to show that it is possible for the letters to be sent in such a way so that no pair of people exchange letters.

   Have the 12 club members sit around a circle. Then have each member send a letter to the 5 people sitting to his or her immediate left. Note that each member will receive a letter from the 5 people sitting to his or her immediate right, and no correspondence at all will take place between people who are sitting opposite from one another. This configuration of letter-sending results in no two people sending and receiving letters from each other.

5.4.5 First, note that if any student gets k questions correct and $10 - k$ questions incorrect, then she will get $\binom{k}{2}$ *pairs* of questions correct and $\binom{10-k}{2}$ pairs of questions incorrect. This gives her a total of

$$\binom{k}{2} + \binom{10-k}{2} = \frac{k(k-1)}{2} + \frac{(10-k)(9-k)}{2} = k^2 - 10k + 45$$

pairs of questions that she answers the same way (either both correct or both incorrect). Note that this number is at least 20 for any value of k, since

$$k^2 - 10k + 45 = (k-5)^2 + 20 \geq 20.$$

So each student answers at least 20 pairs of questions the same way, and hence if there are n students, then there are at least $20n$ pairs of questions answered the same way.

   There are $\binom{10}{2} = 45$ pairs of questions, thus there are 45 pairs of questions that can be answered correctly, and (the same) 45 pairs of questions that can be answered incorrectly. Thus there are 90 different pairs of questions and ways that they can be answered the same – we'll call these "pair-ways."

   Thus, by the Pigeonhole Principle, when we place the $20n$ pairs of questions answered in the same way into the 90 "pair-ways" boxes, there must be at least

$$\left\lfloor \frac{20n - 1}{90} \right\rfloor + 1$$

of them in some box. We want to be able to prove that there are at least 57 in some box, since this corresponds to at least 57 students answering the same pair of questions in the same way, so we will want to have

$$\left\lfloor \frac{20n - 1}{90} \right\rfloor \geq 56 \quad \Leftrightarrow \quad n \geq 253.$$

Thus, we have shown that if there are at least 253 students, then at least 57 of them will answer some pair of questions in the same way.

   To finish, we will have to prove that there is a non-laughable performance of 252 students. When we see a big number like "252" in a counting problem, one good idea is to try to find it in Pascal's Triangle. And indeed, we note that $\binom{10}{5} = 252$, and this gives us a plan.

We can have a group of 252 students, all of whom correctly answered five different problems. Consider any two given problems. If a student answered those two problems correctly, then there are $\binom{8}{3} = 56$ choices for the other 3 problems that he also answered correctly, therefore there are exactly 56 students who answered the two given problems correctly. Similarly, there are exactly 56 students who answered any two given problems incorrectly. Hence, the performance of this group of 252 students is not laughable.

Therefore, the answer is $\boxed{253}$.

Review Problems

5.11

(a) If I only pull out four socks, they may all have different colors, and there will not be any matching pairs. However, if I pull out five socks, then by the Pigeonhole Principle, there must be two socks of the same color, and so I will have a matching pair. Therefore, I must pull out at least $\boxed{5}$ socks to ensure a matching pair.

(b) If I pull out 6 socks, then I might get, for example, three white socks, one black sock, one brown sock, and one blue sock, so six socks do not suffice. But if I pull out seven socks, then either (1) I will get 4 of one color, giving me two pairs of that color, or (2) I will get at least 2 of two different colors, in which case I get two pairs of different colors. In either case, there will always be two matching pairs.

5.12 At any point in the tournament, each team will have played between 0 and 37 games (inclusive). However, we cannot simultaneously have a team that has played 0 games and a team that has played 37 games: the former team hasn't played anybody yet, whereas the latter team has played everyone, and these two conditions can't simultaneously occur. So there are only 37 different possible numbers of games that teams could have played, hence by the Pigeonhole Principle, at least two of them must have played the same number of games.

5.13 Let the positive integers be x_1, x_2, x_3, x_4, and x_5. For $1 \le i \le 5$, let r_i be the remainder when x_i is divided by 3. Each of these remainders r_i must be 0, 1, or 2. So we have five "balls" (the x_i) and three "boxes" (the remainders). There are two cases: Either every remainder appears at least once (meaning there is a ball in each box), or one of the remainders appears at least 3 times (if a box is empty, then there are 2 boxes remaining for the 5 balls, and thus by the Pigeonhole Principle, one of the boxes must have at least 3 balls). Note that these two cases are not exclusive, but that's OK.

If every remainder appears at least once, then choose an x_i corresponding to each of the three remainders. Their sum will be a multiple of 3. If not, then the sum of the three x_i corresponding to the same remainder will be a multiple of 3. In either case, we can find three elements whose sum is divisible by 3.

5.14 The first three students (those who got exactly 1, 2, and 3 questions right) account for 6 of the solved questions. That leaves $35 - 6 = 29$ questions that must be solved by the remaining 7 students. So, by the Pigeonhole Principle, at least one of the remaining students must have solved $\left\lfloor \frac{29-1}{7} \right\rfloor + 1 = 5$ questions.

5.15

(a) If I only buy $4 \times 7 = 28$ apples, specifically 4 of each of the 7 types, then I won't have enough to bake a pie. On the other hand, if I buy 29 apples, then by the Pigeonhole Principle there must be at least $\left\lfloor \frac{29-1}{7} \right\rfloor + 1 = 5$ apples of one type, and thus I can make a pie. So I need to buy $\boxed{29}$ apples.

(b) Thinking about the worst-case scenarios, we see that 38 apples is not enough. For instance, I might buy 14 of one type and 4 of each of the other 6 types, or I might buy 9 of two types and 4 of each of the other 5 types. In either case, I only have enough for 2 pies.

We can prove that 39 apples will do the job. If we buy at least 5 apples of at least 3 types, then we're safe, so suppose that out of our 39 apples, we have at most 4 apples of 5 different types. This accounts for at most 20 apples, so we have 19 apples left for the remaining two types. By the Pigeonhole Principle, at least 10 of these must be of the same type, and that lets us bake two pies. Once we bake those pies, we have 9 apples left, again for two types. By the Pigeonhole Principle, at least 5 must be of the same type, so we can bake a third pie. Thus we need $\boxed{39}$ apples.

Note an interesting phenomenon between these two parts. We needed 29 apples for 1 pie, but we only needed 10 additional apples for two more pies. Can you explain this?

5.16 Let the 11 positive integers be $x_1, x_2, \ldots, x_{11}$, and for $1 \le i \le 11$, let

$$s_i = x_1 + x_2 + \cdots + x_i.$$

For $1 \le i \le 11$, let r_i be the remainder when s_i is divided by 11. If some remainder r_i is equal to 0, then the corresponding sum s_i is divisible by 11, and we are done, so assume that none of the r_i are equal to 0.

Then each of the remainders r_i must be one of 1, 2, ..., 10, for a total of 10 possible remainders. By the Pigeonhole Principle, two of the remainders, say r_i and r_j are equal, where $i < j$. Then the difference between s_j and s_i is divisible by 11. But

$$s_j - s_i = x_{i+1} + x_{i+2} + \cdots + x_j,$$

which gives us a subset whose sum is divisible by 11.

5.17 If all of the friends have a different amount of money, then the minimum amount that they can have will occur if one has \$0, one has \$1, and so on, up to one having \$14. But this gives a total amount of

$$\$0 + \$1 + \cdots + \$14 = \frac{(\$14)(15)}{2} = \$105,$$

which is greater than the allowed total. Therefore, they cannot all have a different amount.

5.18 Since there are 16 people and 20 chairs, there are 4 empty seats. Divide the row of 20 chairs into 5 groups of 4 consecutive seats. Since there are 5 groups and 4 empty chairs, at least one of the 5 groups has no empty seats. So in that group with no empty seats, all four consecutive seats are full.

5.19 Divide the chessboard into 16 2×2 regions, as shown at right. If we tried to place 17 or more kings on the board, then by the Pigeonhole Principle, at least 2 of them would be in the same 2×2 region. But these two kings would necessarily be adjacent, which is not allowed. So we cannot place 17 or more kings.

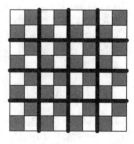

We can legally place 16 kings, by placing a king in the lower-left corner of each 2×2 region, as shown below:

Therefore, the maximum number of kings is $\boxed{16}$.

Challenge Problems

5.20 Since $\binom{6}{3} = 20$, each of the 20 students can enroll in a different combination of three courses. Then given any pair of courses, there are exactly four students who have enrolled in both courses (because there are 4 choices for the third course that each student takes, beyond the given two), and there are exactly four students that have not enrolled in either course (because there are 4 choices for the third course that each student does not take, beyond the given two). Thus, the statement given in the problem is $\boxed{\text{false}}$.

5.21 Let the band members be A, B, C, D, E, and F. Then Sam's band can give three concerts with the following members: A, B, C, D in the first concert, A, B, E, F in the second concert, and C, D, E, F in the third concert. A bit of experimentation may convince you that there's no way to do 4 concerts, so let's try to prove it.

Suppose that the band gives four concerts. Consider the band member A. For every concert he plays, he belongs to each of $\binom{3}{2} = 3$ triples. There are a total of $\binom{5}{2} = 10$ triples that he can belong to, so if no triple can appear twice, then A can play at most three concerts. The same holds for every other band member.

Let a be the number of times that A plays, and define $b, c, d, e,$ and f similarly. Then $a + b + c + d + e + f = 16$, and all six variables are at most 3. Then at least four of them must be equal to 3, for if at most three of them are equal to 3, then $a + b + c + d + e + f \le 3 \cdot 3 + 3 \cdot 2 = 15$, a contradiction. Without loss of generality, assume that $a, b, c,$ and d are equal to 3, so that A, B, C, and D play three times.

If A and B play in the same concert, then there are two triples that contain both A and B from that concert. Among all six band members, there are a total of four triples that contain both A and B, so A and B can play at most two concerts together. The same holds for any pair of A, B, C, and D, which means that there is one concert with A, B, and C; one with A, B, and D; one with A, C, and D; and one with B, C, and D.

This leaves E and F to fill four slots. By the Pigeonhole Principle, at least $\lfloor (4 - 1)/2 \rfloor + 1 = 2$ of these slots have the same member. However, this will always lead to some triple being repeated, since every pair of concerts already has two band members in common, and adding E or F will make an illegally repeated triple. So Sam's band cannot give four concerts.

Therefore, Sam's band can give at most $\boxed{3}$ concerts.

5.22 Consider the sequence

$$1, \quad p, \quad p^2, \quad p^3, \quad \dots$$

Each term p^k can only have one of 10000 different remainders upon division by 10000, but the sequence contains an infinite number of terms, so there exist i and j such that $1 \le i < j$ and $p^i \equiv p^j \pmod{10^4}$. In other words, $p^j - p^i = p^i(p^{j-i} - 1)$ is a multiple of 10000. But if p is any prime other than 2 or 5, then p^i is relatively prime to 10000. Therefore, $p^{j-i} - 1$ is a multiple of 10000, which means that p^{j-i} ends in the digits 0001.

Alternatively, if you know Euler's Theorem, then you can say that $p^{\phi(10^4)} = p^{4000} \equiv 1 \pmod{10^4}$.

5.23 Let $\langle x \rangle$ denote the fractional part of a real number x; that is, $\langle x \rangle = x - \lfloor x \rfloor$. Note that $0 \le \langle x \rangle < 1$ for all real numbers x. For all integers $0 \le i \le n - 1$, define

$$B_i = \left\{ x \in \mathbb{R} \mid \frac{i}{n} \le \langle x \rangle < \frac{i+1}{n} \right\}.$$

In other words, B_i is the set of all real numbers whose fractional parts lie between $\frac{i}{n}$ and $\frac{i+1}{n}$. For a real number to be at most $\frac{1}{n}$ from an integer, it must be in B_0 or B_{n-1} (except that it could be exactly $\frac{1}{n}$ greater than an integer, in which case it would lie in B_1, but it turns out that this detail is not important).

We will proceed by contradiction. Suppose that none of $r, 2r, \dots, (n-1)r$ are in B_0 or in B_{n-1}. Then they are all in $B_1, B_2, \dots B_{n-2}$. So we have $n - 1$ real numbers but only $n - 2$ of the B_i's, so by the Pigeonhole Principle, two different multiples of r in our list must be in the same B_i. Suppose that ar and br are in the same B_i, with $a < b$. Then their difference $(b - a)r$ is in our list of multiple of r, and lies in either B_0 or B_{n-1} (since the fractional parts of ar and br differ by less than $\frac{1}{n}$), giving a contradiction.

Thus one of the elements in the list must be no more than $\frac{1}{n}$ from an integer.

5.24 The Pigeonhole Principle tells us that given any set of 4 points, there must be at least 2 that are the same color. However, we need 4 points that are the same color, and in a particular configuration: corners of a rectangle.

Sets of 4 points have $3^4 = 81$ possible colorings, so we might try to find some sort of Pigeonhole argument with $81 + 1 = 82$ sets of 4 points.

Consider a grid of 4×82 points in the plane, so each column contains 4 points. As discussed above, by the Pigeonhole Principle, there are two columns whose points are colored the same way. Now consider the colors in one of these columns. There are four points in the column, so again by the Pigeonhole Principle, at least two of these points must have the same color. The corresponding points in the other column also have the same color, so these four points form a rectangle where all the vertices have the same color.

Using a more clever argument, one can show that every grid of 4×19 points must contain a rectangle where all the vertices have the same color. Can you find it?

5.25 We claim that a maximum of 16 squares can be colored. The diagram at right shows a possible shading of 16 squares.

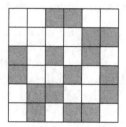

For each row, consider the pairs of columns that are formed by the colored squares in that row. For example, in the bottom row in the diagram at right, the three colored squares form three pairs of columns (namely, the second and fourth columns, second and fifth columns, and fourth and fifth columns). More generally, for $1 \leq i \leq 6$, let a_i be the number of colored squares in the ith row. Then the colored squares in the ith row generate $\binom{a_i}{2}$ pairs of columns.

Now, if the colored squares in two different rows have two columns in common, then the two rows and two columns intersect in four colored squares that form a rectangle. Therefore, if no four squares form a rectangle, then a given pair of columns can be represented in at most one row. In particular, the total number of pairs of columns represented over all rows must be at most $\binom{6}{2} = 15$. This gives us the inequality

$$\binom{a_1}{2} + \binom{a_2}{2} + \binom{a_3}{2} + \binom{a_4}{2} + \binom{a_5}{2} + \binom{a_6}{2} \leq 15.$$

We claim that if $a_1, a_2, \ldots, a_6$ are nonnegative integers that satisfy this inequality, then $a_1 + a_2 + \cdots + a_6$ can be at most 16.

We can turn this problem around, and ask when

$$S = \binom{a_1}{2} + \binom{a_2}{2} + \cdots + \binom{a_6}{2}$$

is minimized for a fixed sum $s = a_1 + a_2 + \cdots + a_6$. We claim that this occurs when no two of the a_i differ by more than 1.

Suppose that two of the a_i differ by more than 1, so $a_j \geq a_i + 2$ for some i, j. Then we claim that S decreases when a_i is replaced by $a_i + 1$ and a_j is replaced by $a_j - 1$. (Note that the sum $s = a_1 + a_2 + \cdots + a_6$ remains the same.) To see this, we expand:

$$\binom{a_i}{2} + \binom{a_j}{2} - \left[\binom{a_i + 1}{2} + \binom{a_j - 1}{2} \right] = \frac{a_i(a_i - 1)}{2} + \frac{a_j(a_j - 1)}{2} - \frac{(a_i + 1)a_i}{2} - \frac{(a_j - 1)(a_j - 2)}{2}$$

$$= a_j - a_i - 1$$

$$\geq 1.$$

This difference is positive, so the sum S does indeed decrease.

Hence, to minimize S, it suffices to look at values $a_1, a_2, \ldots, a_6$ where no two of the a_i differ by more than 1. In particular, when $s = 16$, the minimum value of S is

$$\binom{2}{2} + \binom{2}{2} + \binom{3}{2} + \binom{3}{2} + \binom{3}{2} + \binom{3}{2} = 1 + 1 + 3 + 3 + 3 + 3 = 14.$$

For $s = 17$, the minimum value of S is

$$\binom{2}{2} + \binom{3}{2} + \binom{3}{2} + \binom{3}{2} + \binom{3}{2} + \binom{3}{2} = 1 + 3 + 3 + 3 + 3 + 3 = 16.$$

However, we want S to be at most 15, so s is at most 16. And we have already given an example for 16 colored squares. Therefore, the maximum number of squares that can be colored so that no four form a rectangle is $\boxed{16}$.

5.26 The formal proof is a little hard to follow, so let's first informally explain the procedure. Imagine that we have white stones with weights $x_1, x_2, \ldots, x_m$, and that we have black stones with weights $y_1, y_2, \ldots, y_n$. We also imagine a large balance-type scale, with two pans balancing across a fulcrum. Our goal is to put some number of white stones in the left pan and some number of black stones in the right pan, so that the two sides balance.

We use what is essentially a "greedy" algorithm: start by placing a white stone in the left pan, and then at each step, add a stone to whichever side is lighter, and keep doing this until we run out of stones. Either at some intermediate point the scales will be in balance (in which case we're done), or we'll run out of stones. But the bounds on the weights of the individual stones mean that the scale can never be out-of-balance by more than n on the left side or by more than $m - 1$ on the right side. (It can never be out of balance by m on the right, since we started with a white stone in the left pan.) Since there are $m + n$ total stones and only $m + n - 1$ different ways that the scale can be out of balance, we may conclude by the Pigeonhole Principle that if we run out of stones, the scale must have been out of balance by the same amount at two different times. But this means that all the stones that we added between these two times must balance evenly, thus solving the problem.

Keeping this algorithm in mind, we'll now present a formal proof.

For $1 \le i \le m$, let $s_i = x_1 + x_2 + \cdots + x_i$, and for $1 \le j \le n$, let $t_j = y_1 + y_2 + \cdots + y_j$. Without loss of generality, assume that $s_m \le t_n$. (If $s_m > t_n$, then the same argument works with all the x's and y's reversed.)

For all $1 \le i \le m$, we have $s_i \le s_m \le t_n$, so there always exists an index j such that $s_i \le t_j$. Define $f(i)$ to be the smallest such index. Then for $1 \le i \le m$, let $c_i = t_{f(i)} - s_i$, so $c_i \ge 0$ for all i. If $c_i = 0$ for some i, then $s_i = t_{f(i)}$, which means

$$x_1 + x_2 + \cdots + x_i = y_1 + y_2 + \cdots + y_{f(i)},$$

and we are done, so assume that $c_i \ge 1$ for all i.

We claim that $c_i \le m - 1$ for all i. For the sake of contradiction, suppose that $c_i \ge m$ for some i, so $s_i + m \le t_{f(i)}$. Note that $s_i + m \ge m + 1 > y_1 = t_1$, so $f(i)$ must be at least 2. Then

$$s_i \le t_{f(i)} - m = y_1 + y_2 + \cdots + y_{f(i)-1} + y_{f(i)} - m \le y_1 + y_2 + \cdots + y_{f(i)-1} = t_{f(i)-1}.$$

However, this contradicts the definition of $f(i)$. Therefore, $c_i \le m - 1$ for all i.

Hence, each of the m numbers $c_1, c_2, \ldots, c_m$ must be between 1 and $m - 1$. By the Pigeonhole Principle, there exist indices $p < q$ such that $c_p = c_q$, or $t_{f(p)} - s_p = t_{f(q)} - s_q$. Then $s_q - s_p = t_{f(q)} - t_{f(p)}$, so

$$x_{p+1} + x_{p+2} + \cdots + x_q = y_{f(p)+1} + y_{f(p)+2} + \cdots + y_{f(q)},$$

as desired.

5.27 Since every team has an equal probability of winning, the probability that no two teams win the same number of games is equal to the number of tournaments where no two teams win the same number of games, divided by the total number of possible tournaments.

Label the teams 1 through 40 arbitrarily, and for $1 \le i \le 40$, let w_i be the number of games won by team i. Then $0 \le w_i \le 39$ for all i, so there are 40 possible values of w_i. Hence, if all the w_i are distinct, then all 40 possible values must be represented among the w_i.

We can relabel the teams, if necessary, so that team i wins $i - 1$ games. In particular, team 40 wins all of its 39 games. Since team 39 wins 38 games, the only game it lost was to team 40. Then team 38 wins 37 games, and so the only two games it lost were to teams 39 and 40, and so on. It follows that for any $1 \le i < j \le 40$, team j won against team i.

Hence, any tournament in which no two teams win the same number of games corresponds to a permutation of the 40 teams, of which there are 40!. There are $\binom{40}{2} = 780$ games, and each game has 2 possible outcomes, so there are a total 2^{780} possible tournaments. Therefore, the probability that no two teams win the same number of games is $\boxed{\dfrac{40!}{2^{780}}}$.

5.28 Let A, B, C, D, E, and F be the sets of numbers of the members from the six countries. Then by the Pigeonhole Principle, one of the sets contains at least $\lfloor (1978 - 1)/6 \rfloor + 1 = 330$ elements. Without loss of generality, assume that this set is A, and let the 330 elements be $a_1 < a_2 < \cdots < a_{330}$.

For $1 \le i \le 329$, let $b_i = a_{330} - a_{330-i}$, so $b_1 < b_2 < \cdots < b_{329}$. If one of these b_i belongs to A, then we have

$$b_i = a_{330} - a_{330-i} \quad \Rightarrow \quad a_{330-i} + b_i = a_{330},$$

and a_{330-i}, b_i, and a_{330} are all in A, and we are done.

Otherwise, all of the b_i belong to the other five sets. By the Pigeonhole Principle, one of the five sets contains at least $\lfloor (329 - 1)/5 \rfloor + 1 = 66$ of these differences b_i. Without loss of generality, let this set be B, and let the 66 differences be $b'_1 < b'_2 < \cdots < b'_{66}$. For $1 \le j \le 65$, let $c_j = b'_{66} - b'_{66-j}$.

Then for each j, there exist indices i_1 and i_2 such that $b'_{66} = a_{330} - a_{i_1}$ and $b'_{66-j} = a_{330} - a_{i_2}$, so

$$
\begin{aligned}
c_j &= b'_{66} - b'_{66-j} \\
&= (a_{330} - a_{i_1}) - (a_{330} - a_{i_2}) \\
&= a_{i_2} - a_{i_1}.
\end{aligned}
$$

If c_j belongs to B, then

$$c_j = b'_{66} - b'_{66-j} \quad \Rightarrow \quad b'_{66-j} + c_j = b'_{66},$$

and b'_{66-j}, c_j, and b'_{66} are all in B, and we are done. If c_j belongs to A, then

$$c_j = a_{i_2} - a_{i_1} \quad \Rightarrow \quad a_{i_1} + c_j = a_{i_2},$$

and a_{i_1}, c_j, and a_{i_2} are all in A, and again we are done.

Otherwise, all of the c_j belong to the other four sets, and we can proceed in the same way as above. By the Pigeonhole Principle, one of the four sets contains at least $\lfloor (65 - 1)/4 \rfloor + 1 = 17$ of these differences c_j. Without loss of generality, let this set be C, and let the 17 differences be $c'_1 < c'_2 < \cdots < c'_{17}$. For $1 \le k \le 16$, let $d_k = c'_{17} - c'_{17-k}$.

In the same way as shown above, if d_k is in A, B, or C, then we are done. Otherwise, all of the d_k belong to other three sets. By the Pigeonhole Principle, one of the three sets contains at least $\lfloor (16 - 1)/3 \rfloor + 1 = 6$ of these differences d_k. Without loss of generality, let this set be D, and let the 6 differences be $d'_1 < d'_2 < \cdots < d'_6$. For $1 \le l \le 5$, let $e_l = d'_6 - d'_{6-l}$.

If e_l is in A, B, C, or D, then we are done. Otherwise, all of the e_l belong to other two sets. By the Pigeonhole Principle, one of the two sets contains at least $\lfloor (5 - 1)/2 \rfloor + 1 = 3$ of these differences e_l. Without loss of generality, let this set be E, and let the 3 differences be $e'_1 < e'_2 < e'_3$. For $1 \le m \le 2$, let $f_m = e'_3 - e'_{3-m}$.

If f_m is in A, B, C, D, or E, then we are done. Otherwise, both of the f_m, namely f_1 and f_2, belong to F. Then the difference $f_2 - f_1$ must belong to one of the six sets, and we are finally done.

CHAPTER 6

Constructive Expectation

Exercises for Section 6.2

6.2.1 Each individual coin has a $\frac{1}{2} \cdot \frac{1}{2} = \frac{1}{4}$ of coming up tails twice. Thus, each coin contributes $\frac{1}{4}$ to the total number of tails remaining at the end. Therefore, the expected number of tails remaining is $\frac{1}{4} \cdot 20 = \boxed{5}$.

6.2.2

(a) The expected value of the sum of the blue dice is $2(3.5) = 7$. The expected value of the green die is 3.5. Therefore, the expected value of their difference is $7 - 3.5 = \boxed{3.5}$.

(b) The expected value of the sum of the blue dice is $38(3.5) = 133$. The expected value of the sum of the green dice is $37(3.5) = 129.5$. Therefore, the expected value of their difference is $133 - 129.5 = \boxed{3.5}$.

Another way to see this is that, in terms of expected value, the 37 green dice "cancel out" with 37 of the blue dice, so that the expected value of (37 blue dice) − (37 green dice) is just 0. Therefore, the expected value of (38 blue dice) − (37 green dice) is the same as the expected value of a single blue die, which is 3.5.

6.2.3

(a) The expected value of Kai's number is $pw + (1 - p)x$.

(b) The expected value of Jae's number is $qy + (1 - q)z$.

(c) Let K and J denote Kai's number and Jae's number, respectively. Then

$$P(K = w, J = y) = pq,$$
$$P(K = w, J = z) = p(1 - q),$$
$$P(K = x, J = y) = (1 - p)q,$$
$$P(K = x, J = z) = (1 - p)(1 - q),$$

so the expected value of the sum of Kai's number and Jae's number is

$$\begin{aligned}
E(K + J) &= pq(w + y) + p(1 - q)(w + z) + (1 - p)q(x + y) + (1 - p)(1 - q)(x + z) \\
&= pqw + pqy + p(1 - q)w + p(1 - q)z + (1 - p)qx + (1 - p)qy + (1 - p)(1 - q)x + (1 - p)(1 - q)z \\
&= pqw + p(1 - q)w + (1 - p)qx + (1 - p)(1 - q)x + pqy + (1 - p)qy + p(1 - q)z + (1 - p)(1 - q)z \\
&= pw + (1 - p)x + qy + (1 - q)z.
\end{aligned}$$

From part (a), $E(K) = pw + (1 - p)x$, and from part (b), $E(J) = qy + (1 - q)z$. Thus, we have confirmed that $E(K + J) = E(K) + E(J)$.

6.2.4 Let X be the number of heads before Henry chooses one of the coins, and let Y be the number of heads after Henry has possibly flipped a tail to a head. Then $Y = X$ if Henry chooses heads, and $Y = X + 1$ if Henry chooses tails. The probability of either event occurring is 1/2 (since the coin that we choose is equally likely to be heads or tails), so

$$E(Y) = \frac{1}{2}E(X) + \frac{1}{2}E(X+1) = \frac{1}{2}E(X) + \frac{1}{2}E(X) + \frac{1}{2} = E(X) + \frac{1}{2}.$$

Each coin is equally likely to be a head or a tail, so each coin contributes $\frac{1}{2}$ to the total number of heads. Therefore, $E(X) = 10(\frac{1}{2}) = 5$, and thus $E(Y) = 5 + \frac{1}{2} = \boxed{\frac{11}{2}}$.

6.2.5 A turn occurs when a step to the right is followed by a step upwards, or vice versa. There are 8 intermediate points on each path at which a turn might occur: each path has length 9, but a turn cannot occur at A or B.

Pick an arbitrary point on the path, for instance the 4th intermediate point. Each path from A to B must have 5 steps to the right and 4 steps upwards, so if a turn occurs at the 4th intermediate point of the path, then the two steps surrounding that point must be a step right and a step up (in either order), and the other seven steps in the path must be 4 steps to the right and 3 steps up (in any order). Thus, there are $2 \times \binom{7}{4} = 70$ paths that have a turn at the 4th point of the path.

There are $\binom{9}{5} = 126$ total paths from A to B, and 70 of them have a turn at the 4th intermediate point of the path, therefore a randomly-chosen path has an expected $\frac{70}{126} = \frac{5}{9}$ turns at that point. There are 8 intermediate points, and the calculation of the expected number of turns at each of these points is the same, so a randomly-chosen path has an expected number of turns of $8\left(\frac{5}{9}\right) = \boxed{\frac{40}{9}}$.

Exercises for Section 6.3

6.3.1 Let X be the number of times I laugh, and for $1 \le i \le 20$, let X_i be 1 if the ith and $(i+1)^{\text{st}}$ house have the same color, and 0 otherwise, so $X = X_1 + X_2 + \cdots + X_{20}$. (The 21st house is understood to be the first house.) Then $E(X_i) = \frac{1}{4}$, so

$$E(X) = E(X_1) + E(X_2) + \cdots + E(X_{20}) = 20 \cdot \frac{1}{4} = 5.$$

Therefore, the expected value of the number of times I laugh is $\boxed{5}$.

6.3.2 More generally, suppose we start with n ropes. We choose one of the loose ends, which leaves $2n - 1$ loose ends. Hence, the probability that the second loose end we choose is the other loose end of the first rope is $1/(2n - 1)$. If we choose two loose ends from the same rope, then we form one loop, with $n - 1$ ropes remaining. If we choose two loose ends from different ropes, then we form $n - 1$ ropes.

So at the first step, with 6 initial ropes, we create a loop with probability $\frac{1}{11}$. If we create a loop, we set it aside, so that in any event, we have 5 ropes and 10 loose ends left.

At the second step, we create a loop with probability $\frac{1}{9}$. If we create a loop, we set it aside, so that we are left with 4 ropes and 8 loose ends.

We continue in this fashion, creating a loop with probability $\frac{1}{7}, \frac{1}{5}, \frac{1}{3}$, and 1 at each subsequent step. (Note that we must create a loop at the end.)

Hence, the expected number of loops George ends up with is

$$\frac{1}{11} + \frac{1}{9} + \frac{1}{7} + \frac{1}{5} + \frac{1}{3} + 1 = \boxed{\frac{6508}{3465}}.$$

6.3.3 The expected value of the roll of the first die is $E(a) = (1 + 2 + 3 + 4 + 5 + 6)/6 = 7/2$. To obtain b, we roll a

dice, so

$$E(b) = \frac{7}{2}E(a),$$

so $E(b) = (7/2)^2 = 49/4$. To obtain c, we roll b dice, so

$$E(c) = \frac{7}{2}E(b).$$

Therefore, $E(c) = (7/2)(49/4) = \boxed{343/8}$.

6.3.4 We can divide the square into a 5×5 array of smaller squares, each of which has side length $\frac{1}{5}$. The expected number of points in each of the small squares is $\frac{51}{25} = 2.04$, therefore at least one of the squares must contain at least 3 points. (If they all contained 2 or fewer points, then the average number of points in each square would be at most 2, but we know that it's greater than 2.) Finally, a diagonal of a small square is $\frac{\sqrt{2}}{5}$, so we can completely cover a small square with a circle of radius

$$\frac{\sqrt{2}}{5} \cdot \frac{1}{2} = \frac{\sqrt{2}}{10} = \sqrt{\frac{1}{50}} < \sqrt{\frac{1}{49}} = \frac{1}{7}.$$

Therefore, a circle of radius $\frac{1}{7}$ also completely covers a small square, and there exists a small square with at least 3 points, so there is a circle with radius $\frac{1}{7}$ that covers at least 3 points, and we are done.

6.3.5 Naturally, since we are trying to find the average number of anchors in a randomly-chosen subset, we might think to count the total number of anchors in each subset. However, this is somewhat difficult to count directly. Instead, we'll count how many subsets have each given anchor.

Specifically, let n be a fixed positive integer, where $1 \le n \le 15$. We count the number of subsets S for which n is an anchor. Since the definition of anchor depends on $\#(S)$, it makes sense to try to count them in cases based on $\#(S)$. So let $k = \#(S)$, and note that since S cannot be empty, we must have $k \ge 1$. This means that n and $n + k$ are distinct elements of S, so $k \ge 2$. Also, $n + k \le 15$, so $k \le 15 - n$.

So both n and $n + k$ must be in S, and we can choose any $k - 2$ of the other elements of $\{1, 2, \ldots, 15\}$ to be in S, so there are

$$\binom{13}{k-2}$$

subsets S of size k that have n as an anchor. Summing over $2 \le k \le 15 - n$, we find that there are

$$\binom{13}{0} + \binom{13}{1} + \cdots + \binom{13}{13-n}$$

subsets S that have n as an anchor.

Since $k \ge 2$ and $n + k \le 15$, we can have $1 \le n \le 13$. So summing over $1 \le n \le 13$, we find that the total number of anchors over all subsets of $\{1, 2, \ldots, 15\}$ is

$$\binom{13}{0} + \binom{13}{1} + \cdots + \binom{13}{10} + \binom{13}{11} + \binom{13}{12}$$
$$+ \binom{13}{0} + \binom{13}{1} + \cdots + \binom{13}{10} + \binom{13}{11}$$
$$+ \binom{13}{0} + \binom{13}{1} + \cdots + \binom{13}{10}$$
$$+ \cdots$$
$$+ \binom{13}{0}$$
$$= 13\binom{13}{0} + 12\binom{13}{1} + \cdots + 3\binom{13}{10} + 2\binom{13}{11} + \binom{13}{12}.$$

Let

$$A = 13\binom{13}{0} + 12\binom{13}{1} + \cdots + 2\binom{13}{11} + \binom{13}{12}.$$

Then using the identity $\binom{13}{a} = \binom{13}{13-a}$, we get

$$A = 13\binom{13}{13} + 12\binom{13}{12} + \cdots + 2\binom{13}{2} + \binom{13}{1}$$
$$= \binom{13}{1} + 2\binom{13}{2} + \cdots + 12\binom{13}{12} + 13\binom{13}{13}.$$

Adding these expressions for A gives:

$$2A = 13\binom{13}{0} + 13\binom{13}{1} + \cdots + 13\binom{13}{12} + 13\binom{13}{13}$$
$$= 13\left[\binom{13}{0} + \binom{13}{1} + \cdots + \binom{13}{12} + \binom{13}{13}\right]$$
$$= 13 \cdot 2^{13}.$$

Therefore $A = 13 \cdot 2^{12}$.

The total number of subsets of $\{1, 2, \ldots, 15\}$ is 2^{15}, so the average number of anchors over all subsets of $\{1, 2, \ldots, 15\}$ is $(13 \cdot 2^{12})/2^{15} = \boxed{13/8}$.

Review Problems

6.10 We can approach this problem using the same technique as in Problem 6.7. At any interior point, we obtain a circle if and only if all four of the squares surrounding that point line up correctly. Each square has four different orientations, so the probability of obtaining a circle at any particular interior point is $(1/4)^4 = 1/256$. The number of interior points is $(m-1)(n-1)$, so the expected number of circles is $\boxed{(m-1)(n-1)/256}$.

6.11 In a 10-digit binary number, the leftmost digit must be a 1, so three of the remaining 9 digits must be 1, with the rest 0. For each of the 9 digits after the first, the probability that it is a 1 is $3/9 = 1/3$. Therefore, the expected value is:

$$2^9 + \frac{1}{3} \cdot 2^8 + \frac{1}{3} \cdot 2^7 + \cdots + \frac{1}{3} \cdot 2^1 + \frac{1}{3} \cdot 2^0 = 2^9 + \frac{1}{3}(2^8 + 2^7 + \cdots + 2 + 1)$$

$$= 2^9 + \frac{1}{3}(2^9 - 1)$$

$$= \boxed{\frac{2047}{3}}.$$

6.12 This is essentially the same as Problem 6.6. Each draw will match the number on the ball with probability $\frac{1}{5}$, and there are 5 draws, so the expected winnings are $(5)\left(\$\frac{1}{5}\right) = \boxed{\$1}$.

6.13 For $1 \le i \le 17$, let X_i be 1 if the ith cage and $(i+1)^{\text{st}}$ cage contain different animals, and 0 otherwise, so $A = X_1 + X_2 + \cdots + X_{17}$.

To compute $E(X_i)$, we count the number of arrangements for which $X_i = 1$, and divide by the total number of arrangements. If $X_i = 1$, then either the ith cage contains a dog and the $(i+1)^{\text{st}}$ cage contains a cat, or the ith cage contains a cat and the $(i+1)^{\text{st}}$ cage contains a dog.

If the ith cage contains a dog and the $(i+1)^{\text{st}}$ cage contains a cat, then this leaves 5 dogs and 11 cats to be arranged among the remaining 16 cages, and there are $\binom{16}{5}$ such arrangements. Similarly, there are $\binom{16}{5}$ arrangements where the ith cage contains a cat and the $(i+1)^{\text{st}}$ cage contains a dog.

The total number of arrangements is $\binom{18}{6}$, so

$$E(X_i) = \frac{2\binom{16}{5}}{\binom{18}{6}} = \frac{2 \cdot 16! \cdot 6! \cdot 12!}{18! \cdot 5! \cdot 11!} = \frac{2 \cdot 6 \cdot 12}{17 \cdot 18} = \frac{8}{17}.$$

Therefore, the expected value of A is

$$E(A) = E(X_1) + E(X_2) + \cdots + E(X_{17}) = 17 \cdot \frac{8}{17} = \boxed{8}.$$

6.14

(a) We see that

$$A = \begin{cases} 0 & \text{if } a < \frac{1}{2}, \\ 1 & \text{if } a \ge \frac{1}{2}. \end{cases}$$

and similarly

$$B = \begin{cases} 0 & \text{if } b < \frac{1}{2}, \\ 1 & \text{if } b \ge \frac{1}{2}. \end{cases}$$

Also

$$C = \begin{cases} 0 & \text{if } a + b < \frac{1}{2}, \\ 1 & \text{if } \frac{1}{2} \le a + b < \frac{3}{2}, \\ 2 & \text{if } a + b \ge \frac{3}{2}. \end{cases}$$

We graph these cases below:

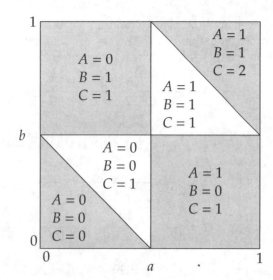

Notice that $A + B = C$ for the shaded regions in the diagram above, which have areas 1/8, 1/4, 1/4, and 1/8, respectively. Therefore, the probability that $A + B = C$ is $1/4 + 1/8 + 1/8 + 1/4 = \boxed{3/4}$.

(b) Note that $E(C - (A + B)) = E(C) - E(A) - E(B)$.

Since $A = 0$ if $a < 1/2$ and $A = 1$ if $a \geq 1/2$, we have $E(A) = 1/2$. Similarly, $E(B) = 1/2$.

Consulting the graph above, the region where $C = 0$ has area 1/8, the region where $C = 1$ has area 3/4, and the region where $C = 2$ has area 1/8, so

$$E(C) = \frac{1}{8} \cdot 0 + \frac{3}{4} \cdot 1 + \frac{1}{8} \cdot 2 = 1.$$

Hence, $E(C - (A + B)) = E(C) - E(A) - E(B) = 1 - 1/2 - 1/2 = \boxed{0}$.

We could have also arrived at the answer by taking advantage of symmetry. Consider a region with values $(A, B, C) = (x, y, z)$. If a rounds to x, b rounds to y, and $c = a + b$ rounds to z, then $1 - a$ rounds to $1 - x$, and $1 - b$ rounds to $1 - y$, so $(1 - a) + (1 - b) = 2 - (a + b) = 2 - c$ rounds to $2 - z$, so there is a corresponding region with values $(A, B, C) = (1 - x, 1 - y, 2 - z)$ of equal area. (Note that the borders of the regions do not correspond, but that's OK as the borders do not contribute anything to the areas of the regions.) All regions can thus be paired up.

Furthermore, the average of $C - (A + B)$ for the two regions is

$$\frac{z - (x + y) + (2 - z) - [(1 - x) + (1 - y)]}{2} = 0.$$

Therefore, the average of $C - (A + B)$ over all regions is 0.

(c) We can use the same symmetry argument as in part (b). Consider a region with values $(A_1, A_2, \ldots, A_{100}, C) = (x_1, x_2, \ldots, x_{100}, z)$. If a_i rounds to A_i for all i, and $c = a_1 + a_2 + \cdots + a_{100}$ rounds to z, then $1 - a_i$ rounds to $1 - A_i$ for all i, and $(1 - a_1) + (1 - a_2) + \cdots + (1 - a_{100}) = 100 - (a_1 + a_2 + \cdots + a_{100}) = 100 - c$ rounds to $100 - z$. Thus, there is a corresponding region with values $(A_1, A_2, \ldots, A_{100}, C) = (1 - x_1, 1 - x_2, \ldots, 1 - x_{100}, 100 - z)$ of equal area.

Furthermore, the average of $C - (A_1 + A_2 + \cdots + A_{100})$ for the two regions is

$$\frac{z - (x_1 + x_2 + \cdots + x_{100}) + (100 - z) - [(1 - x_1) + (1 - x_2) + \cdots + (1 - x_{100})]}{2} = 0.$$

Therefore, the average of $C - (A_1 + A_2 + \cdots + A_{100})$ over all regions is $\boxed{0}$.

6.15 Let X be the number of children in the family of a randomly chosen child. First we compute the probabilities of the different possible values of X. Note that $P(X = 1)$ is *not* $\frac{1}{5}$: although 20% of *families* have 1 child, this does not mean that 20% of *children* come from 1-child families. Instead, we calculate as follows:

$$P(X = 1) = \frac{0.2}{0.2 + 0.3 \cdot 2 + 0.2 \cdot 3 + 0.1 \cdot 4} = \frac{1}{9},$$

$$P(X = 2) = \frac{0.3 \cdot 2}{0.2 + 0.3 \cdot 2 + 0.2 \cdot 3 + 0.1 \cdot 4} = \frac{3}{9},$$

$$P(X = 3) = \frac{0.2 \cdot 3}{0.2 + 0.3 \cdot 2 + 0.2 \cdot 3 + 0.1 \cdot 4} = \frac{3}{9},$$

$$P(X = 4) = \frac{0.1 \cdot 4}{0.2 + 0.3 \cdot 2 + 0.2 \cdot 3 + 0.1 \cdot 4} = \frac{2}{9}.$$

Also note that if a child comes from a family with c children, then he has $c - 1$ siblings. Hence, the expected number of siblings of a randomly-chosen child is $E(X - 1)$, which we compute:

$$E(X - 1) = \frac{1}{9} \cdot 0 + \frac{3}{9} \cdot 1 + \frac{3}{9} \cdot 2 + \frac{2}{9} \cdot 3 = \boxed{\frac{5}{3}}.$$

We could also have solved the problem by using a "representative" population. Consider 100 families, where 20 families have no children, 20 families have 1 child, 30 families have 2 children, 20 families have 3 children, and 10 families have 4 children. This group of families has the same statistical distribution as Aopslandia.

The number of children is $20 \cdot 1 + 30 \cdot 2 + 20 \cdot 3 + 10 \cdot 4 = 180$. Of these 180 children, 20 have no siblings, $30 \cdot 2 = 60$ have 1 sibling, $20 \cdot 3 = 60$ have 2 siblings, and $10 \cdot 4 = 40$ have 3 siblings, so the average number of siblings is

$$\frac{20 \cdot 0 + 60 \cdot 1 + 60 \cdot 2 + 40 \cdot 3}{180} = \frac{5}{3}.$$

Challenge Problems

6.16 Let x be the number we are looking for: the total number of ways to distribute the handouts. Since 6 handouts are going to 15 students, and all of the students are essentially the same, the expected number of handouts received by any individual student is $\frac{6}{15}$. Therefore, if we can compute the number of distributions of handouts in which any given student (call her Sally) receives a handout (call this number y), then we know that $y = \frac{6}{15}x$, so $x = \frac{15}{6}y$. (You can think of this as something like constructive expectation "in reverse.")

If Sally gets a handout, then we must give the other 5 handouts to the other 14 students. Call Sally's handout #1 and number the other five handouts as #2 through #6 as we move around the circle clockwise starting at Sally. For $1 \le i \le 6$, let x_i be the number of students sitting between the student with handout #i and the student with handout #$(i + 1)$ (where handout #7 is understood to be Sally's handout #1).

Each student must either have a handout or be sitting beside a student with a handout, so $x_i \le 2$ for all i. Furthermore, there are $15 - 6 = 9$ students without a handout, so $x_1 + x_2 + \cdots + x_6 = 9$. The only solutions under these conditions are $(0, 1, 2, 2, 2, 2)$ and $(1, 1, 1, 2, 2, 2)$, and their rearrangements. Our next step is to find the number of ways these gaps can appear around the circle.

For the first configuration $(0, 1, 2, 2, 2, 2)$, we have $6 \times 5 = 30$ arrangements (there are 6 slots in which to place the "0", then 5 slots in which to place the "1"). For the second configuration $(1, 1, 1, 2, 2, 2)$, we have $\binom{6}{3} = 20$ arrangements (we must choose 3 of the 6 slots in which to place the "1"s).

Therefore, there are 50 possible configurations of the gaps between the students, so there are 50 ways in which the other 5 handouts can be distributed. Therefore, $y = 50$, and the answer is $x = \frac{15}{6}(50) = \boxed{125}$.

6.17 First, we count the number of 10-element arithmetic sequences in S. Any arithmetic sequence is determined by its smallest element a and its common difference d. The sequence is then

$$a, a + d, a + 2d, \ldots, a + 9d.$$

So we are counting all ordered pairs (a, d) of positive integers such that $a + 9d \leq 2007$. For any value of $a \leq 1998$, we must have $d \leq (2007 - a)/9$. Therefore, the number of sequences is

$$\sum_{a=1}^{1998} \left\lfloor \frac{2007 - a}{9} \right\rfloor.$$

This can be reindexed using the substitution $b = 2007 - a$ to give

$$\sum_{b=9}^{2006} \left\lfloor \frac{b}{9} \right\rfloor.$$

Note that $2006/9 = 222 + \frac{8}{9}$, so that in the above sum, every number from 1 through 222 appears 9 times. Therefore, the sum is equal to

$$9(1 + 2 + \cdots + 222) = 9 \frac{(222)(223)}{2} = 222777.$$

Given a random coloring of S, and random subset of 10 elements of S, the probability that all of the elements are colored with the same color is $\left(\frac{1}{4}\right)^9 = \frac{1}{2^{18}} = \frac{1}{262144}$. Therefore, since there are 222777 arithmetic sequences of length 10, the expected number of them that are colored with the same color in a randomly-chosen coloring of S is $\frac{222777}{262144}$. This is less than 1, which means that there must be some coloring in which 0 of the sequences are colored with the same color: if every coloring had at least 1 monochromatic sequence, then the expected number of such sequences would be at least 1.

6.18 Let us count the expected number of fixed points in a random permutation. On the one hand, each slot in the permutation is fixed with probability $\frac{1}{n}$, and there are n slots in the permutation, so the total expected number of fixed points is $n(\frac{1}{n}) = 1$. On the other hand, a permutation with k fixed points occurs with probability $\frac{p_n(k)}{n!}$, and such a permutation has k fixed points, so the expected number of fixed points is

$$\sum_{k=0}^{n} k \cdot \frac{p_n(k)}{n!}.$$

Therefore, we must have

$$\sum_{k=0}^{n} k \cdot \frac{p_n(k)}{n!} = 1,$$

and multiplying both sides of the above equation by $n!$ gives the desired identity.

6.19 We claim that not only can we find such a line, but we can find such a line that is parallel to one of the sides of the square.

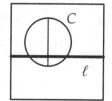

Consider a randomly chosen line ℓ that is parallel to the top and bottom sides of the square, as shown in the picture at right. If C is a circle with diameter d (where $0 < d < 1$, since C must lie entirely within the square), we see that the probability that ℓ intersects C is just d. This means that, given a randomly chosen line, the expected number of circles that it intersects is equal to the sum of the diameters of all the circles. But we know that the sum of the circumferences is 10, so the sum of the diameters is $10/\pi \approx 3.183$. Thus a randomly chosen line will intersect, on average, 3.183 circles. But this means that some line must intersect at least 4 circles, because if they all intersected 3 or fewer circles, then the average would be at most 3.

6.20   The 4 Aces divide the other 48 cards in the deck into 5 groups: the cards before the 1st Ace, the cards between the 1st and 2nd Aces, and so on. Therefore, the expected size of each group is $48/5 = 9.6$ cards. We have to turn over all of the cards in the first group, plus the first Ace, before we see an Ace. Therefore, the expected number of cards that we have to turn over is $\boxed{10.6}$.

6.21   We will compute the expected number of pairs of judges that agree on a randomly-chosen contestant. Given any pair of judges, they agree on that contestant with probability at most $\frac{k}{a}$, since that pair of judges agrees on at most k of the a contestants. There are $\binom{b}{2}$ pairs of judges, so the expected number of pairs of judges that agree on a randomly-chosen contestant is *at most*

$$\frac{k}{a}\binom{b}{2}. \tag{$*$}$$

On the other hand, suppose that p of the judges pass a given contestant, so that $b - p$ of them fail the contestant. Then the number of judges that agree on that contestant is

$$\binom{p}{2} + \binom{b-p}{2}.$$

We can write this as a quadratic in p:

$$\frac{p(p-1) + (b-p)(b-p-1)}{2} = \frac{(p^2 - p) + (p^2 - (2b-1)p + (b^2 - b))}{2} = p^2 - bp + \frac{b^2 - b}{2}.$$

This quadratic is minimized when $p = b/2$, but this is not an integer, so the minimum value occurs when $p = (b-1)/2$. This minimum value is

$$\binom{\frac{b-1}{2}}{2} + \binom{\frac{b+1}{2}}{2} = \frac{(b-1)(b-3) + (b+1)(b-1)}{8} = \frac{(b-1)^2}{4}.$$

Therefore, the expected number of pairs of judges that agree on a randomly-chosen contestant is *at least*

$$\frac{(b-1)^2}{4}. \tag{$**$}$$

Combining $(*)$ and $(**)$, we see that

$$\frac{k}{a}\binom{b}{2} \geq \frac{(b-1)^2}{4},$$

and dividing both sides by $\binom{b}{2}$ gives

$$\frac{k}{a} \geq \frac{(b-1)^2}{4}\frac{2}{b(b-1)} = \frac{b-1}{2b}.$$

CHAPTER 7

Distributions

Exercises for Section 7.2

7.2.1 Line up the 30 cookies in a row. Then we need to insert 9 dividers into 9 of the 29 slots between cookies. So

the number of distributions is $\boxed{\dbinom{29}{9}}$ = 10,015,005.

7.2.2 Give the head of the work crew 2 bills. Then the problem becomes distributing 8 bills, so that each member gets at least one bill. (Since the head already has 2 bills, by getting at least one more bill, she gets at least 3 total.) Therefore, the number of ways the bills can be distributed is $\binom{8-1}{4-1} = \binom{7}{3} = \boxed{35}$.

7.2.3 The problem is equivalent to distributing 100 1's among 3 distinguishable boxes, where the "boxes" are the variables a, b, and c. So, the number of solutions is $\binom{100-1}{3-1} = \binom{99}{2} = \boxed{4851}$.

7.2.4

(a) We distribute each type of candy separately. The 8 licorice sticks are distributed in $\binom{7}{4} = 35$ ways. The 10 chocolate bars are distributed in $\binom{9}{4} = 126$ ways. Since these distributions are independent, the total number of distributions is $\binom{7}{4}\binom{9}{4} = (35)(126) = \boxed{4410}$.

(b) First, we choose which kid(s) will receive licorice and which kid(s) will receive chocolate. We can choose any subset of 1–4 kids to receive licorice, and then the rest will receive chocolate.

Specifically, if $1 \le k \le 4$, then we can choose k kids to receive the licorice in $\binom{5}{k}$ ways. Then, the licorice can be distributed to these kids in $\binom{7}{k-1}$ ways, and the chocolate can be distributed to the remaining $5-k$ kids in $\binom{9}{4-k}$ ways. Therefore, the total number of distributions is

$$\sum_{k=1}^{4} \binom{5}{k}\binom{7}{k-1}\binom{9}{4-k} = \binom{5}{1}\binom{7}{0}\binom{9}{3} + \binom{5}{2}\binom{7}{1}\binom{9}{2} + \binom{5}{3}\binom{7}{2}\binom{9}{1} + \binom{5}{4}\binom{7}{3}\binom{9}{0}$$

$$= (5)(1)(84) + (10)(7)(36) + (10)(21)(9) + (5)(35)(1)$$

$$= 420 + 2520 + 1890 + 175 = \boxed{5005}.$$

Exercises for Section 7.3

7.3.1 To transform the given equation into one involving positive integers, let $a = u + 1$, $b = v + 1$, $c = w + 1$, $d = x + 1$, and $e = y + 1$. Then a, b, c, d, and e are positive integers, and $a + b + c + d + e = u + v + w + x + y + 5 = 27$. Therefore, the number of solutions is $\binom{27-1}{5-1} = \binom{26}{4} = \boxed{14{,}950}$.

7.3.2

(a) Let a, b, and c be the number of glazed, chocolate, and powdered donuts that Pat buys, respectively. Then $a + b + c = 4$, where a, b, and c are nonnegative integers. To transform this equation into one involving positive integers, let $d = a+1$, $e = b+1$, and $f = c+1$. Then d, e, and f are positive integers, and $d+e+f = a+b+c+3 = 7$. Therefore, the number of possible selections is $\binom{7-1}{3-1} = \binom{6}{2} = \boxed{15}$.

(b) Let x, y, and z be the number of chocolate chip, oatmeal, and peanut butter cookies that Pat selects, respectively. Then $x + y + z = 6$, where x, y, and z are nonnegative integers. To transform this equation into one involving positive integers, let $u = x + 1$, $v = y + 1$, and $w = z + 1$. Then u, v, and w are positive integers, and $u + v + w = x + y + z + 3 = 9$. Therefore, the number of possible assortments is $\binom{9-1}{3-1} = \binom{8}{2} = \boxed{28}$.

7.3.3 Let the number of dollar bills received by the seven people be $x_1, x_2, \ldots, x_7$. Then $x_1 + x_2 + \cdots + x_7 = 77$, and $x_i \geq 10$ for all i. Let $y_i = x_i - 9$ for all i, so $y_1 + y_2 + \cdots + y_7 = x_1 + x_2 + \cdots + x_7 - 7 \cdot 9 = 77 - 63 = 14$, and each y_i is a positive integer. Hence, the number of possible distributions is $\binom{14-1}{7-1} = \binom{13}{6} = \boxed{1716}$.

7.3.4 Let $a = 20-x$, $b = 20-y$, and $c = 20-z$, so a, b, and c are all positive integers, and $a+b+c = 60-(x+y+z) = 50$. Hence, the number of solutions is $\binom{50-1}{3-1} = \binom{49}{2} = \boxed{1176}$.

7.3.5 We could use casework and solve $w + x + y + z = 4$, $w + x + y + z = 5$, etc., up to $w + x + y + z = 24$, and add all of the solutions. But there is a more clever approach.

Add a new dummy variable d, and consider solutions in positive integers to $w + x + y + z + d = 25$. Any such solution will also be a solution in positive integers to $w + x + y + z < 25$, since we have $d = 25 - w - x - y - z$. We know that there are $\binom{24}{4}$ solutions to $w + x + y + z + d = 25$, therefore there are $\boxed{\binom{24}{4} = 10{,}626}$ solutions to our original inequality.

If you know the Hockey Stick Identity, then you may recognize that what we have done in this solution is essentially a proof of the identity.

7.3.6 Let a, b, c, and d be the number of candy bars, packages of jelly beans, lollipops, and packs of chewing gum that one sister receives from Andrew, so $a + b + c + d = 20$. Since there are 40 pieces of candy total, the other sister also receives 20 pieces of candy, so the number of ways Andrew can distribute his candy is equal to the number of solutions of $a + b + c + d = 20$ in nonnegative integers no greater than 10.

If there is an infinite supply of each candy, then the problem is fairly straightforward to solve: we can let $w = a+1$, $x = b + 1$, $y = c + 1$, and $z = d + 1$. Then w, x, y, and z are positive integers, and $w + x + y + z = a + b + c + d + 4 = 24$. Hence, the number of solutions is $\binom{24-1}{4-1} = \binom{23}{3} = 1771$.

However, we must have a, b, c, d all at most 10, since our candy supplies are not infinite. Our count of 1771 solutions from about includes solutions in which at least one of w, x, y, z is greater than 11, which is not permitted (recall that we must have $a \leq 10$, so we must have $w \leq 11$, and similarly for x, y, z). Therefore, we must exclude these solutions. Even though we wrote "at least one of $w, x, y, z \ldots$" above, we don't actually need to use PIE, since only one of w, x, y, z can possibly exceed 11 (if two of them do, then the sum must be at least $12+12+1+1 = 26$, which is too big).

If $w > 11$, then let $w' = w - 11$. Then we are counting solutions to $w' + x + y + z = 24 - 11 = 13$ in positive integers, so we know that there are $\binom{13-1}{4-1} = \binom{12}{3} = 220$ solutions. The same holds true for each of other three variables, so this gives us $1771 - 4(220) = \boxed{891}$ solutions to the original problem.

Exercises for Section 7.4

7.4.1 For $1 \le i \le 9$, let a_i be the number of times that i appears on the game piece. Then $a_1 + a_2 + \cdots + a_9 = 6$, and each a_i is a nonnegative integer.

Let $b_i = a_i + 1$, so $b_1 + b_2 + \cdots + b_9 = a_1 + a_2 + \cdots + a_9 + 9 = 15$, and each b_i is a positive integer. Therefore, the number of possible 6-sided game pieces is $\binom{15-1}{9-1} = \binom{14}{8} = \boxed{3003}$.

7.4.2 The key feature of ARMLovian is that there are at most two consonants between any two A's. Once we realize this, we can count the 7-letter words by casework on the number of A's.

There is only 1 word with 7 A's, namely AAAAAAA.

If we have 6 A's, then we have 7 choices for the position of the consonant:

$$\underline{\quad}A\underline{\quad}A\underline{\quad}A\underline{\quad}A\underline{\quad}A\underline{\quad}A\underline{\quad},$$

and 3 choices for which consonant. Therefore, there are $7 \cdot 3 = 21$ words with 6 A's.

If we have 5 A's, we have 6 slots available for the consonants:

$$\underset{1}{\underline{\quad}}A\underset{2}{\underline{\quad}}A\underset{2}{\underline{\quad}}A\underset{2}{\underline{\quad}}A\underset{2}{\underline{\quad}}A\underset{1}{\underline{\quad}},$$

where the numbers underneath the slots indicate the maximum number of consonants that we are allowed to place there. We have 4 choices if we elect to put both consonants in the same slot, plus $\binom{6}{2} = 15$ choices if we elect to put one consonant in two of the six slots, for a total of 19 possible positions for the two consonants. We also have $3^2 = 9$ choices for the two consonants. Therefore, there are $19 \cdot 9 = 171$ words with 5 A's.

If we have 4 A's, we have 5 slots available for the consonants:

$$\underset{1}{\underline{\quad}}A\underset{2}{\underline{\quad}}A\underset{2}{\underline{\quad}}A\underset{2}{\underline{\quad}}A\underset{1}{\underline{\quad}}.$$

We have $\binom{5}{3} = 10$ choices if we elect to put the consonants in 3 different slots, plus we have $3 \cdot 4 = 12$ choices if we elect to put two consonants in one of the middle slots, then the third consonant in one of the 4 remaining slots. This gives us a total of $10 + 12 = 22$ possible positions for the three consonants. We also have $3^3 = 27$ choices for the consonants. Therefore, there are $22 \cdot 27 = 594$ words with 4 A's.

Finally, if we have 3 A's, we have 4 slots available for the consonants:

$$\underset{1}{\underline{\quad}}A\underset{2}{\underline{\quad}}A\underset{2}{\underline{\quad}}A\underset{1}{\underline{\quad}}.$$

We can put one consonant in each of the 4 slots in 1 way. We can put two consonants in one slot, then one consonant in each of two remaining slots, in $2 \cdot \binom{3}{2} = 6$ ways. We can put two consonants in each of two slots in just 1 way (the two middle slots). Thus, we have $1 + 6 + 1 = 8$ ways to position the four consonants. We also have $3^4 = 81$ choices for the consonants. Therefore, we have $8 \cdot 81 = 648$ words with 3 A's.

We cannot have 2 or fewer A's, as then we will not have enough space for the consonants.

Therefore, there are $1 + 21 + 171 + 594 + 648 = \boxed{1435}$ 7-letter ARMLovian words.

7.4.3 We can treat the 3 maple trees and 4 oak trees as 7 indistinguishable non-birch trees. There is a total of $\binom{12}{5}$ arrangements of the 5 birch trees and the 7 non-birch trees.

If no two of the birch trees are next to each other, then we can arrange the trees by first placing the 7 non-birch trees in a row, and then placing the 5 birch trees into 5 of the 8 slots created by the non-birch trees (6 of these slots are between trees, and 2 are at either end). So there are $\binom{8}{5}$ of these arrangements.

Therefore, the probability is

$$\frac{\binom{8}{5}}{\binom{12}{5}} = \frac{8 \cdot 7 \cdot 6 \cdot 5 \cdot 4}{12 \cdot 11 \cdot 10 \cdot 9 \cdot 8} = \boxed{\frac{7}{99}}.$$

7.4.4 Let $f(x) = a_6x^6 + a_5x^5 + a_4x^4 + a_3x^3 + a_2x^2 + a_1x + a_0$, where a_0 through a_6 are positive integers. The given information yields the following equations:

$$f(1) = a_6 + a_5 + a_4 + a_3 + a_2 + a_1 + a_0 = 30,$$
$$f(-1) = a_6 - a_5 + a_4 - a_3 + a_2 - a_1 + a_0 = 12.$$

If we add and subtract these equations, we will get two separate Diophantine equations, one involving the even coefficients and the other involving the odd coefficients:

$$a_6 + a_4 + a_2 + a_0 = 21,$$
$$a_5 + a_3 + a_1 = 9.$$

The first one has $\binom{20}{3} = 1140$ solutions and the second one has $\binom{8}{2} = 28$ solutions, so the number of combined solutions, and thus the answer to the original problem, is $(1140)(28) = \boxed{31{,}920}$.

7.4.5 Let's compute the probability that a drawing has at least one pair of consecutively numbered balls. "At least" usually means either tricky casework or PIE, so let's count the complement instead: the probability that a drawing has no pair of consecutively numbered balls.

If we draw 6 balls, no two of which are consecutive, then the remaining 38 (undrawn) balls are distributed into 7 groups: the balls less than the smallest drawn ball, the balls between the two smallest drawn balls, and so on. To simplify things, imagine that there's a extra undrawn ball labeled 0 and an extra undrawn ball labeled 45. This means that there are 40 undrawn balls in 7 groups, and each of the groups must be nonempty. In other words, we have a 1-1 correspondence:

$$\begin{Bmatrix} \text{Drawing of 6 balls from 1–44, in} \\ \text{which no two are consecutive} \end{Bmatrix} \leftrightarrow \begin{Bmatrix} \text{Solutions to the equation } a_0 + a_1 + \cdots + a_6 = 40, \\ \text{where each } a_i \text{ is a positive integer (for } 0 \leq i \leq 6). \end{Bmatrix}.$$

The number of solutions to the equation in the latter set above is $\binom{39}{6}$. There are $\binom{44}{6}$ possible drawings, so the probability of no two consecutive balls is

$$\frac{\binom{39}{6}}{\binom{44}{6}} = \frac{3262623}{7059052} \approx 46.2\%.$$

So the citizens shouldn't be worried! We expect at least one pair of consecutive balls about 53.8% of the time.

Review Problems

7.14 Part (a) is our "basic" distribution problem. The goal of parts (b)-(d) is to do a manipulation to make them look like a basic problem similar to part (a).

(a) The number of solutions is given by $\binom{10-1}{3-1} = \binom{9}{2} = \boxed{36}$.

(b) Let $a = x + 1$, $b = y + 1$, and $c = z + 1$. Then a, b, and c are positive integers, and $a + b + c = x + y + z + 3 = 13$, so the number of solutions is $\binom{13-1}{3-1} = \binom{12}{2} = \boxed{66}$.

(c) Let $a = x + 3$, $b = y + 3$, and $c = z + 3$. Then a, b, and c are positive integers, and $a + b + c = x + y + z + 9 = 19$, so the number of solutions is $\binom{19-1}{3-1} = \binom{18}{2} = \boxed{153}$.

(d)   Let $a = x/2, b = y/2$, and $c = z/2$. Then a, b, and c are positive integers, and $a + b + c = (x + y + z)/2 = 5$, so the number of solutions is $\binom{5-1}{3-1} = \binom{4}{2} = \boxed{6}$.

7.15   We are told that x_i is a positive odd integer for each $1 \le i \le 5$, so there exists a positive integer y_i such that $x_i = 2y_i - 1$. Then $y_i = (x_i + 1)/2$ for all i, so

$$y_1 + y_2 + y_3 + y_4 + y_5 = \frac{(x_1 + 1) + (x_2 + 1) + (x_3 + 1) + (x_4 + 1) + (x_5 + 1)}{2} = \frac{2003 + 5}{2} = 1004.$$

This is now a straightforward distribution, and the number of solutions is $\binom{1004-1}{5-1} = \boxed{\binom{1003}{4}}$.

7.16

(a)   We can distribute the two types of goodies separately. The candy can be distributed among the 3 children in $\binom{7}{2} = 21$ ways. The cookies can be distributed in $\binom{3}{2} = 3$ ways. These distributions are independent, so there is a total of $(21)(3) = \boxed{63}$ distributions.

(b)   We can distribute the cookies first—after distributing the cookies, we simply hand enough candy to each child so that he or she has 4 items. But now note that we do not necessarily have to make sure that each child gets at least 1 cookie. So we are distributing 4 cookies to 3 children, where each child receives a nonnegative number of cookies; this is equivalent to distributing 7 cookies to 3 children, where each child received a positive number of cookies. (Think of this as baking 3 extra cookies, distributing the 7 cookies, and then cruelly swiping a cookie back from each child.) Therefore, there are $\binom{6}{2} = \boxed{15}$ such distributions.

(c)   As in part (a), consider the two types of goodies separately.

For the candy, note that the girl must receive at least 4 pieces (if she receives 3 or fewer, then by the Pigeonhole Principle, one of the boys must receive at least as many as she does). If she receives 5 or more, then the rest can be distributed to the boys in any manner (which includes one of the boys not getting any), so if the girl gets c candies (where $5 \le c \le 8$), then there are $(8 - c) + 1 = 9 - c$ ways to distribute the rest. If the girl gets 4 candies, we cannot give all 4 remaining candies to either boy, so there are only 3 ways to distribute the remaining 4 candies (2 ways where one boy gets 3 and the other gets 1, and 1 way where both boys get 2). So there is a total of $3 + 4 + 3 + 2 + 1 = 13$ distributions of the candies.

For the cookies, we can choose to give 0, 1, or 2 cookies to each boy, and the rest of the cookies would then go to the girl. This is a total of 3 different distributions.

Therefore, the number of distributions is $(13)(3) = \boxed{39}$.

7.17   Notice that only one of the variables could possibly be larger than 16, given that they all sum to 30. So we can count the number of solutions without restrictions, then subtract those solutions in which one of the variables is larger than 16.

The number of positive integer solutions to $w + x + y + z = 30$, without restriction, is $\binom{29}{3}$.

If $w > 16$, then let $w' = w - 16$. Then w' is a positive integer, and satisfies $w' + x + y + z = 14$. This has $\binom{13}{3}$ solutions. Similarly, there are $\binom{13}{3}$ solutions with any given variable greater than 16.

Therefore, the answer to the original problem is $\binom{29}{3} - 4\binom{13}{3} = \boxed{2510}$.

7.18   From 1 to 36, there are six multiples of 6 (and thus 30 numbers that are not multiples of 6). First, we can order the 30 non-multiples of 6. There are 30! such arrangements.

Next, we can place each of the six multiples of 6 between two of the numbers that we have already arranged, or at the beginning or end. There are $\binom{31}{6}$ choices of slots for the multiples, then 6! ways to arrange them among the chosen slots. Hence, the number of arrangements of the integers from 1 to 36 where no two multiples of 6 are adjacent is $\boxed{30! \cdot \binom{31}{6} \cdot 6!}$.

7.19 Any term in the expansion is of the form $x^a y^b z^c$, where a, b, c are nonnegative integers such that $a+b+c = 100$. The number of terms is the number of solutions of this equation, which is equal to the number of solutions, in positive integers, to the equation $a' + b' + c' = 103$, where $a' = a + 1$, $b' = b + 1$, and $c' = c + 1$. This equation has $\binom{102}{2}$ solutions, and thus there are $\boxed{\binom{102}{2} = 5151}$ terms in the expansion of $(x + y + z)^{100}$.

7.20 First, we determine where teachers and students can sit. We must have at least 2 students between each pair of teachers, so we start with TSSTSST, where T is a teacher and S is a student. We still have 4 students left to place, and 4 slots in which to place them (two slots between teachers and two slots at either end). This is equivalent to solving the equation $a + b + c + d = 4$ in nonnegative integers, which is equivalent to solving the equation $a' + b' + c' + d' = 8$ in positive integers (where $a' = a + 1$, etc.). Therefore, there are $\binom{7}{3}$ ways to place the students.

Once we have the seating positions placed, there are 8! ways to assign students to the student seats and 3! ways to assign teachers to the teacher seats. Therefore, the number of seatings is

$$\binom{7}{3} \cdot 8! \cdot 3! = \boxed{8,467,200}.$$

Challenge Problems

7.21 The 5 seated people divide the 15 empty chairs into 6 groups. Thus, the number of ways to seat 5 people is equal to the number of solutions in nonnegative integers to $x_1 + x_2 + x_3 + x_4 + x_5 + x_6 = 15$. This has $\binom{20}{5}$ solutions (substitute $y_i = x_i + 1$ so that we are solving for 6 positive integers that sum to 21).

If nobody is sitting next to anybody else, then the number of empty chairs in the 4 middle slots must be positive; that is, $x_2, x_3, x_4, x_5 > 0$ in our above equation. Substituting $y_1 = x_1 + 1$ and $y_6 = x_6 + 1$ means that we are looking for positive solutions to $y_1 + x_2 + x_3 + x_4 + x_5 + y_6 = 17$, of which there are $\binom{16}{5}$ solutions.

Since all of these distributions are equally likely, the probability that no one is sitting next to another person is

$$\frac{\binom{16}{5}}{\binom{20}{5}} = \boxed{\frac{91}{323}}.$$

7.22 Since there are fewer B's, they are easier to deal with. The only way that the B's can be arranged, so that all of them are next to each other, is if they all appear in one large group (as BBBBB), or if they are split into two groups, one group of 2 B's and one group of 3 B's. This leads to two cases:

Case 1: All 5 B's appear together in one group. Then some number of A's, possibly 0 but not 1, can appear before the B's, and the rest (again possibly 0 but not 1) appear after the B's. This means that 0, 2, 3, 4, 5, 6, or 8 A's can appear before the B's, leading to 7 possible words.

Case 2: The B's appear in two groups, one BB and one BBB. There are 2 choices for which group to appear first, and at least 2 A's must be in between them. This leaves 6 A's to distribute in the remaining 3 slots (in front the of first group of B's, in between the groups of B's, or after the second group of B's), but we cannot place 1 A in the first or last slot. This is equivalent to solving the equation $x + y + z = 6$ in nonnegative integers where $x \neq 1$ and $z \neq 1$.

If we temporarily ignore the "$\neq 1$" condition, then there are $\binom{8}{2} = 28$ solutions. However, we must exclude the $x = 1$ solutions, which are solutions to $y + z = 5$. There are 6 of these. Similarly, we must exclude the 6 solutions where $z \neq 1$, and add back (using PIE) the 1 solution $x = 1, y = 4, z = 1$ that we have subtracted twice. Therefore, that gives us $28 - 2(6) + 1 = 17$ ways to place the A's. Since there were 2 choices for how to arrange the B's, this gives us $2 \cdot 17 = 34$ possible words in this case.

This gives a total of $7 + 34 = \boxed{41}$ possible words.

7.23 Counting heads and tails based on Amy's observations, we see that

- 8 times a heads follows something,

- 7 times something follows a heads,

- 11 times a tails follows something,

- 12 times something follows a tails.

This implies that any such sequence must have 8 heads and 12 tails, and must start with a T and end with an H.

"3 times a heads followed a heads" means that the 8 heads must occur in $8 - 3 = 5$ groups. There are $\binom{7}{4} = 35$ ways to split the 8 heads into 5 positive groups. Similarly, "7 times a tails followed a tails" means that the 12 tails must occur in $12 - 7 = 5$ groups; there are $\binom{11}{4} = 330$ ways to split them into groups.

Therefore, there are $(35)(330) = \boxed{11{,}550}$ solutions.

7.24 We can re-engineer the problem a bit by thinking of first drawing all 6 balls at once, then ordering them. We'll further break this up into cases based on the number of red balls that we draw. If we draw r red balls and b blue balls, then there are $\binom{10}{r}\binom{8}{b}$ ways to draw this group from our bin, out of a total of $\binom{18}{6}$ ways to draw any 6 balls. For each configuration, we'll determine the probability that the balls are ordered with 2 red balls consecutive.

If $r = 0$ or $r = 1$, then clearly we cannot have two red balls consecutive, so the probability is 0.

If $r = 2$, then there are 5 arrangements of the balls with the two red balls consecutive, and $\binom{6}{2} = 15$ total arrangements. So the probability is $\frac{1}{3}$.

If $r = 3$, then the only arrangements that fail, out of the $\binom{6}{3} = 20$ total arrangements, are the arrangements $RBRBRB$, $BRBRBR$, $RBBRBR$, and $RBRBBR$. So the probability is $\frac{16}{20} = \frac{4}{5}$.

If $r \geq 4$, then we are guaranteed to have two red balls consecutive.

Therefore, the probability is

$$\frac{\frac{1}{3}\binom{10}{2}\binom{8}{4} + \frac{4}{5}\binom{10}{3}\binom{8}{3} + \binom{10}{4}\binom{8}{2} + \binom{10}{5}\binom{8}{1} + \binom{10}{6}}{\binom{18}{6}} = \frac{1050 + 5376 + 5880 + 2016 + 210}{18564} = \frac{14532}{18564} = \boxed{\frac{173}{221}}.$$

7.25 We can choose 7 balls so that no two balls have consecutive labels as follows: First, arrange $n - 7$ white balls in a row. Then we insert 7 black balls among the white balls, so that each black ball goes either between two white balls, or at one of the ends of the row. This gives us $n - 6$ possible slots, so there are $\binom{n-6}{7}$ ways to place the black balls. Finally, label all the balls (black and white) 1 to n, from left to right. Then no two black balls have consecutive labels. Hence, there are $\binom{n-6}{7}$ ways to draw 7 balls so that no two balls have consecutive labels.

Now we calculate the number of ways of drawing 7 balls so that there is exactly one pair of consecutive labels. Choose one of the $n - 6$ slots, as described above, and insert two black balls into that slot. This leaves 5 black balls to be distributed among the remaining $n - 7$ slots. After labeling the balls from 1 to n, there will be exactly one pair of black balls with consecutive labels. Hence, there are $(n - 6)\binom{n-7}{5}$ ways to draw 7 balls so that there is exactly one pair of consecutive labels.

Hence, for the probabilities of the two events to be equal, we must have the number of possibility for the two events to be equal; that is,

$$\binom{n-6}{7} = (n-6)\binom{n-7}{5}.$$

We can expand these out and algebraically solve for n:

$$\frac{(n-6)!}{7!(n-13)!} = (n-6) \cdot \frac{(n-7)!}{5!(n-12)!}$$

$$\Leftrightarrow \quad \frac{(n-12)!}{(n-13)!} = \frac{7!}{5!}$$

$$\Leftrightarrow \quad n - 12 = 42$$

$$\Leftrightarrow \quad n = \boxed{54}.$$

CHAPTER 8

Mathematical Induction

Review Problems

8.7 The first n positive odd integers are $1, 3, 5, \ldots, 2n - 1$, so we must show that

$$1 + 3 + 5 + \cdots + (2n - 1) = n^2.$$

First, we prove that the result is true for the base case. For $n = 1$, the left side is 1, and the right side is $1^2 = 1$, so the result is true for $n = 1$.

Now assume that the result is true for some positive integer $n = k$, so

$$1 + 3 + 5 + \cdots + (2k - 1) = k^2.$$

Adding $2k + 1$ to both sides, we get

$$1 + 3 + 5 + \cdots + (2k - 1) + (2k + 1) = k^2 + 2k + 1 = (k + 1)^2.$$

Hence, the result is true for $n = k + 1$, and by induction, it is true for all positive integers n.

8.8 First, we prove that the formula is true for the base case. For $n = 1$, the left side is a, and the right side is $a(r - 1)/(r - 1)$, so the formula is true for $n = 1$.

Now assume that the formula is true for some positive integer $n = k$, so

$$a + ar + ar^2 + \cdots + ar^{k-1} = a \cdot \frac{r^k - 1}{r - 1}.$$

Adding ar^k to both sides, we get

$$\begin{aligned}
a + ar + ar^2 + \cdots + ar^{k-1} + ar^k &= a \cdot \frac{r^k - 1}{r - 1} + ar^k \\
&= a\left(\frac{r^k - 1}{r - 1} + r^k\right) \\
&= a \cdot \frac{r^k - 1 + r^{k+1} - r^k}{r - 1} \\
&= a \cdot \frac{r^{k+1} - 1}{r - 1}.
\end{aligned}$$

Hence, the formula is true for $n = k + 1$, and by induction, it is true for all positive integers n.

8.9 First, we prove the identity for the base case. For $n = 1$, the left side is $1^2 = 1$, and the right side is $1 \cdot 2 \cdot 3/6 = 1$, so the identity holds for $n = 1$.

Now we assume that the identity holds for some positive integer $n = k$, so

$$1^2 + 2^2 + \cdots + k^2 = \frac{k(k+1)(2k+1)}{6}.$$

Adding $(k+1)^2$ to both sides, we get

$$1^2 + 2^2 + \cdots + k^2 + (k+1)^2 = \frac{k(k+1)(2k+1)}{6} + (k+1)^2$$

$$= (k+1)\left(\frac{k(2k+1)}{6} + k + 1\right)$$

$$= (k+1)\left(\frac{2k^2 + k + 6k + 6}{6}\right)$$

$$= (k+1) \cdot \frac{2k^2 + 7k + 6}{6}$$

$$= \frac{(k+1)(k+2)(2k+3)}{6}.$$

Hence, the identity holds for $n = k + 1$, and by induction, it holds for all positive integers n.

8.10 First, we prove the result for the base case. If $n = 1$, then $7^n - 1 = 6$, which is clearly a multiple of 6, so the result is true for $n = 1$.

Now assume that the result is true for some positive integer $n = k$, so $7^k - 1$ is a multiple of 6. In other words, $7^k - 1 = 6m$ for some positive integer m, so $7^k = 6m + 1$. Then

$$7^{k+1} = 7(6m + 1) = 42m + 7,$$

which implies that $7^{k+1} - 1 = 42m + 6 = 6(7m + 1)$. Hence, $7^{k+1} - 1$ is also a multiple of 6, so the result is true for $n = k + 1$, and by induction, it is true for all positive integers n.

8.11 First, we prove the inequality for the base case. For $n = 1$, the left side is $2! = 2$, and the right side is $2!^1 = 2$, so the inequality holds for $n = 1$.

Now, assume that the inequality holds for some positive integer $n = k$, so

$$2! 4! \cdots (2k)! \geq [(k+1)!]^k.$$

Multiplying both sides by $(2k + 2)!$, we get

$$2! 4! \cdots (2k)!(2k+2)! \geq [(k+1)!]^k (2k+2)!.$$

We want to show that the left side is at least $[(k+2)!]^{k+1}$. Hence, it suffices to show that

$$[(k+1)!]^k (2k+2)! \geq [(k+2)!]^{k+1}.$$

We can simplify this inequality as follows:

$$[(k+1)!]^k (2k+2)! \geq [(k+2)!]^{k+1}$$
$$\Leftrightarrow \quad [(k+1)!]^k (2k+2)! \geq (k+2)![(k+2)!]^k$$
$$\Leftrightarrow \quad (2k+2)! \geq (k+2)!\left(\tfrac{(k+2)!}{(k+1)!}\right)^k = (k+2)!(k+2)^k$$
$$\Leftrightarrow \quad \frac{(2k+2)!}{(k+2)!} \geq (k+2)^k$$
$$\Leftrightarrow \quad (k+3)(k+4)\cdots(2k+2) \geq (k+2)^k.$$

This last inequality is true, because there are k factors in the left side, and each of them is greater than $k + 2$. Since all our steps are reversible, we conclude that

$$[(k + 1)!]^k (2k + 2)! \geq [(k + 2)!]^{k+1}.$$

Hence,

$$2!4! \cdots (2k)!(2k + 2)! \geq [(k + 2)!]^{k+1}.$$

Therefore, the inequality is true for $n = k + 1$, and by induction, it is true for all positive integers n.

8.12 We will prove the statement by induction. Our base case is $n = 2$ (since we are given that $n > 1$), so suppose that there are 4 points in space with $2^2 + 1 = 5$ segments drawn. Note that there are only $\binom{4}{2} = 6$ pairs of points, so only one of the possible segments is missing. In particular, let A and B be the two points that do not have a segment between them, and call the other two points C and D. Then triangles ACD and BCD are both drawn.

Now assume that the statement is true for $2k$ points, and consider $2(k + 1) = 2k + 2$ points and $(k + 1)^2 + 1$ segments connecting pairs of points. Pick any two points A and B that have a line segment between them, and let S be the set of the remaining $2k$ points other than A or B. If A and B each have a segment to a point C in S, then ABC is a triangle. If not, then there are at most $2k$ segments from A or B to the points in S, since there is at most 1 segment from each point in S to either A or B. Therefore, we have accounted for at most $2k + 1$ of the segments (the one segment between A and B, and at most $2k$ segments from A or B to points in S), and thus there are at least

$$(k + 1)^2 + 1 - (2k + 1) = (k^2 + 2k + 1) + 1 - (2k + 1) = k^2 + 1.$$

segments between pairs of points in S. So, by the inductive hypothesis, there is a triangle drawn in S.

8.13 We prove the statement by induction on n, the number of lines. If $n = 1$, then we draw one line, and color one side of the line black and the other side white. This establishes the base case of the induction.

Now suppose that we can color any configuration of k lines, and consider the plane with $k + 1$ lines drawn. Temporarily remove any one line, and legally color the k-line configuration that remains. Then, replace the $(k+1)^{\text{st}}$ line, and reverse the colors of all of the regions on one chosen side of the line (it doesn't matter which side). We claim that this is a legal coloring of the $(k + 1)$-line configuration.

If two regions border along a line other than the $(k + 1)^{\text{st}}$ line, then these regions had opposite colors in the k-line coloring. After adding the $(k+1)^{\text{st}}$ line, these regions either both kept the same color or both had their colors reversed, depending on which side of the $(k + 1)^{\text{st}}$ line they lie on. So they still have opposite color.

On the other hand, if two regions border along the $(k + 1)^{\text{st}}$ line, then prior to adding this line, the two regions were actually the same region in the k-line configuration, and thus had the same color. After adding the $(k+1)^{\text{st}}$ line, we reversed the color of one of the new regions. So the regions now have opposite colors.

Thus the $(k + 1)$-line configuration has a valid coloring, completing the inductive proof.

Challenge Problems

8.14 To prove the general triangle inequality, we first prove it for two variables, i.e.

$$|x + y| \leq |x| + |y|$$

for all real numbers x and y.

To begin, we square both sides (which does not change the inequality, as both sides are nonnegative) to get

$$|x + y|^2 \leq (|x| + |y|)^2 = |x|^2 + 2|x||y| + |y|^2 = |x|^2 + 2|xy| + |y|^2.$$

Since $|a|^2 = a^2$ for all real numbers a, we can replace $|x + y|^2$ with $(x + y)^2 = x^2 + 2xy + y^2$, $|x|^2$ with x^2, and $|y|^2$ with y^2, to obtain the equivalent inequality

$$x^2 + 2xy + y^2 \leq x^2 + 2|xy| + y^2$$
$$\Leftrightarrow \quad xy \leq |xy|$$

This last inequality is true, because if $xy \geq 0$, then both sides are equal, and if $xy < 0$, then the left side is negative and the right side is positive. All of the steps in the above argument are reversible, hence $|x + y| \leq |x| + |y|$ for all real numbers x and y.

Now we prove the generalized triangle inequality. The inequality is clearly true for $n = 1$, and we have just proven the case $n = 2$, so assume that the inequality is true for some positive integer $n = k \geq 2$. We wish to prove that the inequality is true for $k + 1$ variables, i.e.

$$|x_1 + x_2 + \cdots + x_k + x_{k+1}| \leq |x_1| + |x_2| + \cdots + |x_k| + |x_{k+1}|.$$

By the induction hypothesis, the generalized triangle inequality is true for k variables, so we can say that

$$|x_1 + x_2 + \cdots + x_k + x_{k+1}| = |x_1 + x_2 + \cdots + (x_k + x_{k+1})|$$
$$\leq |x_1| + |x_2| + \cdots + |x_k + x_{k+1}|.$$

But we can also say that $|x_k + x_{k+1}| \leq |x_k| + |x_{k+1}|$, so

$$|x_1 + x_2 + \cdots + x_k + x_{k+1}| \leq |x_1| + |x_2| + \cdots + |x_k| + |x_{k+1}|.$$

Hence, the generalized triangle inequality is true for $n = k + 1$ variables, so by induction, it is true for n variables, for all positive integers n.

8.15 Let $a_n = 2^{2^n} + 3^{2^n} + 5^{2^n}$. To get started on the problem, let's try small cases, and list the results in a table. Note that $x^{2^n} = (x^{2^{n-1}})^2$, so we can obtain the numbers in each row by squaring the numbers in the previous row, and then reducing modulo 19.

n	2^{2^n} (mod 19)	3^{2^n} (mod 19)	5^{2^n} (mod 19)	a_n (mod 19)
1	4	9	6	0
2	16	5	17	0
3	9	6	4	0
4	5	17	16	0
5	6	4	9	0
6	17	16	5	0
7	4	9	6	0

Note that the numbers in the first row coincide with the numbers in the seventh row. Since the numbers in each row can be generated from the numbers in the previous row, the result follows quickly from this observation. However, we may also observe that the numbers in the first row are the same as the numbers in the third row (albeit in a different order), and every odd-numbered row, and the same holds for the even-numbered rows. This observation can be proved formally as follows:

$$a_{n+2} = 2^{2^{n+2}} + 3^{2^{n+2}} + 5^{2^{n+2}}$$
$$= 2^{4 \cdot 2^n} + 3^{4 \cdot 2^n} + 5^{4 \cdot 2^n}$$
$$= 16^{2^n} + 81^{2^n} + 625^{2^n}$$
$$\equiv 16^{2^n} + 5^{2^n} + 17^{2^n}$$
$$\equiv (-3)^{2^n} + 5^{2^n} + (-2)^{2^n}$$
$$\equiv 2^{2^n} + 3^{2^n} + 5^{2^n}$$
$$\equiv a_n \quad (\text{mod } 19).$$

To complete the induction argument, we must show that both a_1 and a_2 are divisible by 19. (We must include both of these values in our base cases, since the congruence above relates a_{n+2} and a_n.) To do this, we can consult the table above, or simply plug in and find that $a_1 = 38 = 2 \cdot 19$ and $a_2 = 722 = 38 \cdot 19$.

8.16 We prove by induction. Let $g(n)$ denote the sum of the $f(S)$'s where S is a nonempty subset of $\{1, 2, \ldots, n\}$ with no consecutive elements. If $n = 1$, then the only valid subset is $\{1\}$, and $g(1) = f(\{1\}) = 1 = 2! - 1$. If $n = 2$, then the valid subsets are $\{1\}$ and $\{2\}$, and we have

$$g(2) = f(\{1\}) + f(\{2\}) = 1 + 4 = 5 = 3! - 1.$$

So the result holds for $n \le 2$.

Now assume that the result is true for all $n \le k$ for some integer $k \ge 2$; that is, that $g(n) = (n + 1)! - 1$ for all $n \le k$. We will prove the result for $n = k + 1$.

Suppose that T is a subset of $\{1, 2, \ldots, k + 1\}$ with no two consecutive integers. If $k + 1 \in T$, then we cannot have $k \in T$, so $T \setminus \{k + 1\}$ is a subset of $\{1, 2, \ldots, k - 1\}$. Note also that in this case,

$$f(T) = (k + 1)^2 f(T \setminus \{k + 1\}),$$

unless $T = \{k + 1\}$ (since this would give us $T \setminus \{k + 1\} = \emptyset$), in which case $f(\{k + 1\}) = (k + 1)^2$. So the sum of the $f(T)$'s for subsets containing $k + 1$ is equal to $(k + 1)^2$ times the sum of the $f(T \setminus \{k + 1\})$'s, plus $f(\{k + 1\}) = (k + 1)^2$.

Otherwise, if $k + 1 \notin T$, then T is a valid subset of $\{1, 2, \ldots, k\}$.

Therefore, applying the inductive hypothesis, we see that

$$\begin{aligned}
g(k + 1) &= (k + 1)^2 g(k - 1) + (k + 1)^2 + g(k) \\
&= (k + 1)^2 (k! - 1) + (k + 1)^2 + ((k + 1)! - 1) \\
&= (k + 1)((k + 1)! - (k + 1)) + (k + 1)^2 + (k + 1)! - 1 \\
&= ((k + 1) + 1)(k + 1)! - (k + 1)^2 + (k + 1)^2 - 1 \\
&= (k + 2)! - 1,
\end{aligned}$$

completing the proof.

8.17 If $n = 1$, then there is only one country and only one person, so the problem is trivial. If $n = 2$, then there are two countries with two people each. They can be seated so that both pairs of countrymen are next to each other; this seating satisfies the requirements of the problem.

Suppose that we can seat n countries, each with n people, around a round table as specified in the problem. Now consider the situation with $n + 1$ countries, each with $n + 1$ people. To our existing n-country seating, we need to add 1 additional person from each of the original n countries, plus $n + 1$ people from the new country, which we'll call country Z.

For each original country C, there must be a pair of people from that country seated together at the table, since one of the original n people from country C must have another country C person as his neighbor to the left. We seat the $(n + 1)^{\text{st}}$ person from C and one person from Z (in either order) between the adjacent pair of people from C already seated at the table. We now have the country Z person to the left of a country C person, and also have a country C person to the left of a country Z person. So it's still the case that no two countrymen have people from the same country as their neighbors to the left. We repeat this operation for all n of the original countries.

Finally, we need to add the $(n + 1)^{\text{st}}$ country Z person. We can simply seat her next to any other country Z person. By construction, all of the country Z people will have a different country's citizen to their immediate left.

As an example of this procedure, here is the process by which we go from 2 countries to 3 countries. Letters A and B denote people from the original two countries, and the letter Z denotes people from the new third country. The people added at each step are shown in bold.

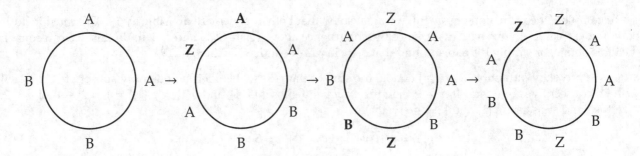

8.18 We will prove the result by induction on n, the number of cars. Obviously, if there is only 1 car on the track, it must have 1 gallon in its tank, and it can make it all the way around the track.

Suppose that the result is true for k cars, and assume that there are $k + 1$ cars on the track satisfying the conditions of the problem. Label the cars $C_1, C_2, \ldots, C_{k+1}$ in counterclockwise order. We first claim that there is at least one car that has enough gas to reach the next car on the track; if not, the sum total of the distances that all of the cars could reach would be less than the entire track (each car would cover a distance strictly less than the distance from it to the next car), which is a contradiction.

So suppose (without loss of generality) that C_1 has enough gas to reach C_2. Then the problem with $k + 1$ cars is reduced to the problem with k cars if we remove all of C_2's gas and place it in C_1's tank, and delete car C_2. Because car C_1 has enough gas to reach C_2, we don't have to worry about running out of gas between C_1 and C_2; therefore, a car that could make it around the track in the new k-car configuration can also make it around the track in the original $(k + 1)$-car configuration.

By induction, one of the cars in the reduced problem (with k cars) can make it around the track, and hence so can this same car in the $(k + 1)$-car problem. This completes the induction.

8.19 We assume that Pick's Theorem is true for all triangles, which establishes the base case. Now, assume that Pick's Theorem is true for all polygons with at most $n = k$ vertices, for some positive integer $k \geq 3$.

Consider a polygon P with $k + 1$ vertices. To apply the inductive hypothesis, we want to dissect P into two polygons, so that each of the new polygons has k vertices or fewer. We can achieve this by dissecting along a diagonal that is contained in P. However, proving that P must contain such a diagonal is a bit tricky.

Choose an arbitrary vertex v_1, and let its neighbors be v_2 and v_3. If the line joining v_2 and v_3 does not intersect any other part of P, then it is contained in P, and we have a suitable diagonal. (There is an amusing bit of terminology for this: we say that the vertex v_1 is an *ear* of the polygon.)

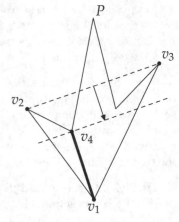

Otherwise, the line joining v_2 and v_3 intersects P, as illustrated at right. In such a case, take the line joining v_2 and v_3 and slide it towards v_1. Let v_4 be the last vertex that this line passes through, before hitting v_1, and so that v_4 is contained in the triangle formed by v_1, v_2, and v_3. Then the line joining v_1 and v_4 cannot intersect any other part of P that is contained in the triangle formed by v_1, v_2, and v_3; hence, it is a diagonal that is completely contained within P.

Now we have a polygon P that has been dissected by a diagonal into two polygons P_1 and P_2, where P_1 and P_2 each have at most k vertices, as shown below:

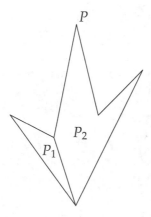

Let I_1 and I_2 be the number of lattice points in the interiors of P_1 and P_2, and let B_1 and B_2 be the number of lattice points on the boundaries of P_1 and P_2, respectively. Then by the inductive hypothesis, the area of P_1 is $I_1 + B_1/2 - 1$, and the area of P_2 is $I_2 + B_2/2 - 1$. Therefore, the area of P is $I_1 + I_2 + (B_1 + B_2)/2 - 2$.

Let I and B be the number of lattice points in the interior and on the boundary of P, respectively. Let m be the number of lattice points on the diagonal dividing P_1 and P_2. Of these m lattice points, $m - 2$ lie in the interior of P (we subtract the two endpoints of the diagonal). Therefore, $I = I_1 + I_2 + (m - 2)$.

To count the number of lattice points that are on the boundary of P, we can add B_1 and B_2, but we must subtract 2 for the endpoints of the diagonal, and 2 for each of the points on the diagonal. Thus

$$B = B_1 + B_2 - 2 - 2(m - 2) = B_1 + B_2 - 2m + 2.$$

Therefore,

$$I + \frac{B}{2} - 1 = I_1 + I_2 + (m - 2) + \frac{1}{2}(B_1 + B_2 - 2m + 2) - 1$$

$$= I_1 + I_2 + \frac{1}{2}(B_1 + B_2) - 2,$$

which is the area of polygon P, so Pick's Theorem holds for P. Since polygon P was chosen arbitrarily, Pick's Theorem is true for all polygons with $k + 1$ vertices, and by induction, it is true for all polygons.

8.20 We prove a more general result by induction: Let n be a positive integer, and let $0 \le N \le 2^n$. Then it is possible to color every subset of $\{1, 2, \ldots, n\}$ either black or white, so that the given conditions hold.

First, we prove the result for $n = 1$. The subsets of $\{1\}$ are $\emptyset$ and $\{1\}$. If $N = 0$, then color both $\emptyset$ and $\{1\}$ black. If $N = 1$, then color $\emptyset$ white and $\{1\}$ black. If $N = 2$, then color both $\emptyset$ and $\{1\}$ white. These coloring all satisfy the conditions of the problem, so the result is true for $n = 1$, which establishes the base case.

Now assume that the result is true for some positive integer $n = k$. Let $0 \le N \le 2^{k+1}$. We must color the subsets of $\{1, 2, \ldots, k, k + 1\}$ so that the given conditions hold.

If $0 \le N \le 2^k$, then by the inductive hypothesis, it is possible to color every subset of $\{1, 2, \ldots, k\}$ so that the given conditions hold for this set. In addition, we color every subset that contains the element $k + 1$ black. Then conditions 1 and 3 clearly hold for the subsets of $\{1, 2, \ldots, k, k + 1\}$, so we check condition 2. Let A and B be two black subsets of $\{1, 2, \ldots, k, k + 1\}$. If either A or B contains the element $k + 1$, then so does their union, and hence it is black. Otherwise, both A and B are subsets of $\{1, 2, \ldots, k\}$, and by the inductive hypothesis, their union is also black. Thus, condition 2 holds as well.

If $2^k + 1 \le N \le 2^{k+1}$, then $0 \le 2^{k+1} - N \le 2^k - 1$. As we showed above, we can color the subsets of $\{1, 2, \ldots, k, k + 1\}$ so that conditions 1 and 2 hold, and there are $2^{k+1} - N$ white subsets. Now, swap the color of each subset. Then conditions 1 and 2 still hold, and there are now N white subsets, as desired.

Hence, the result is true for $n = k + 1$, and by induction, it is true for all positive integers n.

8.21   We claim that there exists a silver matrix, with 1's on the main diagonal, for every positive integer $\begin{pmatrix} 1 & 2 \\ 3 & 1 \end{pmatrix}$
n that is a power of 2. We will prove this by induction. A 2×2 silver matrix with 1's on the diagonal is
shown at right, establishing the base case of the induction.

Assume that a $2^k \times 2^k$ silver matrix A exists with 1's on the diagonal; we will construct a $2^{k+1} \times 2^{k+1}$ silver matrix
with 1's on the diagonal. Let B be the $2^k \times 2^k$ matrix in which 2^{k+1} is added to every entry of A, and let C be the
matrix in which every occurrence of $2^{k+1} + 1$ on the main diagonal of B is replaced by 2^{k+1}. For example, when
$k = 1$, we have:

$$A = \begin{pmatrix} 1 & 2 \\ 3 & 1 \end{pmatrix}, \qquad B = \begin{pmatrix} 5 & 6 \\ 7 & 5 \end{pmatrix}, \qquad C = \begin{pmatrix} 4 & 6 \\ 7 & 4 \end{pmatrix}.$$

Then we construct our $2^{k+1} \times 2^{k+1}$ silver matrix by $M = \begin{pmatrix} A & B \\ C & A \end{pmatrix}$. For example, when $k = 1$, we have:

$$M = \begin{pmatrix} 1 & 2 & 5 & 6 \\ 3 & 1 & 7 & 5 \\ 4 & 6 & 1 & 2 \\ 7 & 4 & 3 & 1 \end{pmatrix}.$$

Note that for every integer i with $1 \le i \le 2^k$, row i of M consists of row i of A and row i of B, and column i of M
consists of column i of A and column i of C. Also, for every integer i with $2^k < i \le 2^{k+1}$, let $j = i - 2^k$. Then row i of
M consists of row j of A and row j of C, and column i of M consists of column j of A and column j of B.

Thus, for any $1 \le i \le 2^{k+1}$, row i and column i of M together consist of a matching row and column of A, which
contain all of the elements $\{1, 2, \dots, 2^{k+1} - 1\}$, together with a row from B and the corresponding column of C (or
vice versa), which contain all of the elements $\{2^{k+1}, 2^{k+1} + 1, \dots, 2^{k+2} - 1\}$. Therefore, M is a silver matrix with 1's
on the diagonal. Hence, by induction, silver matrices exist for all positive powers of 2.

CHAPTER 9

Fibonacci Numbers

Exercises for Section 9.3

9.3.1 If Norman first inserts a nickel, then he has to put in 70 more cents. If Norman first inserts a dime, then he has to put in 65 more cents. If we let c_n be the number of ways that Norman can insert coins totaling n cents, we see that $c_{75} = c_{70} + c_{65}$. More generally, we see that $c_n = c_{n-5} + c_{n-10}$. This is the Fibonacci recursion. Noting that $c_5 = 1$ and $c_{10} = 2$, we conclude that $c_{5k} = F_{k+1}$ for all positive integers k. Therefore, $c_{75} = F_{16} = \boxed{987}$.

9.3.2 Let a_n count the number of paths that a ray can take if it reflects exactly n times. When a ray first enters the sheets, it must take its first reflection off of the middle sheet or the bottom sheet. If the first reflection is off the middle sheet, then (unless $n = 1$) it must then reflect downward off the top sheet, otherwise it will leave the glass altogether. After this second reflection, the ray still has $n - 2$ reflections to make. On the other hand, if the first reflection is off the bottom sheet, then we can treat the ray as if it is entering the glass from the bottom, and it has $n - 1$ reflections to make.

Therefore, $a_n = a_{n-2} + a_{n-1}$, and we have the Fibonacci recurrence. Noting that $a_0 = 1$ (the ray passes through with no reflections) and $a_1 = 2$ (the ray may reflect off of either of the two lower sheets), we see that $a_n = F_{n+2}$. (We check that this works for the given example: $a_3 = F_5 = 5$.) Therefore, if we require exactly 9 reflections, then we have $a_9 = F_{11} = \boxed{89}$ possible paths.

9.3.3 Let A_n be the set of sequences of n tosses, where no two heads are in a row, that end with heads, and let B_n be the set of sequences of n tosses, where no two heads are in a row, that end with tails. Let $a_n = \#(A_n)$ and $b_n = \#(B_n)$. We list the first few terms.

n	A_n	B_n	a_n	b_n
1	{H}	{T}	1	1
2	{TH}	{TT, HT}	1	2
3	{TTH, HTH}	{TTT, THT, HTT}	2	3
4	{TTTH, THTH, HTTH}	{TTTT, TTHT, THTT, HTTT, HTHT}	3	5

We observe that the sequences (a_n) and (b_n) appear to coincide with the Fibonacci sequence. We also observe the following about the sets A_n and B_n: For $n \geq 2$, every element in A_n is generated by appending an H at the end of an element in B_{n-1}. (We cannot append an H at the end of an element in A_{n-1}, since this would result in two consecutive H's.) Hence, $a_n = b_{n-1}$. Also, every element in B_n is generated by appending a T at the end of an element either in A_{n-1} or B_{n-1}. Hence, $b_n = a_{n-1} + b_{n-1}$.

Since $a_n = b_{n-1}$ for $n \geq 2$, we have $a_{n-1} = b_{n-2}$ for $n \geq 3$. Substituting into $b_n = a_{n-1} + b_{n-1}$, we get

$$b_n = b_{n-1} + b_{n-2}.$$

Also, $a_n = b_{n-1}$, so $a_{n+1} = a_n + a_{n-1}$. Shifting the indices by 1, we get

$$a_n = a_{n-1} + a_{n-2}.$$

Let c_n be the total number of sequences of n tosses, where no two heads are in a row, so $c_n = a_n + b_n$. Then adding the two equations above, we get

$$c_n = c_{n-1} + c_{n-2}$$

for all $n \geq 3$. Furthermore, $c_1 = a_1 + b_1 = 2 = F_3$ and $c_2 = a_2 + b_2 = 3 = F_4$. We conclude that $c_n = F_{n+2}$ for all $n \geq 1$.

In particular, the number of sequences of 10 tosses where no two heads are in a row is $F_{12} = 144$. The total number of sequences of 10 tosses is $2^{10} = 1024$, so the probability that in 10 tosses, no two heads are in a row, is $144/1024 = \boxed{9/64}$.

9.3.4 We prove by induction on k that F_{4k} is a multiple of 3 and that F_{4k+1}, F_{4k+2}, and F_{4k+3} are not multiples of 3, for all nonnegative integers k. When $k = 0$, we have $F_0 = 0$, $F_1 = 1$, $F_2 = 1$, and $F_3 = 2$, so the base case holds.

For the inductive step, assume that the result is true for some nonnegative integer k. Then we have that:

$$\begin{aligned}
F_{4k+4} &= F_{4k+3} + F_{4k+2} \\
&= (F_{4k+2} + F_{4k+1}) + (F_{4k+1} + F_{4k}) \\
&= (F_{4k+1} + F_{4k}) + 2F_{4k+1} + F_{4k} \\
&= 3F_{4k+1} + 2F_{4k}.
\end{aligned}$$

By inductive hypothesis, F_{4k} is a multiple of 3, and hence so is $F_{4k+4} = 3F_{4k+1} + 2F_{4k}$.

Similarly, we have that $F_{4k+i+4} = 3F_{4k+i+1} + 2F_{4k+i}$ for any $1 \leq i \leq 3$. Since F_{4k+i} is not a multiple of 3 (by inductive hypothesis), $2F_{4k+i}$ is not a multiple of 3, and neither is $F_{4k+i+4} = 3F_{4k+i+1} + 2F_{4k+i}$.

So the result is true for all Fibonacci numbers, by induction.

9.3.5 We prove the result using induction. For $k = 1$, the left side of the identity is $1 + F_2 = 1 + 1 = 2$ and the right side is $F_3 = 2$, so the result is true for $k = 1$, which establishes the base case.

Now assume that the result is true for some positive integer $k = n$, so

$$1 + F_2 + F_4 + \cdots + F_{2n} = F_{2n+1}.$$

To prove the result for $k = n + 1$, add F_{2n+2} to both sides, to obtain

$$1 + F_2 + F_4 + \cdots + F_{2n} + F_{2n+2} = F_{2n+1} + F_{2n+2}.$$

By the Fibonacci relation, $F_{2n+1} + F_{2n+2} = F_{2n+3}$, so

$$1 + F_2 + F_4 + \cdots + F_{2n} + F_{2(n+1)} = F_{2n+3} = F_{2(n+1)+1}.$$

Thus, the result is true for $k = n + 1$, and by mathematical induction, the result is true for all positive integers k.

9.3.6 Let s_n be the number of minimal selfish subsets of $\{1, 2, \ldots, n\}$. Note that the only minimal selfish subset containing the element 1 is $\{1\}$.

If S is a minimal selfish subset of $\{1, 2, \ldots, n\}$ and $n \notin S$, then S is also a minimal selfish subset of $\{1, 2, \ldots, n-1\}$. On the other hand, if $n \in S$, then we may delete n from S and subtract 1 from each of the remaining elements (since $1 \notin S$), and get a minimal selfish subset of $\{1, 2, \ldots, n-2\}$. This shows that $s_n = s_{n-1} + s_{n-2}$.

There is only 1 minimal selfish subset of $\{1\}$, namely $\{1\}$, so $s_1 = 1$. Similarly, there is only 1 minimal selfish subset of $\{1, 2\}$, again namely $\{1\}$, so $s_2 = 1$. Thus $s_n = \boxed{F_n}$, the nth Fibonacci number.

9.3.7 We relate the identity

$$F_1^2 + F_2^2 + \cdots + F_n^2 = F_n F_{n+1}.$$

to the stair-climbing problem from Problem 9.1. Recall that F_n counts the number of ways to climb an staircase with $(n-1)$ stairs, in which each step is either 1 or 2 stairs. Then the right side of our identity, $F_n F_{n+1}$, counts the number of ways to climb all but 1 stair of an n-step staircase, take 1 step to the top (the nth stair), and then climb back down.

On the other hand, for any particular way that we can climb up and then back down as above, let j be the last staircase that we step on going both upwards and downwards. There are F_{j+1} ways to climb up to the jth step, and F_{j+1} ways to climb back down from it to the ground. The steps from stair j up to the top and back to stair j are fixed: we must hit all the odd stairs on the climb up and all the even stairs on the climb down (or vice versa, depending on whether n is odd or even). So there are F_{j+1}^2 climbs that have the jth as the last stair hit in both directions.

Finally, j can be any integer from 0 to $n-1$, because any stair (including the bottom "0th" ground-level stair) can be the last stair stepped on in both directions. This establishes the identity.

Exercises for Section 9.4

9.4.1   Let $\alpha = (1 + \sqrt{5})/2$ and $\beta = (1 - \sqrt{5})/2$, so that we may write Binet's formula as

$$F_n = \frac{\alpha^n - \beta^n}{\sqrt{5}}.$$

Therefore, we can write the right side of our identity as

$$F_n^2 + F_{n-1}^2 = \frac{(\alpha^n - \beta^n)^2}{5} + \frac{(\alpha^{n-1} - \beta^{n-1})^2}{5}$$
$$= \frac{\alpha^{2n} - 2(\alpha\beta)^n + \beta^{2n} + \alpha^{2n-2} - 2(\alpha\beta)^{n-1} + \beta^{2n-2}}{5}.$$

Note that $\alpha\beta = -1$, so that $(\alpha\beta)^n + (\alpha\beta)^{n-1} = (-1)^n + (-1)^{n-1} = 0$. Let us collect the remaining terms:

$$F_n^2 + F_{n-1}^2 = \frac{\alpha^{2n-2}(\alpha^2 + 1) + \beta^{2n-2}(\beta^2 + 1)}{5} = \frac{\alpha^{2n} + \alpha^{2n-2} + \beta^{2n} + \beta^{2n-2}}{5}.$$

On the other side of the identity, we can use Binet's formula and the facts that $\alpha - \beta = \sqrt{5}$ and $\alpha\beta = -1$ to write:

$$F_{2n-1} = \frac{\alpha^{2n-1} - \beta^{2n-1}}{\sqrt{5}}$$
$$= \frac{\alpha^{2n-1} - \beta^{2n-1}}{\sqrt{5}} \cdot \frac{\alpha - \beta}{\sqrt{5}}$$
$$= \frac{\alpha^{2n} - \beta\alpha^{2n-1} + \beta^{2n} - \alpha\beta^{2n-1}}{5}$$
$$= \frac{\alpha^{2n} + \alpha^{2n-2} + \beta^{2n} + \beta^{2n-2}}{5}.$$

Our expressions for $F_n^2 + F_{n-1}^2$ and F_{2n-1} are identical, thus proving the identity.

9.4.2   The "simplified" formula for F_n is the nearest integer to $\phi^n/\sqrt{5}$, where $\phi = (1 + \sqrt{5})/2$. The number of digits of F_n is $\lfloor \log_{10} F_n \rfloor + 1$, so the number of digits of F_n is:

$$\left\lfloor \log_{10}\left[\frac{\phi^n}{\sqrt{5}}\right] \right\rfloor + 1.$$

Note that

$$\log_{10}(\phi^n/\sqrt{5}) = \log_{10}(\phi^n) - \log_{10}(\sqrt{5}) = n\log_{10}(\phi) - \log_{10}(\sqrt{5}).$$

We compute $\log_{10}(\phi) \approx 0.209$ and $\log_{10}(\sqrt{5}) \approx 0.3495$, so we approximate that for $n > 0$:

$$\text{\# of digits of } F_n \approx \lfloor (0.209)n + 0.6505 \rfloor.$$

9.4.3

(a) Since the Lucas numbers satisfy the same recursion as the Fibonacci numbers, there exist constants λ_1 and λ_2 such that

$$L_n = \lambda_1 \left(\frac{1 + \sqrt{5}}{2} \right)^n + \lambda_2 \left(\frac{1 - \sqrt{5}}{2} \right)^n.$$

Setting $n = 0$ and $n = 1$ gives us the system of equations

$$2 = \lambda_1 + \lambda_2,$$

$$1 = \lambda_1 \left(\frac{1 + \sqrt{5}}{2} \right) + \lambda_2 \left(\frac{1 - \sqrt{5}}{2} \right).$$

The second equation becomes

$$1 = \lambda_1 \left(\frac{1 + \sqrt{5}}{2} \right) + \lambda_2 \left(\frac{1 - \sqrt{5}}{2} \right) = \frac{1}{2}(\lambda_1 + \lambda_2) + \frac{\sqrt{5}}{2}(\lambda_1 - \lambda_2) = 1 + \frac{\sqrt{5}}{2}(\lambda_1 - \lambda_2),$$

so $\lambda_1 = \lambda_2$. Since $\lambda_1 + \lambda_2 = 2$, we get $\lambda_1 = \lambda_2 = 1$. Therefore,

$$\boxed{L_n = \left(\frac{1 + \sqrt{5}}{2} \right)^n + \left(\frac{1 - \sqrt{5}}{2} \right)^n = \frac{(1 + \sqrt{5})^n + (1 - \sqrt{5})^n}{2^n}}$$

for all $n \geq 1$.

(b) To simplify the calculations, let $\nu = 1 + \sqrt{5}$ and $\mu = 1 - \sqrt{5}$, so $\nu\mu = (1 + \sqrt{5})(1 - \sqrt{5}) = -4$. Then

$$F_n = \frac{\nu^n - \mu^n}{2^n \sqrt{5}} \quad \text{and} \quad L_n = \frac{\nu^n + \mu^n}{2^n},$$

and we have:

$$F_n L_n = \left(\frac{\nu^n - \mu^n}{2^n \sqrt{5}} \right) \left(\frac{\nu^n + \mu^n}{2^n} \right)$$

$$= \frac{\nu^{2n} - \mu^{2n}}{2^{2n} \sqrt{5}}$$

$$= F_{2n}.$$

(c) Using the above notation, we have:

$$L_n^2 - 5F_n^2 = \left(\frac{\nu^n + \mu^n}{2^n} \right)^2 - 5 \left(\frac{\nu^n - \mu^n}{2^n \sqrt{5}} \right)^2$$

$$= \frac{\nu^{2n} + 2\nu^n \mu^n + \mu^{2n}}{4^n} - 5 \cdot \frac{\nu^{2n} - 2\nu^n \mu^n + \mu^{2n}}{5 \cdot 4^n}$$

$$= \frac{4\nu^n \mu^n}{4^n}$$

$$= \frac{4(\nu\mu)^n}{4^n}$$

$$= \frac{4(-4)^n}{4^n}$$

$$= 4 \cdot (-1)^n.$$

(d) We construct a table of the Fibonacci and Lucas numbers.

n	F_n	L_n
0	0	2
1	1	1
2	1	3
3	2	4
4	3	7
5	5	11
6	8	18
7	13	29
8	21	47

We note that the Fibonacci and Lucas numbers interlace as follows:

$$F_4 < L_3 < F_5 < L_4 < F_6 < L_5 < F_7 < \cdots.$$

We claim that $F_{n+1} < L_n < F_{n+2}$ for all $n \geq 3$, and we prove this using induction.

Since each Fibonacci number depends on the two previous Fibonacci numbers, this induction argument will require two base cases. We have already seen that the result holds for $n = 3$ and $n = 4$, which establishes the two base cases.

Now assume that the result holds for $n = k$ and $n = k + 1$, for some positive integer $k \geq 3$, so

$$F_{k+1} < L_k < F_{k+2} < L_{k+1} < F_{k+3}.$$

Adding the inequalities $F_{k+1} < L_k$ and $F_{k+2} < L_{k+1}$, we get $F_{k+1} + F_{k+2} < L_k + L_{k+1}$, so $F_{k+3} < L_{k+2}$. Adding the inequalities $L_k < F_{k+2}$ and $L_{k+1} < F_{k+3}$, we get $L_k + L_{k+1} < F_{k+2} + F_{k+3}$, so $L_{k+2} < F_{k+4}$. Hence,

$$F_{(k+2)+1} < L_{k+2} < F_{(k+2)+2},$$

so the result holds for $n = k + 2$, and by mathematical induction, the result holds for all $n \geq 3$.

So, $F_{n+1} < L_n < F_{n+2}$ for all $n \geq 3$, which means that every Lucas number beginning with L_3 lies strictly between two consecutive Fibonacci numbers. Similarly, $L_{n-2} < F_n < L_{n-1}$ for all $n \geq 5$, which means that every Fibonacci number beginning with F_5 lies strictly between two consecutive Lucas numbers.

Therefore, if the Fibonacci and Lucas sequences have any numbers in common, they must be among L_0, L_1, L_2, F_0, F_1, F_2, F_3, and F_4, and the only such numbers are 1, 2, and 3.

Review Problems

9.10 Let c_n be the number of ways that we can fill a parking lot with n spaces. Note that $c_1 = 1$ (we only have room for a compact) and $c_2 = 2$ (we can have either 2 compacts or 1 SUV). If $n \geq 2$, and the car in the first spot is a compact, then we can fill the rest of the lot in c_{n-1} ways. If the car in the first spot is an SUV, then we can fill the rest of the lot in c_{n-2} ways. Thus, $c_n = c_{n-1} + c_{n-2}$. Based on the initial conditions, we see that $c_n = F_{n+1}$, so that the number of ways to fill a 12-space lot is $c_{12} = F_{13} = \boxed{233}$.

9.11 Let s_n be the number of such ordered sums of n. If a given ordered sum has 2 as its first term, then we can remove it and get an ordered sum of $n - 2$. If a given ordered sum has an integer greater than 2 as its first term, then we can subtract 1 from this term and get an ordered sum of $n - 1$. These processes are reversible, and therefore we conclude that $s_n = s_{n-1} + s_{n-2}$.

We note that $s_1 = 0$ and $s_2 = 1$, therefore $s_n = \boxed{F_{n-1}}$.

9.12

(a) Let a_n be the number of rearrangements of n people. We can easily compute that $a_1 = 1$ and $a_2 = 2$, so assume that $n \geq 3$.

Note that the first person (on the far left) must either stay in his seat, or switch seats with the person in the second seat. In the former case, the remaining $n - 1$ people will rearrange themselves according to the condition of the problem. In the latter case, after the first two people have switched seats, the remaining $n - 2$ people will rearrange themselves.

Therefore, $a_n = a_{n-1} + a_{n-2}$ for all $n \geq 3$. Since $a_1 = 1 = F_2$ and $a_2 = 2 = F_3$, we conclude that $a_n = F_{n+1}$ for all positive integers n. In particular, $a_{14} = F_{15} = \boxed{610}$.

(b) Let b_n be the number of rearrangements of n people around a circular table. Pick one person at the table. If that person does not move, then there are $a_{n-1} = F_n$ rearrangements of the other $n - 1$ people (who we now think of as in a row). If the chosen person switches places with the person to her left, then there are $a_{n-2} = F_{n-1}$ rearrangements of the remaining $n - 2$ people. If the chosen person switches places with the person to her right, then there are $a_{n-2} = F_{n-1}$ rearrangements of the remaining $n - 2$ people. The only other possibility is that every person at the table moves 1 space to the left or to the right.

Thus, $b_n = F_n + 2F_{n-1} + 2 = F_{n+1} + F_{n-1} + 2$. If $n = 14$, then $b_{14} = F_{15} + F_{13} + 2 = 610 + 233 + 2 = \boxed{845}$.

9.13 Let m_n be the number of n-generation male ancestors, and f_n the number of n-generation female ancestors. Then for all $n > 0$, we have the relations

$$m_n = f_{n-1},$$
$$f_n = f_{n-1} + m_{n-1}.$$

Substituting the second equation into the first, we see that $f_n = f_{n-1} + f_{n-2}$. The initial conditions are $f_0 = 0$ and $f_1 = 1$, so we have that $f_n = F_n$, the nth Fibonacci number. Then $m_n = f_{n-1} = F_{n-1}$, and the total number of n-generation ancestors is $m_n + f_n = F_{n-1} + F_n = \boxed{F_{n+1}}$.

9.14 We prove the result using induction. For $k = 1$, the left side of the identity is $F_1 = 1$ and the right side is $F_3 - 1 = 2 - 1 = 1$, so the result is true for $k = 1$, which establishes the base case.

Now assume that the result is true for some positive integer $k = n$, so

$$F_1 + F_2 + \cdots + F_n = F_{n+2} - 1.$$

To prove the result for $k = n + 1$, add F_{n+1} to both sides, to obtain

$$F_1 + F_2 + \cdots + F_n + F_{n+1} = F_{n+1} + F_{n+2} - 1.$$

By the Fibonacci relation, $F_{n+1} + F_{n+2} = F_{n+3}$, so

$$F_1 + F_2 + \cdots + F_n + F_{n+1} = F_{n+3} - 1 = F_{(n+1)+2} - 1.$$

Thus, the result is true for $k = n + 1$, and by mathematical induction, the result is true for all positive integers k.

9.15 Let a_n be the number of such n-digit base-4 numbers starting with a 3. Note that $a_1 = 1$ (the only number is 3) and $a_2 = 1$ (the only number is 32), and consider numbers with $n \geq 3$. The first 3 digits of such a number must be either 321 or 323. This suggests looking at the numbers that start with 1, so let b_n be the number of such n-digit base-4 numbers starting with a 1. We then have the equation $a_n = a_{n-2} + b_{n-2}$. The first three digits of such a number starting with 1 must be 101, 121, or 123, hence this gives us the equation $b_n = 2b_{n-2} + a_{n-2}$. So we have the system of equations:

$$a_n = a_{n-2} + b_{n-2},$$
$$b_n = a_{n-2} + 2b_{n-2}.$$

We don't have a good idea how to solve this system, so let's just list some small values of a_n and b_n.

n	#s starting with 3	#s starting with 1	a_n	b_n
1	3	1	1	1
2	32	10, 12	1	2
3	321, 323	101, 121, 123	2	3
4	3210, 3212, 3232	1010, 1012, 1210, 1212, 1232	3	5
5	32101, 32121, 32123, 32321, 32323	10101, 10121, 10123, 12101, 12121, 12123, 12321, 12323	5	8

This should lead to the conjecture $a_n = F_n$ and $b_n = F_{n+1}$ for all $n > 0$. We can verify by induction that these satisfy our system of equations:

$$F_n = F_{n-2} + F_{n-1},$$
$$F_{n+1} = F_{n-2} + 2F_{n-1}.$$

So the number of such n-digit numbers is $\boxed{F_n}$.

9.16 Let p_n be the number of paths in a diagram with n hexes. The first step of the path moves to the point C or the point D below.

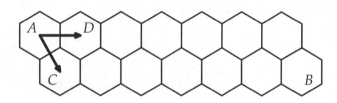

There are p_{n-1} paths from C to B and p_{n-2} paths from D to B, therefore we have $p_n = p_{n-1} + p_{n-2}$, giving us the Fibonacci recurrence. Noting that $p_1 = 1$ and $p_2 = 1$, we conclude that $p_n = F_n$. Since the given example has 14 hexes, the answer is $\boxed{F_{14} = 377}$.

Challenge Problems

9.17 Let b_n be the number ways to assign a row of n seats as specified in the problem, with a boy in the first seat. Let g_n be the number of such seatings with a girl in the first seat.

First, let's count the number of assignments with a boy in the first seat. The next seat must also be a boy, and thus the first three seats must be either BBB (three boys) or BBG (two boys and a girl). In the former case, we can delete the first boy, and what remains is a valid assignment of $n - 1$ seats starting with a boy, so there are b_{n-1} of these. In the latter case, we can delete the first two boys, and what remains is a valid assignment of $n - 2$ seats starting with a girl, so there are g_{n-2} of these. (Note that it might be tempting to delete the first two boys in the BBB case and conclude that there are b_{n-2} such seatings, but this would not count seatings that begin BBBG, which are allowed in the n-seat case but would not be allowed if the first two boys were deleted.)

Therefore, we see that $b_n = b_{n-1} + g_{n-2}$. But $b_k = g_k$ for all k: there is an obvious 1-1 correspondence between seatings that begin with boys and seating that begin with girls, by switching all the boys and girls. So we can replace g_{n-2} with b_{n-2}, giving the recurrence $b_n = b_{n-1} + b_{n-2}$. Noting that $b_2 = 1$ and $b_3 = 1$, we see that $b_n = F_{n-1}$.

Finally, the total number of seatings in our problem is $b_{11} + g_{11} = 2b_{11} = 2F_{10} = \boxed{110}$.

9.18 We conjecture that for all $n > 0$,

$$F_n = \binom{n-1}{0} + \binom{n-2}{1} + \binom{n-3}{2} + \cdots.$$

We prove this by induction on n. The base cases are $F_1 = \binom{0}{0} = 1$ and $F_2 = \binom{1}{0} = 1$. Then for any $n > 0$,

$$F_{n+1} = F_n + F_{n-1}$$

$$= \left(\binom{n-1}{0} + \binom{n-2}{1} + \binom{n-3}{2} + \cdots\right) + \left(\binom{n-2}{0} + \binom{n-3}{1} + \binom{n-4}{2} + \cdots\right)$$

$$= \binom{n-1}{0} + \left(\binom{n-2}{1} + \binom{n-2}{0}\right) + \left(\binom{n-3}{2} + \binom{n-3}{1}\right) + \cdots$$

$$= \binom{n}{0} + \binom{n-1}{1} + \binom{n-2}{2} + \cdots.$$

9.19 We have that

$$\frac{F_k}{F_{k-1}} - \frac{F_k}{F_{k+1}} = \frac{F_k(F_{k+1} - F_{k-1})}{F_{k-1}F_{k+1}} = \frac{F_k^2}{F_{k-1}F_{k+1}}.$$

Therefore,

$$\prod_{k=2}^{100} \left(\frac{F_k}{F_{k-1}} - \frac{F_k}{F_{k+1}}\right) = \prod_{k=2}^{100} \frac{F_k^2}{F_{k-1}F_{k+1}}$$

$$= \frac{F_2^2}{F_1 F_3} \cdot \frac{F_3^2}{F_2 F_4} \cdot \frac{F_4^2}{F_3 F_5} \cdots \frac{F_{100}^2}{F_{99}F_{101}}$$

$$= \boxed{\frac{F_{100}}{F_{101}}}.$$

9.20 Let

$$S = \frac{1}{3} + \frac{1}{9} + \frac{2}{27} + \frac{3}{81} + \frac{5}{243} + \cdots + \frac{F_n}{3^n} + \cdots.$$

Then

$$\frac{S}{3} = \frac{1}{9} + \frac{1}{27} + \frac{2}{81} + \frac{3}{243} + \cdots + \frac{F_{n-1}}{3^n} + \cdots,$$

and

$$\frac{S}{9} = \frac{1}{27} + \frac{1}{81} + \frac{2}{243} + \cdots + \frac{F_{n-2}}{3^n} + \cdots.$$

Adding these expressions, we get

$$\frac{S}{9} + \frac{S}{3} = \frac{4S}{9} = \frac{1}{9} + \frac{1+1}{27} + \frac{1+2}{81} + \frac{2+3}{243} + \cdots + \frac{F_{n-2} + F_{n-1}}{3^n} + \cdots$$

$$= \frac{1}{9} + \frac{2}{27} + \frac{3}{81} + \frac{5}{243} + \cdots + \frac{F_n}{3^n} + \cdots$$

$$= S - \frac{1}{3}.$$

Solving for S, we get $S = \boxed{3/5}$.

9.21 Note that the condition $2 < a^2 < 3$ implies that $\langle a^2 \rangle = a^2 - 2$, and also note that $0 < a^{-1} < 1$, so that $\langle a^{-1} \rangle = a^{-1}$. Therefore, the given condition is $a^{-1} = a^2 - 2$, or $a^3 - 2a - 1 = 0$. We see that $a = -1$ satisfies this equation, so we can factor $(a+1)$ out of this cubic, and get

$$a^3 - 2a - 1 = (a+1)(a^2 - a - 1).$$

Therefore, $a = (1 + \sqrt{5})/2 = \phi$, the golden ratio. At this point, we start think about Fibonacci numbers, and we notice that in the quantity we want to compute, we have the constant $144 = F_{12}$. Also, letting $b = (1 - \sqrt{5})/2$, note that

$$a^{-1} = \frac{2}{1 + \sqrt{5}} = \frac{2(1 - \sqrt{5})}{-4} = -\frac{1 - \sqrt{5}}{2} = -b.$$

Thus, the quantity that we are trying to compute is

$$a^{12} - 144a^{-1} = a^{12} + 144b = a^{12} + F_{12}b.$$

Now we can use Binet's formula:

$$\begin{aligned}
a^{12} + F_{12}b &= a^{12} + \frac{a^{12} - b^{12}}{\sqrt{5}}b \\
&= a^{12} + \frac{a^{12} - b^{12}}{a - b}b \\
&= a^{12} + (a^{11} + a^{10}b + \cdots + b^{11})b \\
&= a^{12} + a^{11}b + a^{10}b^2 + \cdots + b^{12} \\
&= \frac{a^{13} - b^{13}}{a - b} = \frac{a^{13} - b^{13}}{\sqrt{5}} = F_{13}.
\end{aligned}$$

Therefore, the answer is $F_{13} = \boxed{233}$.

CHAPTER 10

Recursion

Exercises for Section 10.2

10.2.1 Let a_n be the number of different ways I can arrange flags on an n-foot flagpole. Then $a_0 = 1$ (the one way with no flags) and $a_1 = 2$.

Now, for $n \geq 2$, consider an arrangement of flags on an n-foot flagpole. The top-most flag is either 1-foot or 2-foot. If it is 1-foot, then it must be one of 2 different types, and the rest of the flags can be arranged in a_{n-1} ways. If it is 2-foot, then it must be one of 3 different types, and the rest of the flags can be arranged in a_{n-2} ways. Hence,

$$a_n = 2a_{n-1} + 3a_{n-2}$$

for all $n \geq 2$.

We can then compute a_{10} using the recursion as follows:

$$a_2 = 2a_1 + 3a_0 = 2 \cdot 2 + 3 \cdot 1 = 7,$$
$$a_3 = 2a_2 + 3a_1 = 2 \cdot 7 + 3 \cdot 2 = 20,$$
$$a_4 = 2a_3 + 3a_2 = 2 \cdot 20 + 3 \cdot 7 = 61,$$
$$a_5 = 2a_4 + 3a_3 = 2 \cdot 61 + 3 \cdot 20 = 182,$$
$$a_6 = 2a_5 + 3a_4 = 2 \cdot 182 + 3 \cdot 61 = 547,$$
$$a_7 = 2a_6 + 3a_5 = 2 \cdot 547 + 3 \cdot 182 = 1640,$$
$$a_8 = 2a_7 + 3a_6 = 2 \cdot 1640 + 3 \cdot 547 = 4921,$$
$$a_9 = 2a_8 + 3a_7 = 2 \cdot 4921 + 3 \cdot 1640 = 14{,}762,$$
$$a_{10} = 2a_9 + 3a_8 = 2 \cdot 14{,}762 + 3 \cdot 4921 = \boxed{44{,}287}.$$

10.2.2 Setting $n = 2^{99}$ in (ii), we get

$$a_{2^{100}} = 2^{99}a_{2^{99}}.$$

Setting $n = 2^{98}$ in (ii), we get

$$a_{2^{99}} = 2^{98}a_{2^{98}},$$

and so forth. We can use (ii) repeatedly, to find

$$a_{2^{100}} = 2^{99} a_{2^{99}}$$
$$= 2^{99} \cdot 2^{98} a_{2^{98}}$$
$$= 2^{99} \cdot 2^{98} \cdot 2^{97} a_{2^{97}}$$
$$= \cdots$$
$$= 2^{99} \cdot 2^{98} \cdot 2^{97} \cdots 2^{1} a_1$$
$$= 2^{99} \cdot 2^{98} \cdot 2^{97} \cdots 2^{1}$$
$$= 2^{99 + 98 + \cdots + 1}$$
$$= 2^{99 \cdot 100 / 2}$$
$$= \boxed{2^{4950}}.$$

10.2.3 Let a_n be the number of such n-digit base 4 numbers. Note that $a_1 = 1$, as the only 1-digit number satisfying the property is 1.

Given an n-digit number satisfying the property, either the first digit is 1, in which case the remaining $n-1$ digits can be anything, or else the first digit is 2 or 3, in which case the remaining $(n-1)$-digit number must satisfy the property. This gives us the recurrence relation $a_n = 4^{n-1} + 2a_{n-1}$.

We can now recursively compute a_6:

$$a_2 = 4 + 2a_1 = 4 + 2(1) = 6,$$
$$a_3 = 16 + 2a_2 = 16 + 2(6) = 28,$$
$$a_4 = 64 + 2a_3 = 64 + 2(28) = 120,$$
$$a_5 = 256 + 2a_4 = 256 + 2(120) = 496,$$
$$a_6 = 1024 + 2a_5 = 1024 + 2(496) = \boxed{2016}.$$

10.2.4 Let's compute the first few values of a_n:

$$a_1 = p,$$
$$a_2 = q,$$
$$a_3 = a_1 a_2 = pq,$$
$$a_4 = a_2 a_3 = q(pq) = pq^2,$$
$$a_5 = a_3 a_4 = (pq)(pq^2) = p^2 q^3,$$
$$a_6 = a_4 a_5 = (pq^2)(p^2 q^3) = p^3 q^5,$$
$$a_7 = a_5 a_6 = (p^2 q^3)(p^3 q^5) = p^5 q^8.$$

Notice the pattern in the exponents of p's and q's: 1,1,2,3,5,8,.... Those look like Fibonacci numbers!

Indeed, we conjecture that for all $n \geq 2$, $a_n = \boxed{p^{F_{n-2}} q^{F_{n-1}}}$. We prove this by induction. We have already proven it for $n \leq 7$ from our computations above, so assume that the formula is true for all $n \leq k$, where $k \geq 7$ is a positive integer. Then:

$$a_{k+1} = a_k a_{k-1}$$
$$= \left(p^{F_{k-2}} q^{F_{k-1}} \right) \left(p^{F_{k-3}} q^{F_{k-2}} \right)$$
$$= p^{(F_{k-2}+F_{k-3})} q^{(F_{k-1}+F_{k-2})}$$
$$= p^{F_{k-1}} q^{F_k}.$$

Thus the formula holds for a_{k+1}, and hence, by induction, for all positive integers n.

10.2.5 Let s_n be the number of spacy subsets of $\{1, 2, \ldots, n\}$. Note that $s_0 = 1$ (the empty set is spacy) and $s_1 = 2$ (both $\emptyset$ and $\{1\}$ are spacy). Also note that the only spacy subsets of s_2 are the empty set and the subsets with one element. So $s_2 = 3$.

For any positive integer $n \geq 3$, if n is an element of a spacy subset of $\{1, 2, \ldots, n\}$, then $n-1$ and $n-2$ cannot be in the subset, and the rest of the subset is a spacy subset of $\{1, 2, \ldots, n-3\}$. On the other hand, if n is not an element, then the subset is a spacy subset of $\{1, 2, \ldots, n-1\}$. This gives the recurrence relation

$$s_n = s_{n-1} + s_{n-3}.$$

Now we can use the recurrence relation to compute values of s_n up to s_{12}:

$$s_3 = s_2 + s_0 = 3 + 1 = 4,$$
$$s_4 = s_3 + s_1 = 4 + 2 = 6,$$
$$s_5 = s_4 + s_2 = 6 + 3 = 9,$$
$$s_6 = s_5 + s_3 = 9 + 4 = 13,$$
$$s_7 = s_6 + s_4 = 13 + 6 = 19,$$
$$s_8 = s_7 + s_5 = 19 + 9 = 28,$$
$$s_9 = s_8 + s_6 = 28 + 13 = 41,$$
$$s_{10} = s_9 + s_7 = 41 + 19 = 60,$$
$$s_{11} = s_{10} + s_8 = 60 + 28 = 88,$$
$$s_{12} = s_{11} + s_9 = 88 + 41 = \boxed{129}.$$

10.2.6 Let a_n be the number of n-digit sequences that have exactly one pair of consecutive 0's, and the b_n be the number of n-digit sequences that have no consecutive 0's. Every sequence with one pair of consecutive 0's (with at least 3 digits) must start with 1, 01, or 001; what follows 1 or 01 is a smaller sequence with exactly one pair of consecutive 0's, but what follows 001 is a smaller sequence with no consecutive 0's. This gives the recurrence relation

$$a_n = a_{n-1} + a_{n-2} + b_{n-3}.$$

Similarly, every sequence with no pair of consecutive 0's (with at least 2 digits) must start with 1 or 01; in each case what follows is also a sequence with no pair of consecutive 0's. This gives the recurrence relation

$$b_n = b_{n-1} + b_{n-2}.$$

Noting that $b_1 = 2$ and $b_2 = 3$, we see that $b_n = F_{n+2}$, the $(n+2)^{\text{nd}}$ Fibonacci number. We can now compute the a_n's, starting with $a_1 = 0$, $a_2 = 1$, and $a_3 = 2$:

$$a_4 = a_3 + a_2 + F_3 = 2 + 1 + 2 = 5,$$
$$a_5 = a_4 + a_3 + F_4 = 5 + 2 + 3 = 10,$$
$$a_6 = a_5 + a_4 + F_5 = 10 + 5 + 5 = 20,$$
$$a_7 = a_6 + a_5 + F_6 = 20 + 10 + 8 = 38,$$
$$a_8 = a_7 + a_6 + F_7 = 38 + 20 + 13 = 71,$$
$$a_9 = a_8 + a_7 + F_8 = 71 + 38 + 21 = 130,$$
$$a_{10} = a_9 + a_8 + F_9 = 130 + 71 + 34 = \boxed{235}.$$

Exercises for Section 10.3

10.3.1 The characteristic polynomial is $c^2 + 2c - 15 = 0$, which factors as $(c + 5)(c - 3) = 0$. Therefore, the general form of the solution is given by

$$a_n = \lambda_1(-5)^n + \lambda_2(3)^n$$

for some constants λ_1 and λ_2.

Substituting the given values for $n = 0$ and $n = 1$ into this equation gives us the system of equations

$$0 = \lambda_1 + \lambda_2,$$
$$1 = -5\lambda_1 + 3\lambda_2.$$

Solving this system yields $\lambda_1 = -\frac{1}{8}$ and $\lambda_2 = \frac{1}{8}$, and hence the solution is

$$a_n = \boxed{-\frac{1}{8}(-5)^n + \frac{1}{8}(3)^n}.$$

10.3.2 The characteristic polynomial is $c^2 - 4c + 3 = 0$, which factors as $(c - 3)(c - 1) = 0$. Therefore, the general form of the solution is given by

$$a_n = \lambda_1(3)^n + \lambda_2(1)^n = \lambda_1(3)^n + \lambda_2$$

for some constants λ_1 and λ_2.

Substituting the given values for $n = 0$ and $n = 1$ into this equation gives us the system of equations

$$1 = \lambda_1 + \lambda_2,$$
$$1 = 3\lambda_1 + \lambda_2.$$

Solving this system yields $\lambda_1 = 0$ and $\lambda_2 = 1$, and hence the solution is

$$a_n = \boxed{1};$$

in other words, this sequence is just the constant sequence 1. (Note that computing $a_2, a_3, \ldots$ could have saved us all this work: we would have immediately seen that $a_n = 1$ for all n.)

10.3.3 The characteristic polynomial of the recursion is $c^2 - 6c + 9 = (c - 3)^2$, so the general term is given by

$$a_n = \lambda_1 3^n + \lambda_2 n 3^n$$

for some constants λ_1 and λ_2.

Substituting $n = 0$ and $n = 1$ gives us the system of equations

$$1 = \lambda_1,$$
$$4 = 3\lambda_1 + 3\lambda_2.$$

Solving gives $\lambda_1 = 1$, $\lambda_2 = 1/3$. Therefore,

$$a_n = 3^n + \frac{1}{3}n \cdot 3^n = \boxed{(n + 3)3^{n-1}}.$$

10.3.4 We are given that $x^2 - px - q = (x - c)^2$, so $p = 2c$ and $q = -c^2$. Thus the recurrence is

$$a_n = 2ca_{n-1} - c^2 a_{n-2}.$$

We plug in $a_n = \lambda_1 c^n + \lambda_2 n c^n$ and verify that it satisfies the recurrence:

$$a_n - 2ca_{n-1} + c^2 a_{n-2} = (\lambda_1 c^n + \lambda_2 n c^n) - 2c(\lambda_1 c^{n-1} + \lambda_2(n-1)c^{n-1}) + c^2(\lambda_1 c^{n-2} + \lambda_2(n-2)c^{n-2})$$
$$= c^{n-2}(\lambda_1(c^2 - 2c^2 + c^2) + \lambda_2(nc^2 - 2(n-1)c^2 + (n-2)c^2))$$
$$= 0.$$

10.3.5   As usual, we write the characteristic polynomial:

$$c^2 - 2c + 5 = 0.$$

Via the quadratic formula, we find the roots:

$$c = \frac{2 \pm \sqrt{4 - 20}}{2} = \frac{2 \pm \sqrt{-16}}{2} = 1 \pm 2i.$$

Even though we have complex roots, we can still continue to find the general solution. We get a general solution of the form

$$a_n = \lambda_1(1 + 2i)^n + \lambda_2(1 - 2i)^n.$$

We plug in our initial conditions $a_1 = 2$ and $a_2 = 1$:

$$2 = \lambda_1(1 + 2i) + \lambda_2(1 - 2i),$$
$$1 = \lambda_1(1 + 2i)^2 + \lambda_2(1 - 2i)^2.$$

We note that $(1 + 2i)^2 = -3 + 4i$ and $(1 - 2i)^2 = -3 - 4i$, so let's rewrite the system as

$$2 = \lambda_1(1 + 2i) + \lambda_2(1 - 2i),$$
$$1 = \lambda_1(-3 + 4i) + \lambda_2(-3 - 4i).$$

Perhaps the easiest way to solve this is to multiply the top equation by $(-3 + 4i)$ and the bottom equation by $(1 + 2i)$ and subtract. The λ_1 terms will cancel, and we'll be left with

$$2(-3 + 4i) - (1 + 2i) = \lambda_2((1 - 2i)(-3 + 4i) - (-3 - 4i)(1 + 2i)) = \lambda_2((5 + 10i) - (5 - 10i)) = \lambda_2(20i).$$

So we can solve for λ_2 by dividing by $20i$:

$$\lambda_2 = \frac{-7 + 6i}{20i} = \frac{3}{10} + \frac{7}{20}i.$$

Substituting back in, we see that

$$\lambda_1 = \frac{3}{10} - \frac{7}{20}i.$$

So our formula is

$$a_n = \boxed{\left(\frac{3}{10} - \frac{7}{20}i\right)(1 + 2i)^n + \left(\frac{3}{10} + \frac{7}{20}i\right)(1 - 2i)^n}.$$

At first glance, a_n looks like a hideous complex number. But in fact, for any value of n, this formula will give us a real number for a_n. You can plug in $n = 3$ and verify that $a_3 = 2(1) - 5(2) = -8$.

10.3.6   The characteristic equation is
$$c^3 - 2c^2 - c + 2 = 0.$$

Generally there's no easy way to find the roots of a cubic polynomial. So what we usually do is search for common roots, like 0, 1, or −1, and hope we get lucky. In fact, in this case, we do get lucky. We see pretty easily that $c = 1$ is a root, so we divide $(c - 1)$ out and the rest easily factors:

$$c^3 - 2c^2 - c + 2 = (c - 1)(c^2 - c - 2) = (c - 1)(c + 1)(c - 2).$$

So the roots are 1, −1, and 2. Therefore our general solution is

$$a_n = \lambda_1 1^n + \lambda_2 (-1)^n + \lambda_3 2^n.$$

To finish finding the formula, we use the initial conditions to get a system of linear equations, so we substitute $n = 0, 1, 2$ into our general solution:

$$0 = \lambda_1 + \lambda_2 + \lambda_3,$$
$$1 = \lambda_1 - \lambda_2 + 2\lambda_3,$$
$$3 = \lambda_1 + \lambda_2 + 4\lambda_3.$$

Subtracting the first equation from the third gives $3 = 3\lambda_3$, so $\lambda_3 = 1$. Then the first two equations become:

$$-1 = \lambda_1 + \lambda_2,$$
$$-1 = \lambda_1 - \lambda_2.$$

Hence $\lambda_1 = -1$ and $\lambda_2 = 0$. Therefore, our solution is $a_n = (-1)1^n + 0(-1)^n + 1(2^n) = \boxed{2^n - 1}$.

Exercises for Section 10.4

10.4.1   If we iterate the recurrence relation

$$a_n = 2(2^{n-1} - a_{n-1} + 1),$$

that is, if we substitute in for a_{n-1} using the same relation, we get:

$$a_n = 2(2^{n-1} - (2(2^{n-2} - a_{n-2} + 1)) + 1) = (2(2^{n-1}) - 4(2^{n-2})) + 4a_{n-2} - 2 = 4a_{n-2} - 2.$$

(Note in particular that the powers of 2 cancel.) So we see that the values of a_n for n even and the values of a_n for n odd form two separate sequences. And since these sequences have the same initial conditions (in particular, $a_1 = a_2 = 2$), they will be equal.

10.4.2   The recursion can be re-written as
$$a_n = -2a_{n-1} + 2^n + 2$$
for all $n \geq 1$. We can solve this recursion systematically as follows: shifting the index by 1, we get

$$a_{n-1} = -2a_{n-2} + 2^{n-1} + 2.$$

Subtracting the two equations, we get

$$a_n = -a_{n-1} + 2a_{n-2} + 2^{n-1}.$$

Shifting the index again by 1, we get

$$a_{n-1} = -a_{n-2} + 2a_{n-3} + 2^{n-2}.$$

Multiplying this by 2, we get

$$2a_{n-1} = -2a_{n-2} + 4a_{n-3} + 2^{n-1}.$$

Subtracting this from the equation $a_n = -a_{n-1} + 2a_{n-2} + 2^{n-1}$, we get

$$a_n = a_{n-1} + 4a_{n-2} - 4a_{n-3}.$$

This recursion relation is homogeneous, and its characteristic polynomial is

$$c^3 - c^2 - 4c + 4 = (c - 2)(c + 2)(c - 1).$$

Hence,

$$a_n = \lambda_1 2^n + \lambda_2 (-2)^n + \lambda_3$$

for some constants λ_1, λ_2, and λ_3.

Setting $n = 0, 1,$ and 2 gives us the system of equations

$$1 = \lambda_1 + \lambda_2 + \lambda_3,$$
$$2 = 2\lambda_1 - 2\lambda_2 + \lambda_3,$$
$$2 = 4\lambda_1 + 4\lambda_2 + \lambda_3.$$

Solving gives $\lambda_1 = 1/2$, $\lambda_2 = -1/6$, and $\lambda_3 = 2/3$. Therefore, the closed-form formula for a_n is given by

$$a_n = \frac{1}{2}2^n - \frac{1}{6}(-2)^n + \frac{2}{3} = \boxed{\frac{3 \cdot 2^n - (-2)^n + 4}{6}}.$$

As a check, we verify that if we substitute $n = 11$, we get:

$$a_{11} = \frac{3 \cdot 2^{11} - (-2)^{11} + 4}{6} = \frac{6144 + 2048 + 4}{6} = \frac{8196}{6} = 1366,$$

matching the value of a_{11} that we found in the solution to Problem 10.7.

Exercises for Section 10.5

10.5.1 There are 6 ways to start the triangulation of an octagon, as shown below:

Two leave a heptagon, which can be triangulated in 42 ways. Two leave a triangle and a hexagon, which can be triangulated in $1 \cdot 14 = 14$ ways. Two leave a quadrilateral and a pentagon, which can be triangulated in $2 \cdot 5 = 10$ ways. Therefore, the number of ways to triangulate an octagon is $2(42 + 14 + 10) = \boxed{132}$ ways.

10.5.2 We will show a 1-1 correspondence between the number of ways to place balls into boxes as in the problem statement and the number of legal arrangements of 5 sets of parentheses as in Problem 10.9. Think of each box as corresponding to a "(" and each ball as corresponding to a ")". For each box, starting at B_1 and ending at B_5, we first write the left parenthesis corresponding to the box, then we write a number of right parentheses, one for each ball in the box. For example, if the boxes B_1, B_2, B_3, B_4, B_5 had 1,0,2,1,1 balls in them, respectively, then we would write the parenthesis-arrangement ()(())()(); the number of balls in each box tells us how many right parentheses to place after each left parenthesis. The condition that boxes B_1 through B_i can have no more than i balls total is equivalent to the condition that the parentheses must be balanced.

Thus, there is a 1-1 correspondence between solutions to this problem and solutions to Problem 10.9, so the answer is $\boxed{42}$.

10.5.3 Note that the first digit must be 1. Delete the first digit and subtract 1 from all the remaining digits; what remains is a 4-digit sequence in which the ith digit is no more than i. This is in 1-1 correspondence with the previous problem 10.5.2: the digit in position i (reading from left-to-right) in our 4-digit sequence tells us the total number of balls in boxes B_1 through B_i, for $1 \le i \le 4$, and then we place the remaining ball(s) in box B_5 so that we use 5 balls total. So the answer to this problem is the same as the answer to the previous problem, which is $\boxed{42}$.

10.5.4   We experiment with smaller-size versions of the same shape.

The smallest shape has only 1 tiling: ▢

The shape with a side length of 2 has 2 tilings:

The shape with a side length of 3 has 5 tilings:

Seeing the pattern 1,2,5 in the first 3 sizes, we might think to look for the Catalan numbers, and we might suspect that the answer to our problem is the next number, 14. So we'll look for a Catalan-style recurrence.

Note that each square on the diagonal has to be covered by a different tile, because there's no way that a rectangular-shaped tile can cover more than one of the diagonal squares. (In the picture at right, the diagonal squares are marked with an "X".) Thus, every tile must cover exactly one of the diagonal squares; in particular, the tile covers the upper-left square (labeled with a "Y" in the picture at right) must also cover one of the diagonal squares. This tile will split the rest of the picture into two parts. In particular, the diagrams below show the possible positions of the tile covering the upper-left square (marked with a "Y"):

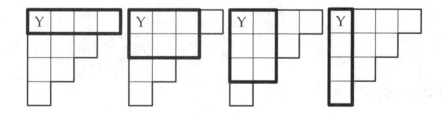

The diagram on the left leaves a size-3 picture to tile, which we know can be done in 5 ways; the same is true for the diagram on the right. The two diagrams in the middle each leave a size-1 picture and a size-2 picture to be tiled, which can be done in $1 \times 2 = 2$ ways. Thus there are $5 + 2 + 2 + 5 = \boxed{14}$ possible tilings.

10.5.5   We can first solve this using PIE. There are $\binom{12}{6}$ total paths (without worrying about whether they pass through any of the X's). There are $\binom{2}{1}\binom{10}{5}$ paths that pass through the X at $(1,1)$, and the same number of paths that pass through the X at $(5,5)$. There are $\binom{6}{3}\binom{6}{3}$ paths that pass through the X at $(3,3)$. There are $\binom{2}{1}\binom{4}{2}\binom{6}{3}$ paths that pass through both $(1,1)$ and $(3,3)$, and the same number of paths that pass through $(3,3)$ and $(5,5)$. There are $\binom{2}{1}\binom{8}{4}\binom{2}{1}$ paths that pass through $(1,1)$ and $(5,5)$. There are $\binom{2}{1}\binom{4}{2}\binom{4}{2}\binom{2}{1}$ that pass through all three X's. Therefore, by PIE, the number of paths that pass through none of the X's is:

$$\binom{12}{6} - 2\binom{2}{1}\binom{10}{5} - \binom{6}{3}\binom{6}{3} + 2\binom{2}{1}\binom{4}{2}\binom{6}{3} + \binom{2}{1}\binom{8}{4}\binom{2}{1} - \binom{2}{1}\binom{4}{2}\binom{4}{2}\binom{2}{1} = \boxed{132}.$$

Noticing that our answer, 132, is a Catalan number (see Exercise 10.5.1 above), we might try to look for a Catalan recurrence that would explain it. Let p_n be the number of paths from $(0,0)$ to $(2n, 2n)$, where we are not allowed to pass through $(2i-1, 2i-1)$ for all $1 \le i \le n$. We have shown in our PIE calculation above that $p_3 = C_6 = 132$, so we conjecture that $p_n = C_{2n}$ for all n. Note trivially by inspection that $p_1 = 2 = C_2$.

For any path, let j be the smallest positive integer such that the path passes through (j, j). Note that j must be even, since the diagonal points with odd coordinates are not allowed. So we have $j = 2k$, where $1 \leq k \leq n$. To get from $(0, 0)$ to $(2k, 2k)$ without touching the diagonal, we must either go entirely below the diagonal or entirely above the diagonal. Either way, the number of paths is C_{2k-1}, so there are $2C_{2k-1}$ paths from $(0, 0)$ to $(2k, 2k)$ that avoid the diagonal (except at $(0, 0)$ and $(2k, 2k)$). Then, by definition, there are p_{n-k} remaining paths from $(2k, 2k)$ to $(2n, 2n)$.

Thus, we have the recurrence

$$p_n = \sum_{k=1}^{n} 2C_{2k-1}p_{n-k}.$$

If we assume as our inductive hypothesis that $p_j = C_{2j}$ for all $j < n$, then we have:

$$p_n = \sum_{k=1}^{n} 2C_{2k-1}C_{2n-2k} = \sum_{k=1}^{n} (C_{2k-1}C_{2n-2k} + C_{2n-2k}C_{2k-1}).$$

Writing this out, we see that the first terms of each entry of the sum give

$$C_1C_{2n-2} + C_3C_{2n-4} + \cdots + C_{2n-1}C_0,$$

and that the second terms of each entry of the sum give

$$C_{2n-2}C_1 + C_{2n-4}C_3 + \cdots + C_0C_{2n-1}.$$

In particular, the first terms give all terms of the form C_mC_{2n-1-m} where m is odd, and the second terms give all terms of the form C_mC_{2n-1-m} where m is even. When we combine them, we get:

$$\sum_{m=0}^{2n-1} C_mC_{2n-1-m} = C_{2n},$$

completing the inductive proof.

Exercises for Section 10.6

10.6.1 By recursion:

$$
\begin{aligned}
C_8 &= C_0C_7 + C_1C_6 + C_2C_5 + C_3C_4 + C_4C_3 + C_5C_2 + C_6C_1 + C_7C_0 \\
&= (1)(429) + (1)(132) + (2)(42) + (5)(14) + (14)(5) + (42)(2) + (132)(1) + (429)(1) \\
&= 429 + 132 + 84 + 70 + 70 + 84 + 132 + 429 \\
&= 1430.
\end{aligned}
$$

By formula:

$$C_8 = \frac{1}{9}\binom{16}{8} = \frac{12870}{9} = 1430.$$

10.6.2 Let c_n be the number of ways that we can place coins on top of a row of n coins, and let j be the number of consecutive coins on the left edge of the second row. For example, in the picture at right, $n = 5$ and $j = 2$. (If there is no coin on the far left side of the 2nd row, then $j = 0$.) Then the number of ways to complete the arrangement is the number of ways to place coins on top of the j coins in the second row, which is c_j,

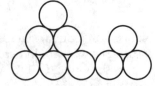

times the number of ways to place coins on top of the $n - j - 1$ coins on the first row to the right of the row of j coins, which is c_{n-j-1}. This gives the recurrence relation

$$c_n = \sum_{j=0}^{n-1} c_j c_{n-j-1},$$

and since $c_0 = c_1 = 1$, we recognize that $c_n = \boxed{C_n}$, the nth Catalan number.

10.6.3 If Brazil and Germany were never tied, then Brazil was always ahead of Germany, except at the start when it was 0-0. Then this sequence of goals corresponds to a path from $(0,0)$ to $(8,6)$, going only upwards and to the right, that stays strictly below the main diagonal, except at the point $(0,0)$.

Note that the first two steps must be to the right, and consider the portion of the path from $(1,0)$ to $(8,6)$. This portion of the path stays on or below the line $y = x - 1$, so by shifting this portion of the path one unit to the left, we obtain a path from $(0,0)$ to $(7,6)$ that stays on or below the main diagonal. But every path from $(0,0)$ to $(7,7)$ that goes only upwards and to the right and stays on or below the main diagonal must pass through the point $(7,6)$. Hence, we have a 1-1 correspondence

$$\begin{Bmatrix} \text{Paths from } (0,0) \text{ to } (8,6) \text{ that stay strictly below} \\ \text{the main diagonal except at } (0,0) \end{Bmatrix} \leftrightarrow \begin{Bmatrix} \text{Paths from } (0,0) \text{ to } (7,7) \text{ that stay on or below the} \\ \text{main diagonal} \end{Bmatrix}.$$

The number of paths in each set is

$$C_7 = \frac{1}{8}\binom{14}{7} = 429.$$

The number of different orders in which Brazil could have scored 8 goals and Germany 6 is $\binom{14}{8} = 3003$. Therefore, the probability that the score was never tied (except at 0-0) is

$$\frac{429}{3003} = \boxed{\frac{1}{7}}.$$

10.6.4 The root node must be one of the internal nodes (if $n \geq 1$). Then, j of the internal nodes will go on the left branch of the tree and the remaining $n - 1 - j$ internal nodes will go on the right branch of the tree. If we let t_n be the number of trees with n internal nodes, this gives us the recurrence

$$t_n = \sum_{j=0}^{n-1} t_j t_{n-1-j}.$$

This is the Catalan recurrence, and since $t_0 = 1$, we conclude that $t_n = \boxed{C_n}$, the nth Catalan number.

10.6.5 We list the first few Catalan numbers:

n	0	1	2	3	4	5	6	7	8	9
C_n	1	1	2	5	14	42	132	429	1430	4862

We see odd Catalan numbers for $n = 0, 1, 3, 7$ so far in our list. This might lead to the conjecture that:

$$\boxed{C_n \text{ is odd if and only if } n \text{ is one less than a power of 2.}}$$

We can quickly check C_{15} using our formula:

$$C_{15} = \frac{1}{16}\binom{30}{15} = 9694845,$$

and indeed this is odd.

We can prove our conjecture using induction. The conjecture is true for $n = 0$. For the inductive step, recall the Catalan recurrence:

$$C_n = \sum_{j=0}^{n-1} C_j C_{n-1-j}.$$

All of the terms of this sum come in matching pairs: $C_0 C_{n-1}$ matches with $C_{n-1} C_0$, $C_1 C_{n-2}$ matches with $C_{n-2} C_1$, and so on, with the exception of the middle term $C_{\frac{n-1}{2}} C_{\frac{n-1}{2}}$ when n is odd. So if n is even, then

$$C_n = 2 \left(\sum_{j=0}^{\frac{n}{2}-1} C_j C_{n-1-j} \right),$$

and thus C_n is even. If n is odd, then

$$C_n = 2 \left(\sum_{j=0}^{\frac{n-1}{2}-1} C_j C_{n-1-j} \right) + (C_{\frac{n-1}{2}})^2,$$

so C_n has the same parity as $C_{\frac{n-1}{2}}$. Finally, note that n is 1 less than a power of 2 if and only if $\frac{n-1}{2}$ is also 1 less than a power of 2. This completes the proof.

Review Problems

10.16 We see that $a_1 = 1$, so let $n \geq 2$. Choose one of the $2n$ students arbitrarily. Then there are $2n - 1$ other students that can be paired with that student, and after this pair is formed, there are $2n - 2$ students left, from which we want to form $n - 1$ more pairs. Hence, $a_n = (2n - 1)a_{n-1}$. Therefore,

$$\begin{aligned}
a_n &= (2n - 1)a_{n-1} \\
&= (2n - 1)(2n - 3)a_{n-2} \\
&= (2n - 1)(2n - 3)(2n - 5)a_{n-3} \\
&= \cdots \\
&= (2n - 1)(2n - 3)(2n - 5) \cdots 3 \cdot a_1 \\
&= \boxed{(2n - 1)(2n - 3)(2n - 5) \cdots 3 \cdot 1}.
\end{aligned}$$

Another formula is $a_n = \dfrac{(2n)!}{2^n n!}$. Do you see why?

10.17

(a) Let's consider a small case. If we draw three lines as shown, then we form 7 different regions. To maximize the number of regions that are created when we draw another line, we want this new line to pass through as many regions as possible.

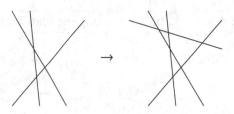

The new line can pass through at most four regions, because every pair of successive regions is divided by a line that is already present, of which there are only three. We can always pick a new line through 4 regions: we pick a line that does not pass through any existing intersection points and is not parallel to any existing line. When the new line is drawn, it splits each region it passes through into two new regions, creating a total of $7 + 4 = 11$ regions.

More generally, let R_n be the maximum number of different regions formed by n lines. Then $R_1 = 2$, and for $n \geq 2$, if there are $n - 1$ lines in the plane, then a new line can pass through n regions, so $R_n = R_{n-1} + n$. Therefore,

$$
\begin{aligned}
R_n &= n + R_{n-1} \\
&= n + (n - 1) + R_{n-2} \\
&= \cdots \\
&= n + (n - 1) + (n - 2) + \cdots + 2 + R_1 \\
&= n + (n - 1) + (n - 2) + \cdots + 2 + 2 \\
&= n + (n - 1) + (n - 2) + \cdots + 2 + 1 + 1 \\
&= \frac{n(n + 1)}{2} + 1 \\
&= \boxed{\frac{n^2 + n + 2}{2}}.
\end{aligned}
$$

(b) As above, let R_n denote the maximum number of regions formed by n circles. Note that $R_1 = 2$ and that each new circle can intersect the other $n - 1$ circles in $2n - 2$ points. Thus the new circle divides $2n - 2$ regions in two. This gives the recurrence relation $R_n = R_{n-1} + 2(n - 1)$, and thus:

$$
\begin{aligned}
R_n &= 2(n - 1) + R_{n-1} \\
&= 2(n - 1) + 2(n - 2) + R_{n-2} \\
&\;\;\vdots \\
&= 2\left((n - 1) + (n - 2) + \cdots + 2 + 1\right) + R_1 \\
&= 2\left((n - 1) + (n - 2) + \cdots + 2 + 1\right) + 2 \\
&= \boxed{n(n - 1) + 2}.
\end{aligned}
$$

(c) As above, let R_n denote the maximum number of regions formed by n pairs of parallel lines. Note that $R_1 = 3$. If we already have $n - 1$ pairs of lines drawn, then we can draw a new n^{th} pair such that each line of our n^{th} pair will intersect each of the $2n - 2$ lines already drawn. Thus, each new line will create $2n - 1$ new regions. This gives us the recurrence $R_n = R_{n-1} + 2(2n - 1)$. Therefore,

$$
\begin{aligned}
R_n &= 2(2n - 1) + R_{n-1} \\
&= 2(2n - 1) + 2(2n - 3) + R_{n-2} \\
&\;\;\vdots \\
&= 2\left((2n - 1) + (2n - 3) + \cdots + 3\right) + 3 \\
&= 2\left((2n - 1) + (2n - 3) + \cdots + 3 + 1\right) + 1 \\
&= \boxed{2n^2 + 1}.
\end{aligned}
$$

10.18 The characteristic equation of this recurrence is $c^2 - 2c - 1 = 0$, whose roots (by the quadratic formula) are

$$
c = \frac{2 \pm \sqrt{8}}{2} = 1 \pm \sqrt{2}.
$$

Therefore, we know that the solution is of the form

$$a_n = \lambda_1 \left(1 + \sqrt{2}\right)^n + \lambda_2 \left(1 - \sqrt{2}\right)^n.$$

To determine the unknown coefficient, we use the initial conditions $a_0 = 2$ and $a_1 = 3$ to get the system of equations

$$2 = \lambda_1 + \lambda_2,$$
$$3 = \lambda_1 \left(1 + \sqrt{2}\right) + \lambda_2 \left(1 - \sqrt{2}\right).$$

This system has the solution $\lambda_1 = 1 + \frac{\sqrt{2}}{4}$, $\lambda_2 = 1 - \frac{\sqrt{2}}{4}$, so the solution to the recurrence is

$$a_n = \left(1 + \frac{\sqrt{2}}{4}\right)\left(1 + \sqrt{2}\right)^n + \left(1 - \frac{\sqrt{2}}{4}\right)\left(1 - \sqrt{2}\right)^n.$$

10.19   More generally, let p_n be the probability that the player wins when beginning with n pairs of tiles. We see that $p_1 = 1$, so assume $n \geq 2$. After drawing three tiles, the player may keep playing as long as two of the three tiles he draws match. There are $n(2n - 2)$ ways to draw (without regard to order) 3 tiles that include a matching pair (n choices for the matching pair and $2n - 2$ choices for the third tile), so the probability of this occurring is

$$\frac{n(2n - 2)}{\binom{2n}{3}} = \frac{n(2n - 2)}{\frac{2n(2n-1)(2n-2)}{6}} = \frac{3}{2n - 1}.$$

At this stage, if the player is still in the game, then he is at the same point as having drawn only one tile after beginning with $n - 1$ pairs of tiles. This gives us the recurrence

$$p_n = \frac{3}{2n - 1} p_{n-1}$$

for $n \geq 2$. Hence,

$$\begin{aligned}
p_6 &= \frac{3}{11} p_5 = \frac{3}{11} \cdot \frac{3}{9} p_4 \\
&= \frac{3}{11} \cdot \frac{3}{9} \cdot \frac{3}{7} p_3 \\
&= \frac{3}{11} \cdot \frac{3}{9} \cdot \frac{3}{7} \cdot \frac{3}{5} p_2 \\
&= \frac{3}{11} \cdot \frac{3}{9} \cdot \frac{3}{7} \cdot \frac{3}{5} \cdot \frac{3}{3} p_1 \\
&= \frac{3^4}{11 \cdot 9 \cdot 7 \cdot 5} = \boxed{\frac{9}{385}}.
\end{aligned}$$

10.20   Let a_n denote the number of ways to tile a $3 \times n$ rectangle.

First note that if n is odd, then it is impossible to tile: the total number of squares in the rectangle is odd, but each tile covers 2 squares. So $a_n = 0$ if n is odd.

If n is even, then look at the left column of our $3 \times n$ rectangle. If we tile it with 3 horizontal tiles, then what's left is a $3 \times (n - 2)$ rectangle that can be tiled in a_{n-2} ways. Otherwise, we must use one vertical tile and one horizontal tile. This leaves two untiled spaces in the 2nd column. If we tile them with a single vertical tile, then what's left is a $3 \times (n - 2)$ rectangle. If not, then we tile them with 2 horizontal tiles. After placing another horizontal tile (in the remaining row), we're again left with 2 untiled squares in the left column. If we tile them with a single vertical tile, then what's left is a $3 \times (n - 4)$ rectangle; if not, we repeat and we again get back to 2 untiled squares in the left column.

This gives the recurrence relation

$$a_n = a_{n-2} + 2(a_{n-2} + a_{n-4} + \cdots + a_2 + a_0),$$

where the factor of 2 comes from the fact that a vertical tile can be placed in the initial column in 2 different ways. Noting that $a_0 = 1$, we compute:

$$a_2 = a_0 + 2a_0 = 3a_0 = 3,$$
$$a_4 = a_2 + 2(a_2 + a_0) = 3 + 2(3 + 1) = 11,$$
$$a_6 = a_4 + 2(a_4 + a_2 + a_0) = 11 + 2(11 + 3 + 1) = 41,$$
$$a_8 = a_6 + 2(a_6 + a_4 + a_2 + a_0) = 41 + 2(41 + 11 + 3 + 1) = 153,$$
$$a_{10} = a_8 + 2(a_8 + a_6 + a_4 + a_2 + a_0) = 153 + 2(153 + 41 + 11 + 3 + 1) = \boxed{571}.$$

10.21 Let T_n denote the number of legal n-block towers. Note that if $n \le 3$, then there is no condition on the order of the blocks in the tower, so $T_3 = 3! = 6$. For $n > 3$, given an $(n-1)$-block tower, we can create an n-block tower by placing block n directly on top of the block of size $n-1$, directly on top of the block of size $n-2$, or at the bottom of the tower; these are the only legal positions. Furthermore, removing block n from an n-block tower leaves a valid $(n-1)$-block tower. Therefore, we have the recurrence $T_n = 3T_{n-1}$ for all $n > 3$. We therefore see that $T_n = 3^{n-3}(6) = 3^{n-2}(2)$ for all $n \ge 3$, and in particular $T_8 = 3^6(2) = \boxed{1458}$.

10.22 Let $a(n, k)$ denote the entry in column k of row n, for all integers $0 \le k \le n$. Note that $a(n, 0) = 1$ for all n, and more generally $a(n, k) = a(n, k-1) + a(n-1, k)$ for all $0 < k \le n$, where we define $a(n-1, n) = 0$. The key observation is that each entry counts the number of paths to that point on the grid, where we start at the top and each step is either down or to the right, since each path to a point must come from the point to the left or from the point directly above. Therefore, the last entry in Row n counts the number of paths from the top "1" to that point, which (rotating the picture 90 degrees counterclockwise) is the same as the number of paths from $(0, 0)$ to (n, n) which do not go above the diagonal. Thus, the number of paths to that point is C_n.

Challenge Problems

10.23 Let a_n, b_n, and c_n denote the number of such words of length n that end with A, B, and C, respectively. We see that $a_1 = b_1 = c_1 = 1$.

For $n \ge 2$, a word of length n ending with A can be formed by appending an A to a string of length $n-1$ ending with A or B (but not C), so $a_n = a_{n-1} + b_{n-1}$.

A word of length n ending with B can be formed by appending a B to any string of length $n-1$, so $b_n = a_{n-1} + b_{n-1} + c_{n-1}$.

Finally, a word of length n ending with C can be formed by appending a C to a string of length $n-1$ ending with B or C (but not A), so $c_n = b_{n-1} + c_{n-1}$.

We notice that $a_n = c_n$ for all $n \ge 1$, because there is a natural 1-1 correspondence

$$\{\text{words ending in } A\} \quad \leftrightarrow \quad \{\text{words ending in } C\},$$

achieved by changing every A to a C and vice versa.

Hence, we can write the relations above as

$$a_n = a_{n-1} + b_{n-1},$$
$$b_n = 2a_{n-1} + b_{n-1}.$$

We can isolate one sequence in one equation and substitute it into the other. In particular, we can rewrite the first equation as

$$b_{n-1} = a_n - a_{n-1},$$

then substitute this into the second equation to get

$$a_{n+1} - a_n = 2a_{n-1} + (a_n - a_{n-1}).$$

Rearranging, we get

$$a_{n+1} = 2a_n + a_{n-1}.$$

Similarly, $b_{n+1} = 2b_n + b_{n-1}$.

Finally, if we let t_n denote the number of allowable words of length n (ending in any letter), then $t_n = a_n + b_n + c_n = 2a_n + b_n$, so $t_{n+1} = 2t_n + t_{n-1}$ for all $n \geq 2$.

We now compute the initial values of the sequence t_n. Note that $t_1 = 3$ (any letter is allowed) and $t_2 = 7$ (any 2-letter sequence is allowed except for AC and CA). Hence,

$$t_3 = 2t_2 + t_1 = 2 \cdot 7 + 3 = 17,$$
$$t_4 = 2t_3 + t_2 = 2 \cdot 17 + 7 = 41,$$
$$t_5 = 2t_4 + t_3 = 2 \cdot 41 + 17 = 99,$$
$$t_6 = 2t_5 + t_4 = 2 \cdot 99 + 41 = 239,$$
$$t_7 = 2t_6 + t_5 = 2 \cdot 239 + 99 = 577,$$
$$t_8 = 2t_7 + t_6 = 2 \cdot 577 + 239 = \boxed{1393}.$$

Note that we could have explicitly solved the recurrence $t_{n+1} = 2t_n + t_{n-1}$ to get a closed-form formula for t_n, but since we only needed t_8 it was easy to simply crunch the numbers.

10.24 We can reformulate (and generalize) the problem as follows: call a string of 0's and 1's *allowable* if the substrings 11 and 000 never appear. There is a natural 1-1 correspondence between allowable strings of length 19 and permitted subsets of houses: a 1 represents a house that gets mail, and a 0 represents a house that does not.

Let A_n be the number of allowable strings of length n (for $n \geq 2$). We'll break up the allowable strings into cases. For $n \geq 2$, let B_n, C_n, and D_n be the number of allowable strings of 0s and 1s of length n that end with 00, 01, and 10, respectively. (Since the substring 11 can't appear, an allowable string can't end with 11.) We see that $A_n = B_n + C_n + D_n$ for all $n \geq 2$, and that $B_2 = C_2 = D_2 = 1$.

Then for $n \geq 3$, a string of length n ending with 00 can only be obtained by appending a 0 to a string of length $n - 1$ ending with 10 (since the substring 000 cannot appear), so $B_n = D_{n-1}$.

A string of length n ending with 01 can be obtained by appending a 1 to a string of length $n - 1$ ending with either 00 or 10, so $C_n = B_{n-1} + D_{n-1}$.

Finally, a string of length n ending with 10 can only be obtained by appending a 0 to a string of length $n - 1$ ending with 01, so $D_n = C_{n-1}$.

Thus, we have the following system of recurrence relations for all $n \geq 3$:

$$B_n = D_{n-1},$$
$$C_n = B_{n-1} + D_{n-1},$$
$$D_n = C_{n-1}.$$

We can now simply make a chart of all the B_n, C_n, and D_n:

n	2	3	4	5	6	7	8	9	10	11	12	13	14	15	16	17	18	19
B_n	1	1	1	2	2	3	4	5	7	9	12	16	21	28	37	49	65	86
C_n	1	2	2	3	4	5	7	9	12	16	21	28	37	49	65	86	114	151
D_n	1	1	2	2	3	4	5	7	9	12	16	21	28	37	49	65	86	114

Thus our answer is $A_{19} = B_{19} + C_{19} + D_{19} = 86 + 151 + 114 = \boxed{351}$.

We notice in our above chart that all three sequences are the same, except shifted to the left or right. So we might achieve a simple solution by solving for just one of the sequences. If we substitute $B_n = D_{n-1}$ and $D_n = C_{n-1}$ into the recurrence relation for C_n, we get:

$$C_n = B_{n-1} + D_{n-1} = D_{n-2} + D_{n-1} = C_{n-3} + C_{n-2}.$$

This is valid for all $n \geq 5$. We can then use this recurrence to get all of the values of C_n for $n \leq 19$, and then finish by:

$$A_{19} = B_{19} + C_{19} + D_{19} = C_{17} + C_{19} + C_{18} = 86 + 114 + 151 = 351.$$

10.25 Let p_n be the probability of an odd number of heads appearing when the coins $C_1, C_2, \ldots, C_n$ are tossed. Then $p_1 = 1/3$, and for $n \geq 2$, we calculate p_n in terms of p_{n-1}.

The probability of an odd number of heads appearing when the coins $C_1, C_2, \ldots, C_{n-1}$ are tossed is p_{n-1}, so the probability of an even number of heads appearing is $1 - p_{n-1}$.

Now suppose that an odd number of heads appear when the coins $C_1, C_2, \ldots, C_{n-1}$, and C_n are tossed. If C_n comes up heads, then the number of heads among the first $n - 1$ coins must be even, and if C_n comes up tails, then the number of heads among the first $n - 1$ coins must be odd. Hence,

$$p_n = \frac{1}{2n+1}(1 - p_{n-1}) + \frac{2n}{2n+1}p_{n-1} = \frac{2n-1}{2n+1}p_{n-1} + \frac{1}{2n+1}.$$

Multiplying both sides by $2n + 1$, we get

$$(2n+1)p_n = (2n-1)p_{n-1} + 1.$$

Set $q_n = (2n + 1)p_n$. Then the above equation becomes

$$q_n = q_{n-1} + 1.$$

Since $q_1 = 3p_1 = 1$, we have that $q_n = n$ for all $n \geq 1$. Therefore,

$$p_n = \frac{q_n}{2n+1} = \boxed{\frac{n}{2n+1}}$$

for all $n \geq 1$.

10.26 Let a_n be the number of positive integers whose digit-sum is n, and whose digits are all 1, 3, or 4. Then $a_1 = 1$ (the number 1), $a_2 = 1$ (the number 11), $a_3 = 2$ (the numbers 111 and 3), and $a_4 = 4$ (the numbers 1111, 31, 13, and 4).

Assume that $n \geq 5$, and consider a positive integer whose digit-sum is n, and whose digits are all 1, 3, or 4. Such a number must end with 1, 3, or 4. If this last digit is truncated, then the digit-sum of the remaining number must be $n - 1$, $n - 3$, or $n - 4$, respectively. Hence,

$$a_n = a_{n-1} + a_{n-3} + a_{n-4}$$

for all $n \geq 5$.

We could factor the characteristic polynomial, and solve for a_n in the usual way. But since this is a quartic polynomial, it may be easier to list the first few terms of the sequence to see if we can find a pattern:

$$a_1 = 1,$$
$$a_2 = 1,$$
$$a_3 = 2,$$
$$a_4 = 4,$$
$$a_5 = a_4 + a_2 + a_1 = 4 + 1 + 1 = 6,$$
$$a_6 = a_5 + a_3 + a_2 = 6 + 2 + 1 = 9,$$
$$a_7 = a_6 + a_4 + a_3 = 9 + 4 + 2 = 15,$$
$$a_8 = a_7 + a_5 + a_4 = 15 + 6 + 4 = 25,$$
$$a_9 = a_8 + a_6 + a_5 = 25 + 9 + 6 = 40,$$
$$a_{10} = a_9 + a_7 + a_6 = 40 + 15 + 9 = 64.$$

We can verify that a_n is a perfect square when n is even: $a_2 = 1 = 1^2$, $a_4 = 4 = 2^2$, $a_6 = 9 = 3^2$, $a_8 = 25 = 5^2$, and $a_{10} = 64 = 8^2$. These are the squares of the Fibonacci numbers! With the Fibonacci numbers in mind, we can now see that the odd terms are the products of consecutive Fibonacci numbers: $a_1 = 1 = 1 \cdot 1, a_3 = 2 = 1 \cdot 2, a_5 = 6 = 2 \cdot 3$, $a_7 = 15 = 3 \cdot 5$, and $a_9 = 40 = 5 \cdot 8$.

We now have a conjecture for a formula for a_n: For all $n \geq 1$, $a_{2n-1} = F_n F_{n+1}$ and $a_{2n} = F_{n+1}^2$. We prove this using induction. We have already verified that these formulas hold for $1 \leq n \leq 2$, so assume that these formulas hold for $1 \leq n \leq k$, for some positive integer $k \geq 2$.

Then

$$a_{2k+1} = a_{2k} + a_{2k-2} + a_{2k-3}$$
$$= F_{k+1}^2 + F_k^2 + F_{k-1} F_k$$
$$= F_{k+1}^2 + F_k(F_{k-1} + F_k)$$
$$= F_{k+1}^2 + F_k F_{k+1}$$
$$= F_{k+1}(F_k + F_{k+1})$$
$$= F_{k+1} F_{k+2},$$

and

$$a_{2k+2} = a_{2k+1} + a_{2k-1} + a_{2k-2}$$
$$= F_{k+1} F_{k+2} + F_k F_{k+1} + F_k^2$$
$$= F_{k+1} F_{k+2} + F_k(F_k + F_{k+1})$$
$$= F_{k+1} F_{k+2} + F_k F_{k+2}$$
$$= F_{k+2}(F_k + F_{k+1})$$
$$= F_{k+2}^2.$$

Hence, the formulas hold for $1 \leq n \leq k + 1$, and by strong induction, they hold for all positive integers n. In particular, $a_{2n} = F_{n+1}^2$ is a perfect square for all positive integers n.

10.27 We seek a way of building valid connections on a $2 \times n$ grid from valid connections on smaller grids. This will give us a recursion that can be used to calculate T_n.

For a $2 \times n$ grid, there are $2n$ possible outer edges and $n - 2$ possible inner edges. For a valid connection on a $2 \times n$ grid, locate the outer edge that is absent and furthest to the right, which we will refer to as the *missing edge*. (If all the outer edges are present, then they would form a loop, so at least one must be absent.) For example, in the valid connection below, the missing edge is the edge between A and B.

We will count valid connections on a $2 \times n$ grid by grouping them based on the location of their missing edge.

Case 1 The missing edge is the rightmost vertical edge.

In this case, the valid connection can be built from a valid connection on a $2 \times (n-1)$ grid by attaching two horizontal edges at the right, as in the following example:

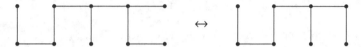

Thus there is a 1-1 correspondence

$$\left\{ \begin{array}{l} \text{Valid connections on a } 2 \times n \text{ grid whose missing} \\ \text{edge is the rightmost vertical edge} \end{array} \right\} \quad \leftrightarrow \quad \{\text{Valid connections on a } 2 \times (n-1) \text{ grid}\}.$$

Thus there are T_{n-1} valid connections in this case.

Case 2 The missing edge is horizontal.

Let the nodes of the missing edge be A and B, where A is on the left and B is on the right. Let A' and B' be the corresponding nodes on the other side (that is, on the top row if A and B are on the bottom row, and vice versa). We may conclude that all of the outer edges starting at A' and going clockwise around the outside of the grid to B must be present in the valid connection, as follows. First, the missing edge is the outer edge that is absent and furthest to the right, so all the outer edges from B' to B must be present. Second, the edge $A'B'$ must also be present; otherwise, not all the nodes in the grid could be connected. (In particular, nodes A and B could not be connected.)

Thus, the valid connection on the $2 \times n$ grid can be built from a valid connection on a $2 \times k$ grid, where $1 \le k \le n-1$, by attaching the outer edges from A' to B. Some examples are shown below:

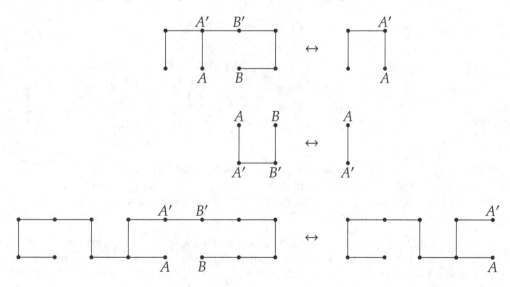

We can attach the outer edges from A' to B to a $2 \times k$ grid in two ways (with the missing edge either on the top or on the bottom), so each valid connection on a $2 \times k$ grid produces 2 valid connections on a $2 \times n$ grid. Summing over $1 \le k \le n-1$, we find that this case contributes $2T_{n-1} + 2T_{n-2} + \cdots + 2T_1$ valid connections on the $2 \times n$ grid.

Case 3 The missing edge is the leftmost vertical edge.

There is only one possible valid connection in this case:

Adding up over all three cases, we find that

$$T_n = T_{n-1} + 2T_{n-1} + 2T_{n-2} + \cdots + 2T_1 + 1$$
$$= 3T_{n-1} + 2T_{n-2} + 2T_{n-3} + \cdots + 2T_1 + 1$$

for all $n \geq 2$. Also, $T_1 = 1$, so this recursion is sufficient to compute T_{10}.

However, by substituting $n - 1$ for n in the formula above, we also have

$$T_{n-1} = 3T_{n-2} + 2T_{n-3} + \cdots + 2T_1 + 1,$$

so

$$T_{n-1} - T_{n-2} = 2T_{n-2} + 2T_{n-3} + \cdots + 2T_1 + 1.$$

Substituting this into our formula for T_n, we find that

$$T_n = 3T_{n-1} + 2T_{n-2} + 2T_{n-3} + \cdots + 2T_1 + 1$$
$$= 3T_{n-1} + T_{n-1} - T_{n-2}$$
$$= 4T_{n-1} - T_{n-2},$$

for all $n \geq 3$.

Since $T_1 = 1$ and $T_2 = 4$, we can now compute T_{10} easily by recursion:

$$T_3 = 4T_2 - T_1 = 15,$$
$$T_4 = 4T_3 - T_2 = 56,$$
$$T_5 = 4T_4 - T_3 = 209,$$
$$T_6 = 4T_5 - T_4 = 780,$$
$$T_7 = 4T_6 - T_5 = 2911,$$
$$T_8 = 4T_7 - T_6 = 10864,$$
$$T_9 = 4T_8 - T_7 = 40545,$$
$$T_{10} = 4T_9 - T_8 = \boxed{151316}.$$

10.28 Label the colors 1, 2, and 3. Choose one of the triangles, and suppose its color is 1. Then beginning with this triangle, and going counterclockwise, we read off the colors of the triangles. This generates a string of 1's, 2's, and 3's of length 10, beginning with 1, such that no two consecutive numbers are equal and the last number is not equal to 1. For example, the sequence could be 1213212312.

Thus, we can reformulate the problem as follows: Consider the set of strings consisting of 1's, 2's, and 3's of length n, beginning with 1, such that no two consecutive numbers are equal. Let A_n be the set of such strings that end with 1, and let B_n be the set of such strings that do not end with 1. Let $a_n = \#(A_n)$ and $b_n = \#(B_n)$. Then the total number of colorings of the decagon is given by $3b_{10}$. (We multiply by 3 to account for the fact that the originally chosen triangle can also have colors 2 or 3.)

To get a feel for these numbers, we list the first few cases.

n	A_n	B_n	a_n	b_n
1	$\{1\}$	$\emptyset$	1	0
2	$\emptyset$	$\{12, 13\}$	0	2
3	$\{121, 131\}$	$\{123, 132\}$	2	2
4	$\{1231, 1321\}$	$\{1212, 1213, 1312, 1313, 1232, 1323\}$	2	6

We see that $a_1 = 1$ and $b_1 = 0$, so assume that $n \geq 2$. Then we can generate an element in A_n by appending a 1 to an element in B_{n-1}, so $a_n = b_{n-1}$.

To generate an element in B_n, we can either append to an element in A_{n-1} or an element in B_{n-1}. If we append to an element in A_{n-1}, then we can always append a 2 or a 3, resulting in $2a_{n-1}$ possible strings. If we append to an element in B_{n-1}, then the number we append is uniquely determined, because it can't be the same as the last number, nor a 1. (For example, if we have the string 123, we can only append a 2 to get 1232.) This results in b_{n-1} strings. Hence, $b_n = 2a_{n-1} + b_{n-1}$.

Since $a_n = b_{n-1}$ for $n \geq 2$, we have $a_{n-1} = b_{n-2}$ for $n \geq 3$. Substituting into $b_n = 2a_{n-1} + b_{n-1}$, we get

$$b_n = b_{n-1} + 2b_{n-2}$$

for all $n \geq 3$, with initial conditions $b_1 = 0$ and $b_2 = 2$. We can now compute b_{10} recursively, or we can solve the recursion relation.

The characteristic polynomial is $c^2 - c - 2 = (c - 2)(c + 1)$, so

$$b_n = \lambda_1 2^n + \lambda_2 (-1)^n$$

for some constants λ_1 and λ_2. Substituting $n = 1$ and $n = 2$ gives us the system of equations

$$0 = 2\lambda_1 - \lambda_2,$$
$$2 = 4\lambda_1 + \lambda_2.$$

Solving the system, we obtain $\lambda_1 = 1/3$ and $\lambda_2 = 2/3$. Therefore,

$$b_n = \frac{1}{3}2^n + \frac{2}{3}(-1)^n = \frac{2^n + 2(-1)^n}{3}.$$

In particular, $b_{10} = [2^{10} + 2(-1)^{10}]/3 = 342$, so the total number of colorings is $3b_{10} = \boxed{1026}$.

10.29

(a) We claim that the largest element of S_n is F_{n+1}. To prove this by induction, we must make a stronger claim, namely: The largest element of S_n is F_{n+1}, and the numbers F_n and F_{n+1} appear as consecutive terms in S_n. It is easy to check that the result is true for $n = 1$ and $n = 2$, so assume that the result is true for all $1 \leq n \leq k$, for some positive integer $k \geq 2$.

In particular, the largest element of S_{k-1} is F_k, the largest element of S_k is F_{k+1}, and F_k and F_{k+1} appear consecutively somewhere in S_k, so S_k is of the form

$$S_k = \ldots, F_k, F_{k+1}, \ldots.$$

(The case where F_{k+1} precedes F_k is similarly argued.)

Then S_{k+1} is of the form

$$S_{k+1} = \ldots, F_k, F_{k+2}, F_{k+1}, \ldots,$$

so F_{k+1} and F_{k+2} appear as consecutive terms in S_{k+1}. Furthermore, by the construction of S_{k+1}, each newly inserted term in S_{k+1} is the sum of a term in S_{k-1} and a term in S_k, so each term in S_{k+1} can be at most $F_k + F_{k+1} = F_{k+2}$.

Hence, the result is true for all $1 \leq n \leq k + 1$, so by strong induction, the result is true for all positive integers n.

(b) Let T_n be the sequence that results from reducing every element of S_n modulo 2. We list the first few such sequences.

n	T_n
2	$1,0,1$
3	$1,1,0,1,1$
4	$1,0,1,1,0,1,1,0,1$
5	$1,1,0,1,1,0,1,1,0,1,1,0,1,1,0,1,1$

Let B denote the block $1, 0, 1$. Then assuming that symbols that are consecutive are concatenated, we can rewrite the terms as follows:

n	T_n
2	B
3	$1B1$
4	BBB
5	$1BBBBB1$

We claim that T_{2n} is of the form $BB\cdots B$, and T_{2n+1} is of the form $1BB\cdots B1$ for all $n \geq 1$. We prove this by induction. The result is true for $n = 1$, so assume that it is true for some positive integer $n = k$, where $k \geq 1$, so T_{2k} is of the form $BB\cdots B$, and T_{2k+1} is of the form $1BB\cdots B1$.

For any sequence P of 0's and 1's, let $f(P)$ denote the sequence of 0's and 1's obtained by applying the algorithm in the problem to P, and then reducing modulo 2. Note that $f((1)) = 1$ and $f(B) = 1B1$. Also note that for any such sequences P and Q, we have $f(PQ) = f(P)Df(Q)$, where D is the sum of the last number of P and the first number of Q, reduced modulo 2.

Using these observations, we can write

$$
\begin{aligned}
T_{2k+2} &= f(T_{2k+1}) \\
&= f(1BB\cdots B1) \\
&= (1)(0)(1B1)(0)(1B1)(0)\cdots(0)(1B1)(0)(1) \\
&= (101)B(101)B\cdots B(101) \\
&= BB\cdots B.
\end{aligned}
$$

Also,

$$
\begin{aligned}
T_{2k+3} &= f(T_{2k+2}) \\
&= f(BB\cdots B) \\
&= (1B1)(0)(1B1)(0)\cdots(0)(1B1) \\
&= 1B(101)B\cdots(101)B1 \\
&= 1BB\cdots B1.
\end{aligned}
$$

Hence, the result is true for $n = k + 1$, and by mathematical induction, the result is true for all positive integers n.

So T_{2n} consists of a number of blocks B, for all positive integers n. But each block B consists of two 1's and one 0, which means that in S_{2n}, the number of odd terms is equal to twice the number of even terms.

10.30 Consider an arrangement of n left parentheses and $2n$ right parentheses. Then the arrangement is double-good if for all positive integers k, as we read left-to-right, at most $2(k - 1)$ right parentheses have appeared before the kth left parenthesis. If the arrangement is not double-good, then call it k-bad if the first time this condition fails is after the kth left parenthesis but before the $(k + 1)^{\text{st}}$ left parenthesis. For example, ())())() is 1-bad, (()))))() is 2-bad, and)()()) is 0-bad. We also extend the definition of k-bad to an arrangement of any number of left parentheses and right parentheses, not just those where the number of right parentheses is double the number of left parentheses.

First, we prove the following lemma.

Lemma. For all $0 \leq k < n$, the number of k-bad arrangements with n left parentheses and $2n$ right parentheses is twice the number of k-bad arrangements with $n - 1$ left parentheses and $2n + 1$ right parentheses.

Proof. If an arrangement is k-bad, then the arrangement begins with a double-good arrangement of k "("s and $2k$ ")"s, followed by a right parenthesis. So, we have used k left parentheses and $2k + 1$ right parentheses, which leaves the last $3n - 3k - 1$ parentheses to be determined.

For such an arrangement with n left parentheses and $2n$ right parentheses, the remaining $n - k$ left parentheses can be arranged among the last $3n - 3k - 1$ parentheses arbitrarily, so there are $\binom{3n-3k-1}{n-k}$ possible ways to arrange the last $3n - 3k - 1$ parentheses. Hence there are $\binom{3n-3k-1}{n-k}$ k-bad arrangements with n "("s and $2n$ ")"s that begin with a given double-good arrangement of k "("s and $2k$ ")"s.

Similarly, each k-bad arrangement with $n - 1$ left parentheses and $2n + 1$ right parentheses begins with a double-good arrangement of k "("s and $2k$ ")"s. There are $\binom{3n-3k-1}{n-k-1}$ possible ways to arrange the last $3n - 3k - 1$ parentheses, and thus there are $\binom{3n-3k-1}{n-k-1}$ k-bad arrangements with $n-1$ "("s and $2n+1$ ")"s that begin with a given double-good arrangement of k "("s and $2k$ ")"s.

To finish the proof of the lemma, we compute:

$$
\begin{aligned}
\binom{3n - 3k - 1}{n - k} &= \frac{(3n - 3k - 1)!}{(n - k)!(2n - 2k - 1)!} \\
&= \frac{(3n - 3k - 1)!(2n - 2k)}{(n - k)(n - k - 1)!(2n - 2k)(2n - 2k - 1)!} \\
&= \frac{2n - 2k}{n - k} \cdot \frac{(3n - 3k - 1)!}{(n - k - 1)!(2n - 2k)!} \\
&= 2 \cdot \frac{(3n - 3k - 1)!}{(n - k - 1)!(2n - 2k)!} \\
&= 2\binom{3n - 3k - 1}{n - k - 1}.
\end{aligned}
$$

Let $\mathcal{D}$ be an arbitrary double-good arrangement of k "("s and $2k$ ")"s. Our argument above shows that there are twice as many k-bad arrangements of n "("s and $2n$ ")"s that start with $\mathcal{D}$ as there are k-bad arrangements of $n - 1$ "("s and $2n + 1$ ")"s that start with $\mathcal{D}$. Since all k-bad arrangements begin with some double-good arrangement of k "("s and $2k$ ")"s, we conclude (summing over all possible $\mathcal{D}$) that there are twice as many k-bad arrangements of n "("s and $2n$ ")"s as there are k-bad arrangements of $n - 1$ "("s and $2n + 1$ ")"s.

Thus the Lemma is proved.

Since the Lemma holds for all $0 \leq k < n$, it follows that the number of arrangements with n left parentheses and $2n$ right parentheses that are not double-good is twice the number of arrangements with $n - 1$ left parentheses and $2n + 1$ right parentheses that are not double-good. But *all* of the latter arrangements are not double-good, and there are $\binom{3n}{n-1}$ such arrangements.

Thus, we have shown that the number of arrangements with n left parentheses and $2n$ right parentheses that are not double-good is $2\binom{3n}{n-1}$. Therefore, the number of arrangements that are double-good is

$$
\begin{aligned}
\binom{3n}{n} - 2\binom{3n}{n-1} &= \frac{(3n)!}{n!(2n)!} - 2 \cdot \frac{(3n)!}{(n-1)!(2n+1)!} = \frac{(3n)!}{(n-1)!(2n)!}\left(\frac{1}{n} - \frac{2}{2n+1}\right) \\
&= \frac{(3n)!}{(n-1)!(2n)!} \cdot \frac{1}{n(2n+1)} = \frac{1}{2n+1} \cdot \frac{(3n)!}{n!(2n)!} = \boxed{\frac{1}{2n+1}\binom{3n}{n}}.
\end{aligned}
$$

10.31 For each possible sequence of goals, we plot a path in the coordinate plane as follows. We start at the origin (0,0). Each time Germany scores a goal, we move 1 unit to the right, and each time Brazil scores a goal, we move 1 unit upward. Hence, if we are at the point (x, y), then Germany has scored x goals and Brazil has scored y goals. Since the final score is Germany $n - m$ and Brazil $n + m$, the final point on the path is $(n - m, n + m)$.

Furthermore, since Germany is never more than $2m$ goals behind, $y - x \leq 2m$ for all points (x, y) on the path. In other words, the path lies entirely on or below the line $y = x + 2m$. To count the number of such paths, we use the same reflection argument as in Problem 10.14.

Consider a path that goes from $(0,0)$ to $(n - m, n + m)$ that goes above the line $y = x + 2m$. Circle the first point on the path that goes above the line $y = x + 2m$. Since this circled point is one unit above the line $y = x + 2m$, it is of the form $(t, t + 2m + 1)$ for some integer t.

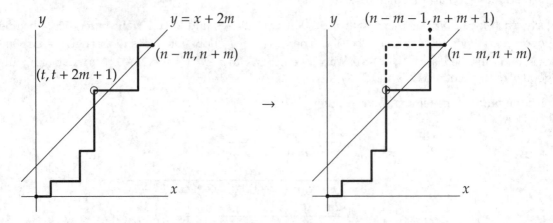

Now, reflect the portion of the path that goes from $(t, t + 2m + 1)$ to $(n - m, n + m)$. This portion of the path goes $n - m - t$ units to the right and $n + m - (t + 2m + 1) = n - m - t - 1$ units upwards. So the reflected portion goes $n - m - t - 1$ units to the right and $n - m - t$ units upwards. Hence, the final point of the reflected portion is

$$(t + n - m - t - 1, t + 2m + 1 + n - m - t) = (n - m - 1, n + m + 1).$$

Thus, this process generates a path going from $(0,0)$ to $(n - m - 1, n + m + 1)$.

Conversely, given a path that goes from $(0,0)$ to $(n - m - 1, n + m + 1)$, we can reverse the process to generate a path that goes from $(0,0)$ to $(n - m, n + m)$ that goes above the line $y = x + 2m$. This establishes a 1-1 correspondence:

$$\left\{\begin{matrix}\text{paths from } (0,0) \text{ to } (n - m, n + m) \text{ that} \\ \text{go above the line } y = x + 2m\end{matrix}\right\} \quad \leftrightarrow \quad \{\text{paths from } (0,0) \text{ to } (n - m - 1, n + m + 1)\}.$$

The number of paths that go from $(0,0)$ to $(n - m - 1, n + m + 1)$ is $\binom{2n}{n-m-1}$. Therefore, the number of paths that go from $(0,0)$ to $(n - m, n + m)$ and that do not go above the line $y = x + 2m$ is

$$\begin{aligned}
\binom{2n}{n-m} - \binom{2n}{n-m-1} &= \frac{(2n)!}{(n-m)!(n+m)!} - \frac{(2n)!}{(n-m-1)!(n+m+1)!} \\
&= \frac{(2n)!}{(n-m-1)!(n+m)!}\left(\frac{1}{n-m} - \frac{1}{n+m+1}\right) \\
&= \frac{(2n)!}{(n-m-1)!(n+m)!} \cdot \frac{2m+1}{(n-m)(n+m+1)} \\
&= \frac{2m+1}{n+m+1} \cdot \frac{(2n)!}{(n-m)!(n+m)!} \\
&= \boxed{\frac{2m+1}{n+m+1}\binom{2n}{n-m}}.
\end{aligned}$$

Note that when $m = 0$, we recover the nth Catalan number $\frac{1}{n+1}\binom{2n}{n}$.

10.32 Throughout this solution, the word "sequence" will mean a sequence that satisfies the conditions of the problem (all elements are integers less than or equal to 1 and all partial sums are nonnegative).

First, note that for any sequence $(a_1, a_2, \ldots, a_n)$, we can add an additional term $a_{n+1} = -(a_1 + \cdots + a_n)$ to create a sequence of length $n + 1$ whose sum is 0. This operation is reversible, so there is a 1-1 correspondence

$$\{\text{Sequences of length } n\} \quad \leftrightarrow \quad \{\text{Sequences of length } n + 1 \text{ that sum to } 0\}.$$

Let s_n be the number of sequences of length n that sum to 0.

For any sequence $(a_1, a_2, \ldots, a_n)$ that sums to 0, let k be the point at which the partial sum is *first* 0; that is $a_1 + a_2 + \cdots + a_k = 0$ but $a_1 + a_2 + \cdots + a_l \neq 0$ for all $l < k$. There are two cases.

Case 1: $k = 1$. Then $a_1 = 0$, and $(a_2, \ldots, a_n)$ is a valid sequence summing to 0.

Case 2: $k > 1$. Then $a_1 = 1$ and $a_k < 0$. In this case, $(a_2, \ldots, a_k + 1)$ is a valid sequence summing to 0.

In either case, $(a_{k+1}, \ldots, a_n)$ is also a sequence summing to 0. (This is the empty sequence if $k = n$.) So the sequence corresponds to two subsequences, one of length $k - 1$ and one of length $n - k$.

This sets up a Catalan recurrence. Setting $s_0 = 1$, we see that

$$s_n = \sum_{k=1}^{n} s_{k-1} s_{n-k}.$$

Thus we see that $s_n = C_n$, the nth Catalan number. Therefore, the answer to the problem is $s_6 = C_6 = \boxed{132}$.

CHAPTER 11

Conditional Probability

Exercises for Section 11.2

11.2.1 If we roll a pair of fair dice, so that neither die shows $\boxed{\cdot}$, then there are 5 possible outcomes for each die. Therefore, there are 25 ways to roll a pair of fair dice and not get a $\boxed{\cdot}$ on either die. Four of these outcomes sum to 7, namely $\boxed{\cdot}\,\boxed{\because}$, $\boxed{\because}\,\boxed{\therefore}$, $\boxed{\therefore}\,\boxed{\because}$, and $\boxed{\because}\,\boxed{\cdot}$. Thus the probability is $\boxed{\dfrac{4}{25}}$.

11.2.2 Let the rolls of the die be a, b, and c. Then for a fixed value of c, there are $c-1$ rolls of the first two dice that sum to c, namely $(1, c-1), (2, c-2), \ldots, (c-1, 1)$. Summing over $2 \le c \le 6$, we find that there are $1+2+3+4+5 = 15$ possible rolls such that $a + b = c$.

Now, of these 15 possible rolls, we count the number in which a 2 appears. Either 2 is the sum of the other two rolls, or 2 is part of the sum. If 2 is the sum of the other two rolls, then (a, b, c) must be $(1,1,2)$. If 2 is part of the sum, then (a, b, c) must be one of $(2,1,3)$, $(2,2,4)$, $(2,3,5)$, or $(2,4,6)$, or one of these with the first two rolls reversed. The triples $(2,1,3)$, $(2,3,5)$, and $(2,4,6)$ each give two different rolls, but the triple $(2,2,4)$ only gives one. This gives us a total of $1 + 2(3) + 1 = 8$ rolls containing a 2.

Therefore, the desired probability is $\boxed{8/15}$.

11.2.3 On this last flip, the coins must show either heads-heads, heads-tails, or tails-heads, with equal probability. Hence, the probability that both coins show heads is $\boxed{1/3}$. (Note that all of the two-tails flips that occur before the last flip are irrelevant.)

11.2.4 The desired probability is:
$$\frac{\#(\text{ways to get 4 } \heartsuit \text{s})}{\#(\text{ways to get at least 3 } \heartsuit \text{s})}.$$
There are $\binom{13}{3} \times 39$ ways to choose 3 $\heartsuit$s and a non-$\heartsuit$, and $\binom{13}{4}$ ways to choose 4 $\heartsuit$s. Therefore, the desired probability is:
$$\frac{\binom{13}{4}}{\binom{13}{4} + 39\binom{13}{3}} = \frac{715}{11869} = \boxed{\frac{5}{83}}.$$

11.2.5 First, we note that in the set $\{1, 2, 3, \ldots, 99\}$, there are 10 numbers that have a units digit of 1 through 9 each, but only 9 that have a units digit of 0. This means there are 49 even numbers and 50 odd numbers.

If $x + y$ is even, then either both x and y are even, or both x and y are odd. The number of ordered pairs (x, y) where both x and y are even is 49^2, and the number where both x and y are odd is 50^2, for a total of $49^2 + 50^2 = 4901$ ordered pairs.

Now, let x_0 be the units digit of x, and let y_0 be the units digit of y. Of these 4901 ordered pairs (x, y), we wish to count the number of ordered pairs where $x_0 + y_0 < 10$. Again, either both x_0 and y_0 are even, or both x_0 and y_0 are odd.

If both x_0 and y_0 are even, then (x_0, y_0) must be one of the following ordered pairs:

$$(0,0), (0,2), (0,4), (0,6), (0,8),$$
$$(2,0), (2,2), (2,4), (2,6),$$
$$(4,0), (4,2), (4,4),$$
$$(6,0), (6,2),$$
$$(8,0).$$

Recall that there are 10 numbers in $\{1, 2, \ldots, 99\}$ for every units digits except for 0, and there are 9 numbers in the set with units digit 0. Therefore, the total number of ordered pairs (x, y) with x_0 and y_0 both even is:

$$9 \cdot 9 + 9 \cdot 10 + 9 \cdot 10 + 9 \cdot 10 + 9 \cdot 10$$
$$+ 10 \cdot 9 + 10 \cdot 10 + 10 \cdot 10 + 10 \cdot 10$$
$$+ 10 \cdot 9 + 10 \cdot 10 + 10 \cdot 10$$
$$+ 10 \cdot 9 + 10 \cdot 10$$
$$+ 10 \cdot 9$$
$$= 1401.$$

If both x_0 and y_0 are odd, then (x_0, y_0) must be one of the following ordered pairs:

$$(1,1), (1,3), (1,5), (1,7),$$
$$(3,1), (3,3), (3,5),$$
$$(5,1), (5,3),$$
$$(7,1).$$

For each such pair (x_0, y_0), there are $10 \cdot 10 = 100$ possible pairs (x, y), so the total number of such ordered pairs (x, y) is $10 \cdot 100 = 1000$.

Therefore, the probability that if $x + y$ is even then $x_0 + y_0 < 10$ is

$$\frac{1401 + 1000}{4901} = \boxed{\frac{2401}{4901}}.$$

Exercises for Section 11.3

11.3.1 Let A be the event that Bag X is chosen, and let B be the event that the ball drawn is white. We wish to compute $P(A|B) = P(A \cap B)/P(B)$.

If Bag X is chosen, then the probability of drawing a white ball is $1/10$, so $P(A \cap B) = 1/2 \cdot 1/10 = 1/20$. If Bag Y is chosen, then the probability of drawing a white ball is 1, so

$$P(B) = \frac{1}{2} \cdot \frac{1}{10} + \frac{1}{2} \cdot 1 = \frac{11}{20}.$$

Therefore, $P(A|B) = (1/20)/(11/20) = \boxed{1/11}$.

11.3.2

(a) We see that A is more likely than B. Also, $P(A \cap B) \le P(B)$ by common sense: the probability of A and B occurring is certainly less than the probability of just B occurring. If B is such that it occurs only when A occurs too, then $P(A \cap B) = P(B)$, and hence the maximum possible value of $P(A \cap B)$ is $\boxed{\frac{2}{3}}$.

On the other hand, $P(A \cap B)$ is minimized when A and B are as "disjoint" as possible. This happens when at least one of A or B always happens, meaning that $P(A \cup B) = 1$. Then, by PIE,

$$P(A \cup B) = P(A) + P(B) - P(A \cap B),$$

giving us $P(A \cap B) = P(A) + P(B) - P(A \cup B) = \dfrac{3}{4} + \dfrac{2}{3} - 1 = \boxed{\dfrac{5}{12}}$.

(b)   We know that

$$P(A|B) = \frac{P(A \cap B)}{P(B)}.$$

We are given that $P(B) = 2/3$, and from part (a), the minimum and maximum values of $P(A \cap B)$ are 5/12 and 2/3, respectively, so the minimum and maximum values of $P(A|B)$ are $(5/12)/(2/3) = \boxed{5/8}$ and $(2/3)/(2/3) = \boxed{1}$, respectively.

Similarly,

$$P(B|A) = \frac{P(A \cap B)}{P(A)},$$

and we are given that $P(A) = 3/4$. Therefore, the minimum and maximum values of $P(B|A)$ are $(5/12)/(3/4) = \boxed{5/9}$ and $(2/3)/(3/4) = \boxed{8/9}$, respectively.

11.3.3   Let A be the event that the color face-down is red, and let B be the event that the color face-up is red. Then we wish to compute $P(A|B) = P(A \cap B)/P(B)$.

If the card with two red sides is chosen, then the probability that the color face-up is red is 1. If the card with one red side and one green side is chosen, then the probability that the color face-up is red is 1/2. Therefore,

$$P(B) = \frac{1}{2} \cdot 1 + \frac{1}{2} \cdot \frac{1}{2} = \frac{3}{4}.$$

For the event $A \cap B$ to occur, both sides of the card must be red, so $P(A \cap B) = 1/2$.

Therefore, $P(A|B) = (1/2)/(3/4) = \boxed{2/3}$.

11.3.4 $\boxed{\text{False}}$. There are many examples we could cite. For example, consider rolling a 6-sided die. If A is the event "an odd number is rolled" and B is the event "a ⚀ is rolled," then $P(A|B) = 1$ (since all rolls of ⚀ are odd) whereas $P(B|A) = \frac{1}{3}$ (since only $\frac{1}{3}$ of odd rolls are ⚀).

In general, we can see this algebraically. We have the formulas

$$P(A|B) = \frac{P(A \cap B)}{P(B)} \quad \text{and} \quad P(B|A) = \frac{P(A \cap B)}{P(A)}.$$

Therefore, $P(A|B) = P(B|A)$ if and only if $P(A) = P(B)$ or $P(A \cap B) = 0$, which is generally not the case.

11.3.5   Let X be the event that the first ball drawn is red, and let Y be the event that the second ball drawn is black. Then we wish to compute $P(X|Y) = P(X \cap Y)/P(Y)$.

If Urn A is chosen as the first urn, then the probability of drawing a white ball is $4/6 = 2/3$, and the probability of drawing a red ball is $2/6 = 1/3$. If Urn B is chosen as the first urn, then the probability of drawing a red ball is $3/6 = 1/2$, and the probability of drawing a black ball is $3/6 = 1/2$. Thus, after the first ball has been drawn, we have one of the following four scenarios, with their respective probabilities:

First Urn and ball	Balls left in Urn A	Balls left in Urn B	Probability
A white	3 white balls, 2 red balls	3 red balls, 3 black balls	$1/2 \cdot 2/3 = 1/3$
A red	4 white balls, 1 red ball	3 red balls, 3 black balls	$1/2 \cdot 1/3 = 1/6$
B red	4 white balls, 2 red balls	2 red balls, 3 black balls	$1/2 \cdot 1/2 = 1/4$
B black	4 white balls, 2 red balls	3 red balls, 2 black balls	$1/2 \cdot 1/2 = 1/4$

For the second ball to be black, the second urn chosen must be Urn B. The probability of drawing a black ball from Urn B, under the scenarios listed above, are $3/6 = 1/2$, $3/6 = 1/2$, $3/5$, and $2/5$, in that order. Therefore,

$$P(Y) = \frac{1}{2}\left(\frac{1}{3}\cdot\frac{1}{2} + \frac{1}{6}\cdot\frac{1}{2} + \frac{1}{4}\cdot\frac{3}{5} + \frac{1}{4}\cdot\frac{2}{5}\right) = \frac{1}{4}.$$

The first ball is red in 2nd and 3rd scenarios listed above, so

$$P(X \cap Y) = \frac{1}{2}\left(\frac{1}{6}\cdot\frac{1}{2} + \frac{1}{4}\cdot\frac{3}{5}\right) = \frac{7}{60}.$$

Therefore, $P(X|Y) = (7/60)/(1/4) = \boxed{7/15}$.

Exercises for Section 11.4

11.4.1 Let A be the event that the chosen kernel is yellow, and let B be the event that the kernel is popped. We wish to compute $P(A|B) = P(A \cap B)/P(B)$.

The probability of choosing a yellow kernel is $1/3$, and the probability that it pops is $2/3$, so $P(A \cap B) = 1/3 \cdot 2/3 = 2/9$. The probability of choosing a white kernel is $2/3$, and the probability that it pops is $1/2$, so

$$P(B) = \frac{1}{3}\cdot\frac{2}{3} + \frac{2}{3}\cdot\frac{1}{2} = \frac{5}{9}.$$

Therefore, $P(A|B) = (2/9)/(5/9) = \boxed{2/5}$.

11.4.2 If a permutation does not have first term 1, then there are 5 choices for the first term of the permutation, and then 5! ways to order the remaining numbers. Therefore, there are $5 \cdot 5!$ permutations with the first term not 1.

If the third term is 3 and the first term is not 1, then there are 4 choices for the first term, and 4! ways to arrange the remaining four numbers. So there are $4 \cdot 4!$ such permutations.

Therefore, the fraction is $\dfrac{4 \cdot 4!}{5 \cdot 5!} = \boxed{\dfrac{4}{25}}$.

11.4.3 We show possible ordered pairs (r, s) on the Cartesian plane in the picture at the right. The "possible outcomes" region where $|r - s| < \frac{1}{4}$ is lightly shaded: this is the region between the lines $r - s = -\frac{1}{4}$ and $r - s = \frac{1}{4}$. The lines $r = \frac{1}{2}$ and $s = \frac{1}{2}$ are shown as dashed lines in the diagram, and the region $r < \frac{1}{2} < s$ is shaded darkly.

The entire shaded region has area 1 minus the area of the white region. Together, the two white triangular regions form a square of side length $\frac{3}{4}$, so the white area is $\frac{9}{16}$, and hence the shaded area is $1 - \frac{9}{16} = \frac{7}{16}$. The darkly-shaded "successful outcomes" region is an isosceles right triangle with side length $\frac{1}{4}$, so its area is $\frac{1}{32}$. Therefore, the desired probability is

$$\frac{\frac{1}{32}}{\frac{7}{16}} = \boxed{\frac{1}{14}}.$$

11.4.4 Let A be the event that the King's right foot has six toes, and let B be the event that four inhabitants say that the King's right foot has six toes. We wish to compute $P(A|B) = P(A \cap B)/P(B)$.

If the King does have six toes on his right foot, then the probability that four inhabitants say that he does have six toes is $(2/5)^4$, so

$$P(A \cap B) = \frac{1}{3} \cdot \left(\frac{2}{5}\right)^4 = \frac{16}{1875}.$$

If the King does not have six toes on his right foot, then the probability that four inhabitants say that he does have six toes is $(3/5)^4$, so

$$P(B) = \frac{1}{3} \cdot \left(\frac{2}{5}\right)^4 + \frac{2}{3} \cdot \left(\frac{3}{5}\right)^4 = \frac{178}{1875}.$$

Therefore, $P(A|B) = (16/1875)/(178/1875) = \boxed{8/89}$.

11.4.5   As in the solution in the text, we will compute

$$P(\text{a blivet is good} \mid \text{the blivet passes } n \text{ tests}).$$

The probability that a randomly-chosen blivet is good is 0.85, and a good blivet will always pass any number of tests. The probability that a randomly-chosen blivet is bad is 0.15, and it will pass n tests with probability $(0.90)^n$. Therefore, the probability that a blivet that passes n tests is good is:

$$\frac{0.85}{0.85 + (0.15)(0.90)^n}.$$

We need this quantity to be at least 0.95, so we must solve the inequality

$$\frac{0.85}{0.85 + (0.15)(0.90)^n} \geq 0.95.$$

This simplifies as follows:

$$
\begin{aligned}
& 0.85 \geq 0.95(0.85 + (0.15)(0.9)^n) \\
\Leftrightarrow \quad & 0.85 \geq 0.8075 + (0.1425)(0.9)^n \\
\Leftrightarrow \quad & 0.0425 \geq (0.1425)(0.9)^n \\
\Leftrightarrow \quad & \tfrac{17}{57} \geq (0.9)^n.
\end{aligned}
$$

Therefore, $n \geq \log_{0.9}(17/57) \approx 11.48$, so we need to test the blivet $\boxed{12}$ times.

11.4.6

(a) Let A be the event that you have arachnophobia, and let B be the event that you never shiver when shown a picture of a black widow spider three times. We wish to compute $P(A|B) = P(A \cap B)/P(B)$.

   If you have arachnophobia, then the probability that you never shiver when shown a picture of a black widow spider three times is $(1/10)^3 = 1/1000$, so

$$P(A \cap B) = \frac{3}{10} \cdot \frac{1}{1000} = \frac{3}{10000}.$$

   If you do not have arachnophobia, then the probability that you never shiver when shown a picture of a black widow spider three times is $(4/5)^3 = 64/125$, so

$$P(B) = \frac{3}{10} \cdot \frac{1}{1000} + \frac{7}{10} \cdot \frac{64}{125} = \frac{3587}{10000}.$$

   Therefore, $P(A|B) = (3/10000)/(3587/10000) = \boxed{3/3587}$.

(b) Let C be the event that you always shiver when shown a picture of a black widow spider three times. Then we wish to compute $P(A|C) = P(A \cap C)/P(C)$.

If you have arachnophobia, then the probability that you always shiver when shown a picture of a black widow spider three times is $(9/10)^3 = 729/1000$, so

$$P(A \cap C) = \frac{3}{10} \cdot \frac{729}{1000} = \frac{2187}{10000}.$$

If you do not have arachnophobia, then the probability that you always shiver when shown a picture of a black widow spider three times is $(1/5)^3 = 1/125$, so

$$P(C) = \frac{3}{10} \cdot \frac{729}{1000} + \frac{7}{10} \cdot \frac{1}{125} = \frac{2243}{10000}.$$

Therefore, $P(A|C) = (2187/10,000)/(2243/10000) = \boxed{2187/2243}$.

(c) Let D be the event that you shiver exactly twice when shown a picture of a black widow spider three times. Then we wish to compute $P(A|D) = P(A \cap D)/P(D)$.

If you have arachnophobia, then the probability that you shiver exactly twice when shown a picture of a black widow spider three times is $1/10 \cdot 9/10 \cdot 9/10 + 9/10 \cdot 1/10 \cdot 9/10 + 9/10 \cdot 9/10 \cdot 1/10 = 243/1000$, so

$$P(A \cap D) = \frac{3}{10} \cdot \frac{243}{1000} = \frac{729}{10000}.$$

If you do not have arachnophobia, then the probability that you shiver exactly twice when shown a picture of a black widow spider three times is $4/5 \cdot 1/5 \cdot 1/5 + 1/5 \cdot 4/5 \cdot 1/5 + 1/5 \cdot 1/5 \cdot 4/5 = 12/125$, so

$$P(D) = \frac{3}{10} \cdot \frac{243}{1000} + \frac{7}{10} \cdot \frac{12}{125} = \frac{1401}{10000}.$$

Therefore, $P(A|D) = (729/10000)/(1401/10000) = \boxed{243/467}$.

Exercises for Section 11.5

11.5.1 Since there are 9 goats and 1 car, the probability that the contestant originally chose the car is 1/10, and the revealing of the 8 goats does not change this probability. Therefore, the probability of winning if the contestant switches is $\boxed{9/10}$.

11.5.2 There are essentially four different strategies: The contestant can choose to switch after the first reveal or not, and the contestant can choose to switch after the second reveal or not.

Case 1: The contestant does not switch after either reveal.

   The probability that the contestant originally chose the car is 1/4, and this does not change after either of the reveals, so the probability that the contestant wins the car in this case is 1/4.

Case 2: The contestant switches after the first reveal, but not the second reveal.

   The probability that the contestant originally chose the car is 1/4, so the probability that the contestant did not originally choose the car is 3/4. The only way the contestant can win the car is to choose a goat originally (with probability 3/4), and then switch to the car (with probability 1/2), so the probability that the contestant wins the car in this case is $3/4 \cdot 1/2 = 3/8$.

Case 3: The contestant switches after the second reveal, but not the first reveal.

   Like in Case 2, the only way the contestant can win the car is to choose a goat originally (with probability 3/4), and then switch to the car (with probability 1), so the probability that the contestant wins the car in this case is $3/4 \cdot 1 = 3/4$.

Case 4: The contestant switches after both the first reveal and the second reveal.

If the contestant originally chooses the car (which occurs with probability $\frac{1}{4}$, then the contestant wins by switching to a goat (with probability 1) and then switching back to the car (with probability 1). So the probability that the contestant wins the car if initially he chooses it is 1.

If the contestant originally chooses a goat (which occurs with probability $\frac{3}{4}$, then the contestant wins by switching to another goat (with probability $\frac{1}{2}$) and then switching to the car (with probability 1 after the contestant's initially chosen goat is revealed). So the probability that the contestant wins the car if he initially chooses a goat is $\frac{1}{2}$.

Thus the overall probability of this strategy is $\frac{1}{4} \cdot 1 + \frac{3}{4} \cdot \frac{1}{2} = \frac{5}{8}$.

Thus, the best strategy is to $\boxed{\text{switch only after the second reveal}}$, which has a probability of winning of $\boxed{3/4}$.

Review Problems

11.11 There are only 8 primes from 1 to 20 (namely 2, 3, 5, 7, 11, 13, 17, and 19) and only one of them is even (namely 2), so the probability that the chosen prime is even is $\boxed{1/8}$.

11.12 Let X be the event that the marble taken from Bag A is white, and let Y be the event that the marble taken from Bag B is white. Then we wish to compute $P(X|Y) = P(X \cap Y)/P(Y)$.

The probability that a white marble is taken from Bag A is 3/5. After it has been placed in Bag B, the bag will then contain five white marbles and three black marbles. Then the probability a white marble is drawn from Bag B is 5/8, so

$$P(X \cap Y) = \frac{3}{5} \cdot \frac{5}{8} = \frac{3}{8}.$$

The probability that a black marble is taken from Bag A is 2/5. After it has been placed in Bag B, it will then contain four white marbles and four black marbles. Then the probability a white marble is drawn from Bag B is $4/8 = 1/2$, so

$$P(Y) = \frac{3}{5} \cdot \frac{5}{8} + \frac{2}{5} \cdot \frac{1}{2} = \frac{23}{40}.$$

Therefore, $P(X|Y) = (3/8)/(23/40) = \boxed{15/23}$.

11.13 Let A be the event that the chosen coin has two heads, and let B be the event that when the coin is flipped 9 times, it comes up heads each time. We wish to compute $P(A|B) = P(A \cap B)/P(B)$.

The probability that the coin with two heads is chosen is 1/500, and if it is chosen, then of course it must come up heads each time, so $P(A \cap B) = 1/500$.

The probability that a fair coin is chosen is 499/500, and if it is chosen, then the probability that 9 heads come up is $1/2^9 = 1/512$, so

$$P(B) = \frac{1}{500} + \frac{499}{500} \cdot \frac{1}{512} = \frac{1011}{256000}.$$

Therefore, $P(A|B) = (1/500)/(1011/256000) = \boxed{512/1011}$.

11.14 The probability that it is raining and that the Martians are all telling the truth is

$$\frac{3}{10} \times \left(\frac{4}{5}\right)^3 = \frac{96}{625}.$$

The probability that it is not raining and that the Martians are all lying is

$$\frac{7}{10} \times \left(\frac{1}{5}\right)^3 = \frac{7}{1250}.$$

Therefore, the probability that it is raining is

$$\frac{\frac{96}{625}}{\frac{96}{625} + \frac{7}{1250}} = \boxed{\frac{192}{199}}.$$

11.15 First we look at the size of the region of possible outcomes. If the quarter does not hang over the edge of the table, then the center of the quarter must be at least 1 cm from the edge of the table. Therefore, the center of the quarter must lie within the circle whose center is the center of the table and whose radius is 4 cm, as in the top diagram at right.

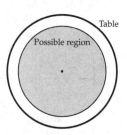

If such a quarter is going to overlap the center of the table, then the quarter's center must be within 1 cm of the center of the table. Therefore, the center of the quarter must lie within the circle whose center is the center of the table and whose radius is 1 cm, as in the bottom diagram at right.

The area of the possible region is 16π cm^2, and the area of the successful region is π cm^2, so the probability is $\frac{\pi}{16\pi} = \boxed{\frac{1}{16}}$.

11.16 Let L be the event of Louise attending the convention and let T be the event of Thelma attending the convention. We wish to compute $P(L|T) = P(L \cap T)/P(T)$.

If Louise attends, Thelma has an 80% chance of attending, so $P(L \cap T) = \frac{3}{4} \cdot \frac{4}{5} = \frac{3}{5}$. If Louise does not attend, then Thelma has 50% chance of attending, so

$$P(T) = \frac{3}{4} \cdot \frac{4}{5} + \frac{1}{4} \cdot \frac{1}{2} = \frac{29}{40}.$$

Therefore, $P(L|T) = (3/5)/(29/40) = \boxed{24/29}$.

Challenge Problems

11.17 Let A be the event that Royals win the World Series and let B be the event that the series went to six games. Then we wish to compute $P(A|B) = P(A \cap B)/P(B)$.

Let R and C denote a win by the Royals and Cubs, respectively. If the Royals win in six games, then the series must have been of the form XXXXXR, where X stands for R or C. There are three Rs and two Cs among the Xs, so the number of possible series is $\binom{5}{3} = 10$. The probability of each such series occurring is $(2/3)^4(1/3)^2 = 16/729$, so $P(A \cap B) = 10 \cdot 16/729 = 160/729$.

Similarly, if the Cubs win in six games, then the series must have been of the form XXXXXC. There are two Rs and three Cs among the Xs, so again the number of possible series is 10. The probability of each such series occurring is $(2/3)^2(1/3)^4 = 4/729$, so

$$P(B) = 10 \cdot \frac{16}{729} + 10 \cdot \frac{4}{729} = \frac{200}{729}.$$

Therefore, $P(A|B) = (160/729)/(200/729) = \boxed{4/5}$.

11.18 Let r be Roger's arrival time expressed in hours after noon, so that $0 \le r \le 6$; similarly, let s be Stacy's arrival time, so that $0 \le s \le 6$. If they were both at the fair at the same time, then Roger must have arrived sometime between 1 hour before Stacy arrived and 2 hours after Stacy arrived. Therefore, we have the inequalities $s - 1 \le r \le s + 2$. We plot the region of possible arrival times subject to the condition in the Cartesian plane at right.

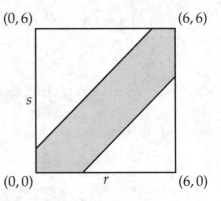

If Roger and Stacy were both there at 3:00, then $2 \le r \le 3$ and $1 \le s \le 3$. We draw dashed lines representing these conditions, and darkly shade the corresponding outcomes, giving us the diagram on the left below. The probability we seek is the area of the dark shaded region divided by the area of the total shaded region.

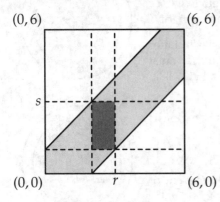

The overall shaded area is the area of the square minus the area of the two white triangles, which is $36 - 8 - (25/2) = 31/2$. The darker shaded area has area 2. Therefore, the desired probability is $2/(31/2) = \boxed{4/31}$.

11.19 Since all of the outcomes are equally likely, we can just count outcomes.

The number of ways that 14 heads appear is just $\binom{20}{14}$.

Now we count the number of ways that 14 heads can appear, such that no two tails occur on consecutive flips. Let H and T denote a head and a tail, respectively, and consider 14 Hs in a row. Then we can insert 6 Ts, where each T is inserted either between two Hs or at the ends of the row. The number of such ways of inserting 6 Ts is $\binom{15}{6}$.

Therefore, the probability is $\dfrac{\binom{15}{6}}{\binom{20}{14}} = \dfrac{5005}{38760} = \boxed{\dfrac{1001}{7752}}$.

11.20 Suppose that the boss rolls k ⚃'s. We will compute the probability that the die is loaded.

If the die is the loaded die, then the probability of rolling k ⚃'s (out of 10 rolls) is

$$\binom{10}{k}\left(\frac{1}{2}\right)^{10}.$$

If the die is a fair die, then this probability is

$$\binom{10}{k}\left(\frac{1}{6}\right)^{k}\left(\frac{5}{6}\right)^{10-k}.$$

Therefore, the probability that the die is loaded is (note that the $\binom{10}{k}$ terms cancel):

$$\frac{\frac{1}{5}\left(\frac{1}{2}\right)^{10}}{\frac{1}{5}\left(\frac{1}{2}\right)^{10} + \frac{4}{5}\left(\frac{1}{6}\right)^{k}\left(\frac{5}{6}\right)^{10-k}} = \frac{3^{10}}{3^{10} + 4 \cdot 5^{10-k}},$$

where the last fraction is the result of multiplying numerator and denominator by $5 \cdot 6^{10}$. Let's compute some probabilities (approximated to 3 decimal places) for the values of k:

k	10	9	8	7	6	5	
P(die is loaded given k ⚃'s)	99.993%	99.966%	99.831%	99.160%	95.938%	82.529%	...

So the pit boss must see $\boxed{6}$ ⚃'s to be at least 90% sure that the die is loaded.

11.21 Fix the first point (say, A). Then each of B and C is located between $-180°$ and $180°$ counterclockwise from A. If both B and C are a positive number of degrees (counterclockwise) from A, then all three points will lie on a common semicircle—in particular, they will all lie on the semicircle starting at A and extending $180°$ counterclockwise from A. Similarly, if both B and C are a negative number of degrees (counterclockwise) from A, then all three points will again lie on a common semicircle. Finally, if one point is a positive number of degrees from A and the other is a negative number of degrees from A, then the points will lie on a semicircle if and only if the absolute value of the difference of the distances (in degrees) from A is less than $180°$.

We can represent the outcomes where all three points lie on a semicircle as the shaded region shown in the Cartesian plane at right.

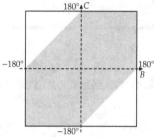

To determine the "successful" region in which triangle ABC has no angle above $120°$, we instead think of the complement, that is, the region in which the triangle ABC has an angle of at least $120°$. This is equivalent to the condition that the points A, B, C all lie on an arc of length $120°$, which is just a scaled version of the condition that A, B, C all lie on a semicircle (an arc of length $180°$).

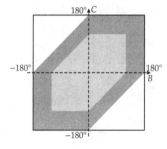

So we can use the same analysis, and we see that the successful region is the complement of a similar region to our possible region, scaled by $120°/180° = 2/3$. The successful region is the darker-shaded region in the picture at left. By similarity, the light region in the center of the picture has $(2/3)^2 = 4/9$ the area of the entire possible region. Therefore, the ratio of the area of the successful region to that of the entire possible region, and thus the desired probability, is $1 - (4/9) = \boxed{5/9}$.

Combinatorial Identities

Exercises for Section 12.2

12.2.1 By the Binomial Theorem,

$$\binom{n}{0}x^n + \binom{n}{1}x^{n-1}y + \binom{n}{2}x^{n-2}y^2 + \cdots + \binom{n}{n}y^n = (x+y)^n$$

for all real numbers x and y. Letting $x = 1$ and $y = -1$, we get

$$\binom{n}{0} - \binom{n}{1} + \binom{n}{2} - \cdots + (-1)^n\binom{n}{n} = \boxed{0}.$$

12.2.2

(a) We expand the left side:

$$\begin{aligned}
k\binom{n}{k} &= k\frac{n!}{k!(n-k)!} \\
&= \frac{n!}{(k-1)!(n-k)!} \\
&= n\frac{(n-1)!}{(k-1)!(n-k)!} \\
&= n\binom{n-1}{k-1}.
\end{aligned}$$

(b) The LHS counts the number of ways to first choose a k-person committee from a club of n people, and then to choose one of the k committee members to be its president. The RHS counts the same thing, by first choosing one of the n club members to be the committee president, and then choosing the remaining $k-1$ committee members from the $n-1$ club members remaining.

12.2.3

(a) By the Binomial Theorem,

$$\binom{n}{0} + \binom{n}{1}x + \binom{n}{2}x^2 + \cdots + \binom{n}{n}x^n = (1+x)^n.$$

for all real numbers x. Taking $x = 2$, we get

$$\binom{n}{0} + 2\binom{n}{1} + 2^2\binom{n}{2} + \cdots + 2^n\binom{n}{n} = 3^n.$$

(b) We have n people, and we wish to form a committee from these n people. Each person can either be a junior member of the committee, a senior member of the committee, or not on the committee, and any size committee is possible (including an empty committee). Since there are three possible states for each person, the total number of possible committees is 3^n.

We also count the number of possible committees as follows: First, we choose k people to be on the committee, where $0 \le k \le n$. This can be done in $\binom{n}{k}$ ways. Then, we designate each person to be a junior member or a senior member, which can be done in 2^k ways. Hence, the number of committees with k people is $2^k\binom{n}{k}$. Summing over $0 \le k \le n$, we get that the total number of possible committees is

$$\binom{n}{0} + 2\binom{n}{1} + 2^2\binom{n}{2} + \cdots + 2^n\binom{n}{n} = 3^n.$$

12.2.4

(a) Starting with a club with n members, the LHS counts the number of ways to form an r-person committee and then form an k-person subcommittee from the committee. The RHS counts the same thing, by first choosing the k people to be on the subcommittee, and then choosing the remaining $r - k$ people (from the club's remaining $n - k$ members) to complete the committee.

(b) Expanding the LHS gives:
$$\binom{n}{r}\binom{r}{k} = \frac{n!}{r!(n-r)!}\frac{r!}{k!(r-k)!} = \frac{n!}{k!(r-k)!(n-r)!}.$$

Expanding the RHS gives:
$$\binom{n}{k}\binom{n-k}{r-k} = \frac{n!}{k!(n-k)!}\frac{(n-k)!}{(r-k)!((n-k)-(r-k))!} = \frac{n!}{k!(r-k)!(n-r)!}.$$

Thus the LHS and RHS are equal.

12.2.5 For every positive integer k,

$$k\binom{n}{k} = k \cdot \frac{n!}{k!(n-k)!} = \frac{n!}{(k-1)!(n-k)!} = n \cdot \frac{(n-1)!}{(k-1)!(n-k)!} = n\binom{n-1}{k-1},$$

so

$$\binom{n}{1} + 3\binom{n}{3} + 5\binom{n}{5} + \cdots = n\binom{n-1}{0} + n\binom{n-1}{2} + n\binom{n-1}{4} + \cdots$$
$$= n\left[\binom{n-1}{0} + \binom{n-1}{2} + \binom{n-1}{4} + \cdots\right].$$

The problem is now to find the sum

$$\binom{n-1}{0} + \binom{n-1}{2} + \binom{n-1}{4} + \cdots.$$

If $n = 1$, then this sum is equal to $\binom{0}{0} = 1$, so assume that $n \ge 2$. By the Binomial Theorem,

$$\binom{n-1}{0} + \binom{n-1}{1}x + \binom{n-1}{2}x^2 + \binom{n-1}{3}x^3 + \cdots = (1+x)^{n-1}.$$

Taking $x = 1$ and $x = -1$ gives the relations

$$\binom{n-1}{0} + \binom{n-1}{1} + \binom{n-1}{2} + \binom{n-1}{3} + \cdots = 2^{n-1},$$
$$\binom{n-1}{0} - \binom{n-1}{1} + \binom{n-1}{2} - \binom{n-1}{3} + \cdots = 0,$$

respectively. Adding these and dividing by 2, we get

$$\binom{n-1}{0} + \binom{n-1}{2} + \binom{n-1}{4} + \cdots = \frac{2^{n-1}}{2} = 2^{n-2}.$$

Hence,

$$\binom{n}{1} + 3\binom{n}{3} + 5\binom{n}{5} + \cdots = \boxed{n2^{n-2}}$$

for $n \geq 2$.

Exercises for Section 12.3

12.3.1

(a) Expand the LHS:

$$\binom{\binom{n}{2}}{2} = \frac{\binom{n}{2}(\binom{n}{2} - 1)}{2}$$

$$= \frac{\frac{n(n-1)}{2}[\frac{n(n-1)}{2} - 1]}{2}$$

$$= \frac{n(n-1)[n(n-1) - 2]}{8}$$

$$= \frac{n(n-1)(n^2 - n - 2)}{8}$$

$$= \frac{n(n-1)(n+1)(n-2)}{8}$$

$$= 3 \cdot \frac{(n+1)n(n-1)(n-2)}{4!}$$

$$= 3\binom{n+1}{4}.$$

(b) Let $P_1, P_2, \ldots, P_n$ be n points in the plane. Then $\binom{n}{2}$ is the number of line segments formed by these n points when taken as endpoints, and $\binom{\binom{n}{2}}{2}$ is the number of pairs of line segments.

   Now, let Q be another point and choose a set of 4 points from the $n+1$ points $P_1, P_2, \ldots, P_n, Q$. Each such set of 4 points either contains Q or it does not contain Q. If the set contains Q, then list the three pairs of line segments formed by the other three points. For example, if the set is $\{P_1, P_2, P_3, Q\}$, then list

$$(\overline{P_1P_2}, \overline{P_1P_3}), \quad (\overline{P_1P_2}, \overline{P_2P_3}), \quad (\overline{P_1P_3}, \overline{P_2P_3}).$$

If the set does not contain Q, then list the three pairs of line segments formed by the four points, such that the line segments in each pair have no end-points in common. For example, if the set is (P_1, P_2, P_3, P_4), then list

$$(\overline{P_1P_2}, \overline{P_3P_4}), \quad (\overline{P_1P_3}, \overline{P_2P_4}), \quad (\overline{P_1P_4}, \overline{P_2P_3}).$$

   Thus, each quadruple of points generates three pairs of line segments. Furthermore, note that each pair of line segments appears exactly once: if the pair does not have an endpoint in common, then it will be listed as corresponding to the set of its 4 endpoints, and if the pair does have an endpoint in common, then it will be listed as corresponding to the set of its 3 endpoints plus Q. Therefore,

$$\binom{\binom{n}{2}}{2} = 3\binom{n+1}{4}.$$

12.3.2 Let π be a permutation of the numbers $1, 2, \ldots, n+1$, and let $f(\pi)$ denote the greatest integer k such that $\pi(i) = i$ for all $1 \le i \le k$. For example, if $n = 6$ and π is the permutation $(1, 2, 3, 4, 6, 7, 5)$, then $f(\pi) = 4$. Then for each $0 \le k \le n + 1$, we count the number of permutations π such that $f(\pi) = k$.

For $k = n + 1$, there is only one permutation π such that $f(\pi) = n + 1$, namely the permutation $(1, 2, \ldots, n+1)$, so assume that $1 \le k \le n$. If $f(\pi) = k$, then $\pi(i) = i$ for $1 \le i \le k$, and $\pi(k+1) \ne k+1$. Hence, $\pi(k+1)$ must be one of the values $k+2, k+3, \ldots, n+1$, for a total of $n - k$ possible values for $\pi(k+1)$. Once $\pi(k+1)$ has been determined, this leaves $n - k$ values that can be assigned to $\pi(k+2), \pi(k+3), \ldots, \pi(n+1)$ in any order, so the number of permutations π such that $f(\pi) = k$ is $(n-k) \cdot (n-k)!$.

Finally, for $k = 0$, we only require that $\pi(1) \ne 1$, so $\pi(1)$ must be one of the values $2, 3, \ldots, n+1$, for a total of n possible values for $\pi(1)$. Once $\pi(1)$ has been determined, this leaves n values that can be assigned to $\pi(2), \pi(3), \ldots, \pi(n+1)$ in any order, so the number of permutations π such that $f(\pi) = 1$ is $n \cdot n!$. Thus, the formula above works for $k = 0$ as well.

The total number of permutations of the numbers $1, 2, \ldots, n+1$ is $(n+1)!$, so summing over $0 \le k \le n + 1$, we get

$$
\begin{aligned}
f(0) + f(1) + \cdots + f(n) + f(n+1) &= (n+1)! \\
\Leftrightarrow \quad n \cdot n! + (n-1) \cdot (n-1)! + \cdots + 1 \cdot 1! + 1 &= (n+1)! \\
\Leftrightarrow \quad 1 \cdot 1! + 2 \cdot 2! + 3 \cdot 3! + \cdots + n \cdot n! &= (n+1)! - 1.
\end{aligned}
$$

12.3.3 *Method 1:* We notice that each term has the form $(17 - k)\binom{20}{k}$ for some value of k. Let's rewrite that in terms of things that we've seen in previous identities. We write:

$$
\begin{aligned}
\sum_{k=0}^{20} (17 - k)\binom{20}{k} &= 17\sum_{k=0}^{20}\binom{20}{k} - \sum_{k=0}^{20} k\binom{20}{k} \\
&= 17(2^{20}) - 20(2^{19}) \\
&= 14(2^{19}) = \boxed{7(2^{20})}.
\end{aligned}
$$

Method 2: Write

$$
S = 17\binom{20}{0} + 16\binom{20}{1} + 15\binom{20}{2} + \cdots + 0\binom{20}{17} + (-1)\binom{20}{18} + (-2)\binom{20}{19} + (-3)\binom{20}{20}.
$$

Using $\binom{20}{k} = \binom{20}{20-k}$, we can rewrite S as:

$$
S = (-3)\binom{20}{0} + (-2)\binom{20}{1} + (-1)\binom{20}{2} + \cdots + 14\binom{20}{17} + 15\binom{20}{18} + 16\binom{20}{19} + 17\binom{20}{20}.
$$

Then add the two equations together:

$$
\begin{aligned}
2S &= 14\binom{20}{0} + 14\binom{20}{1} + 14\binom{20}{2} + \cdots + 14\binom{20}{17} + 14\binom{20}{18} + 14\binom{20}{19} + 14\binom{20}{20} \\
&= 14\left(\binom{20}{0} + \binom{20}{1} + \binom{20}{2} + \cdots + \binom{20}{17} + \binom{20}{18} + \binom{20}{19} + \binom{20}{20}\right) \\
&= 14(2^{20}).
\end{aligned}
$$

So $S = 14(2^{19}) = \boxed{7(2^{20})}$.

12.3.4 Let's take a closer look at what happens when $m = 6$, $n = 8$, and $r = 10$. In this case, Vandermonde's identity states that

$$
\binom{6}{0}\binom{8}{10} + \binom{6}{1}\binom{8}{9} + \binom{6}{2}\binom{8}{8} + \cdots + \binom{6}{6}\binom{8}{4} + \binom{6}{7}\binom{8}{3} + \cdots + \binom{6}{10}\binom{8}{0} = \binom{14}{10}.
$$

The terms in the middle, from $\binom{6}{2}\binom{8}{8}$ to $\binom{6}{6}\binom{8}{4}$, make sense, but the terms on the outside contain binomial coefficients such as $\binom{8}{10}$ and $\binom{6}{10}$, where the number on the top is less than the number on the bottom. We need to make sure these terms make sense as well.

According to the proof, the number $\binom{8}{10}$ is the number of ways of choosing 10 people from a group of 8 women. This is impossible, so the only way to make sense of this binomial coefficient is to say $\binom{8}{10} = 0$. In fact, by convention, we say that $\binom{n}{k} = 0$ if $n < k$. Hence, $\binom{6}{10} = 0$ as well, and all the terms on the outside disappear, and the equation above becomes

$$\binom{6}{2}\binom{8}{8} + \binom{6}{3}\binom{8}{7} + \binom{6}{4}\binom{8}{6} + \binom{6}{5}\binom{8}{5} + \binom{6}{6}\binom{8}{4} = \binom{14}{10}.$$

But if all these terms disappear, then are there any committees we might be missing? In the above example, we want to form a committee of 10 people from 6 men and 8 women. Since there only 8 women, there must be at least 2 men. Similarly, since there are only 6 men, there must be at least 4 women. Hence, all the terms in the equation above do capture all possible committees. Thus, in general, the committee-forming argument still works when $r > m$ or $r > n$, and Vandermonde's identity still holds.

12.3.5

(a) If $a = 4$ and $b = 6$, then we can write

$$\frac{10 + 6 + 3 + 1}{15} = \frac{\binom{5}{2} + \binom{4}{2} + \binom{3}{2} + \binom{2}{2}}{\binom{6}{4}} = \frac{\binom{6}{3}}{\binom{6}{4}},$$

where the last step is the application of the Hockey Stick identity. Similarly, if $a = 4$ and $b = 7$, then we write

$$\frac{20 + 10 + 4 + 1}{35} = \frac{\binom{6}{3} + \binom{5}{3} + \binom{4}{3} + \binom{3}{3}}{\binom{7}{4}} = \frac{\binom{7}{4}}{\binom{7}{4}}.$$

(b) We rewrite each term of the sum over the common denominator $\binom{b}{a}$, as follows. For all $1 \leq k \leq a$, we have

$$\frac{a(a-1)(a-2)\cdots(a-(k-1))}{b(b-1)(b-2)\cdots(b-(k-1))} = \frac{\frac{a!}{(a-k)!}}{\frac{b!}{(b-k)!}}$$

$$= \frac{\frac{a!}{(a-k)!}}{\frac{b!}{a!(b-a)!} \cdot \frac{a!(b-a)!}{(b-k)!}}$$

$$= \frac{\frac{a!}{(a-k)!} \cdot \frac{(b-k)!}{a!(b-a)!}}{\frac{b!}{a!(b-a)!}}$$

$$= \frac{\frac{(b-k)!}{(b-a)!(a-k)!}}{\frac{b!}{a!(b-a)!}}$$

$$= \frac{\binom{b-k}{b-a}}{\binom{b}{a}}.$$

Therefore, the sum that we want to compute is:

$$\frac{a}{b} + \frac{a(a-1)}{b(b-1)} + \frac{a(a-1)(a-2)}{b(b-1)(b-2)} + \cdots + \frac{a!}{b(b-1)\cdots(b-a+1)} = \frac{\binom{b-1}{b-a}}{\binom{b}{a}} + \frac{\binom{b-2}{b-a}}{\binom{b}{a}} + \frac{\binom{b-3}{b-a}}{\binom{b}{a}} + \cdots + \frac{\binom{b-a}{b-a}}{\binom{b}{a}}$$

$$= \frac{\binom{b-1}{b-a} + \binom{b-2}{b-a} + \binom{b-3}{b-a} + \cdots + \binom{b-a}{b-a}}{\binom{b}{a}}.$$

By the Hockey Stick identity, the numerator of this is equal to $\binom{b}{b-a+1}$, and thus our sum is equal to

$$\frac{\binom{b}{b-a+1}}{\binom{b}{b-a}} = \frac{\frac{b!}{(b-a+1)!(a-1)!}}{\frac{b!}{(b-a)!a!}}$$

$$= \frac{(b-a)!a!}{(b-a+1)!(a-1)!}$$

$$= \frac{a}{b-a+1}.$$

Plugging in $a = 19$ and $b = 99$ gives the answer $\frac{19}{81}$, as before.

Review Problems

12.11 Since $\binom{n}{k} = \binom{n}{n-k}$,

$$\sum_{k=0}^{n}\binom{n}{k}\binom{m}{k} = \sum_{k=0}^{n}\binom{n}{n-k}\binom{m}{k}.$$

By Vandermonde's identity,

$$\sum_{k=0}^{n}\binom{n}{n-k}\binom{m}{k} = \boxed{\binom{m+n}{n}}.$$

12.12 Since $\binom{n}{k} = \binom{n}{n-k}$,

$$\sum_{k=1}^{n}\binom{n}{k}\binom{n}{k-1} = \sum_{k=1}^{n}\binom{n}{n-k}\binom{n}{k-1}.$$

The sum is a candidate for Vandermonde's identity, since the sum of the bottom numbers of the binomial coefficients is constant. We can see the application of the identity more clearly if we make the substitution $j = k - 1$:

$$\sum_{k=1}^{n}\binom{n}{n-k}\binom{n}{k-1} = \sum_{j=0}^{n-1}\binom{n}{n-(j+1)}\binom{n}{j}.$$

The $j = n$ term is missing from the sum, but note that $\binom{n}{n-(n+1)} = \binom{n}{-1} = 0$. So the $j = n$ term is 0, so we can extend the sum to $j = n$, and then apply Vandermonde's identity to give

$$\sum_{j=0}^{n}\binom{n}{n-(j+1)}\binom{n}{j} = \binom{2n}{n-1}.$$

12.13

(a) The LHS counts the number of ways to choose an r-person committee from a club of n people, and then choose one of the $n - r$ people not on the committee to be club president. The RHS counts the same thing, by first choosing one of the n club members to be club president, and then choosing the r-person committee from the remaining $n - 1$ members.

(b)   We expand the LHS:

$$(n-r)\binom{n}{r} = (n-r)\frac{n!}{r!(n-r)!}$$

$$= \frac{n!}{r!(n-r-1)!}$$

$$= n\frac{(n-1)!}{r!(n-1-r)!}$$

$$= n\binom{n-1}{r}.$$

12.14

(a)   We simply expand each term on the LHS:

$$\binom{n}{1} + 6\binom{n}{2} + 6\binom{n}{3} = n + \frac{6n(n-1)}{2} + \frac{6n(n-1)(n-2)}{6}$$

$$= n + 3n(n-1) + n(n-1)(n-2)$$

$$= n + 3n^2 - 3n + n^3 - 3n^2 + 2n = n^3.$$

(b)   The RHS counts the number of ordered triples (a, b, c), where $1 \le a, b, c \le n$ are positive integers. The LHS also counts those triples, by breaking them into three exclusive cases. The $\binom{n}{1}$ counts those triples in which all three numbers are the same, and the $(3!)\binom{n}{3}$ term counts those triples in which all three numbers are different. Finally, the $3 \times 2 \times \binom{n}{2}$ term counts those triples in which two of the numbers are the same and the third is different: there are $\binom{n}{2}$ choices for the two numbers, then 2 choices for which number appears twice and which appears once, then 3 choices for the slot in which the single number appears.

12.15   We can prove the identity algebraically:

$$\binom{q+2}{2}\binom{p}{0} + \binom{q+1}{1}\binom{p+1}{1} + \binom{q}{0}\binom{p+2}{2} = \frac{(q+2)(q+1)}{2} + (q+1)(p+1) + \frac{(p+2)(p+1)}{2}$$

$$= \frac{q^2 + 3q + 2 + 2pq + 2p + 2q + 2 + p^2 + 3p + 2}{2}$$

$$= \frac{p^2 + 2pq + q^2 + 5p + 5q + 6}{2}$$

$$= \frac{(p+q)^2 + 5(p+q) + 6}{2}$$

$$= \frac{(p+q+3)(p+q+2)}{2}$$

$$= \binom{p+q+3}{2}.$$

We can also prove the identity combinatorially, as follows. Let A be a set of $p + 2$ points in the plane, and let B be a set of $q + 2$ points, such that A and B have exactly one point in common, say X. Then $\#(A \cup B) = \#(A) + \#(B) - \#(A \cap B) = (p+2) + (q+2) - 1 = p + q + 3$, so the number of line segments whose end-points are in A or B is equal to $\binom{p+q+3}{2}$.

We can count the number of line segments in a different way. Every such line segment comes under one of the following exclusive categories:

*   Both end-points are in B.

- One end-point is in B and the other end-point is in A, and neither end-point is X.

- Both end-points are in A.

The set B consists of $q + 2$ points, so there are $\binom{q+2}{2}$ line segments with both end-points in B.

There are $q + 1$ points in B other than X, and $p + 1$ points in A other than X, so the number of line segments with one end-point in B and the other end-point in A, and neither end-point is X, is $\binom{p+1}{1}\binom{q+1}{1}$.

The set A consists of $p + 2$ points, so there are $\binom{p+2}{2}$ line segments with both end-points in A.

Finally, $\binom{p}{0} = \binom{q}{0} = 1$, so the total number of line segments is

$$\binom{q+2}{2}\binom{p}{0} + \binom{q+1}{1}\binom{p+1}{1} + \binom{q}{0}\binom{p+2}{2} = \binom{p+q+3}{2}.$$

12.16 Let S_n denote the given sum. We divide into the cases where n is odd and n is even. If n is odd, then $n = 2m + 1$ for some nonnegative integer m, and

$$S_n = \sum_{i=0}^{\lfloor n/2 \rfloor} \binom{n}{i} = \binom{2m+1}{0} + \binom{2m+1}{1} + \cdots + \binom{2m+1}{m}.$$

This looks like half of the elements in a binomial expansion. In fact, since $\binom{2m+1}{k} = \binom{2m+1}{2m+1-k}$,

$$2S_n = \binom{2m+1}{0} + \binom{2m+1}{1} + \cdots + \binom{2m+1}{m} + \binom{2m+1}{m} + \cdots + \binom{2m+1}{1} + \binom{2m+1}{0}$$

$$= \binom{2m+1}{0} + \binom{2m+1}{1} + \cdots + \binom{2m+1}{m} + \binom{2m+1}{m+1} + \cdots + \binom{2m+1}{2m} + \binom{2m+1}{2m+1}$$

$$= 2^{2m+1},$$

so $S_n = 2^{2m} = 2^{n-1}$.

Now if n is even, then $n = 2m$ for some nonnegative integer m, and

$$S_n = \sum_{i=0}^{\lfloor n/2 \rfloor} \binom{n}{i} = \binom{2m}{0} + \binom{2m}{1} + \cdots + \binom{2m}{m}.$$

By the same argument as above,

$$2S_n = \binom{2m}{0} + \binom{2m}{1} + \cdots + \binom{2m}{m} + \binom{2m}{m} + \cdots + \binom{2m}{1} + \binom{2m}{0}$$

$$= \left[\binom{2m}{0} + \binom{2m}{1} + \cdots + \binom{2m}{m} + \cdots + \binom{2m}{2m-1} + \binom{2m}{2m}\right] + \binom{2m}{m}$$

$$= 2^{2m} + \binom{2m}{m},$$

so $S_n = 2^{2m-1} + \frac{1}{2}\binom{2m}{m} = 2^{n-1} + \frac{1}{2}\binom{n}{n/2}$.

To summarize,

$$\sum_{i=0}^{\lfloor n/2 \rfloor} \binom{n}{i} = \begin{cases} 2^{n-1} & \text{if } n \text{ is odd,} \\ 2^{n-1} + \frac{1}{2}\binom{n}{n/2} & \text{if } n \text{ is even.} \end{cases}$$

Challenge Problems

12.17 To get started on the problem, let's look at a small case, say with three numbers a, b, and c. Then the geometric means generated by these three numbers are

$$a, \quad b, \quad c, \quad \sqrt{ab} = a^{1/2}b^{1/2}, \quad \sqrt{ac} = a^{1/2}c^{1/2}, \quad \sqrt{bc} = b^{1/2}c^{1/2}, \quad \sqrt[3]{abc} = a^{1/3}b^{1/3}c^{1/3},$$

and the geometric mean of these geometric means is

$$(a \cdot b \cdot c \cdot a^{1/2}b^{1/2} \cdot a^{1/2}c^{1/2} \cdot b^{1/2}c^{1/2} \cdot a^{1/3}b^{1/3}c^{1/3})^{1/7} = (a^{7/3}b^{7/3}c^{7/3})^{1/7}$$
$$= a^{1/3}b^{1/3}c^{1/3}$$
$$= \sqrt[3]{abc}.$$

Thus, the result is true for three numbers.

Now, we are set to prove the general result. Let k be a positive integer, where $1 \le k \le n$. Then the $\binom{n}{k}$ geometric means involving k numbers are

$$(a_1 a_2 \cdots a_{k-1} a_k)^{1/k}, \quad (a_1 a_2 \cdots a_{k-1} a_{k+1})^{1/k}, \quad \ldots, \quad (a_{n-k+1} a_{n-k+2} \cdots a_{n-1} a_n)^{1/k}.$$

To compute the product of these $\binom{n}{k}$ numbers, we first determine how many times each number a_i appears among them. For example, the number a_1 appears in $\binom{n-1}{k-1}$ of these $\binom{n}{k}$ geometric means, because once we have chosen a_1, there are $k-1$ numbers left to choose from the remaining $n-1$ numbers. By symmetry, all of the a_i also appear $\binom{n-1}{k-1}$ times. Therefore, the product of these $\binom{n}{k}$ geometric means is

$$(a_1^{\binom{n-1}{k-1}} a_2^{\binom{n-1}{k-1}} \cdots a_n^{\binom{n-1}{k-1}})^{1/k}.$$

Multiplying over $1 \le k \le n$, we find that the product of all $2^n - 1$ geometric means is

$$\prod_{k=1}^{n} (a_1^{\binom{n-1}{k-1}} a_2^{\binom{n-1}{k-1}} \cdots a_n^{\binom{n-1}{k-1}})^{1/k}.$$

(There are $2^n - 1$ geometric means because there are 2^n subsets of $\{a_1, a_2, \ldots, a_n\}$, but we must exclude the empty set.)

The exponent of each number a_i in this product is

$$\sum_{k=1}^{n} \frac{1}{k}\binom{n-1}{k-1},$$

so the next step is to find this sum explicitly. Note that

$$\frac{1}{k}\binom{n-1}{k-1} = \frac{1}{k} \cdot \frac{(n-1)!}{(k-1)!(n-k)!} = \frac{(n-1)!}{k!(n-k)!} = \frac{1}{n} \cdot \frac{n!}{k!(n-k)!} = \frac{1}{n}\binom{n}{k}.$$

Hence,

$$\sum_{k=1}^{n} \frac{1}{k}\binom{n-1}{k-1} = \sum_{k=1}^{n} \frac{1}{n}\binom{n}{k}$$

$$= \frac{1}{n}\sum_{k=1}^{n} \binom{n}{k}$$

$$= \frac{1}{n}\left[\binom{n}{1} + \binom{n}{2} + \cdots + \binom{n}{n}\right]$$

$$= \frac{1}{n}\left[\binom{n}{0} + \binom{n}{1} + \binom{n}{2} + \cdots + \binom{n}{n} - 1\right]$$

$$= \frac{1}{n}(2^n - 1).$$

Therefore, the product of all $2^n - 1$ geometric means is

$$\prod_{k=1}^{n}(a_1^{\binom{n-1}{k-1}} a_2^{\binom{n-1}{k-1}} \cdots a_n^{\binom{n-1}{k-1}})^{1/k} = a_1^{(2^n-1)/n} a_2^{(2^n-1)/n} \cdots a_n^{(2^n-1)/n},$$

which implies that the geometric mean of all $2^n - 1$ geometric means is

$$(a_1^{(2^n-1)/n} a_2^{(2^n-1)/n} \cdots a_n^{(2^n-1)/n})^{1/(2^n-1)} = a_1^{1/n} a_2^{1/n} \cdots a_n^{1/n} = \sqrt[n]{a_1 a_2 \cdots a_n},$$

which is the geometric mean of the original n numbers, as desired.

12.18 First, observe that we can let the sum go from $k = 1$ to $n/2$, because the summand for $k = 0$ is 0. As derived in previous problems, $2k\binom{n}{2k} = n\binom{n-1}{2k-1}$, so the given sum is equal to

$$\sum_{k=1}^{n}\left[2^{2k} \cdot n\binom{n-1}{2k-1}\right] = n\sum_{k=1}^{n/2} 2^{2k}\binom{n-1}{2k-1}$$

$$= n\left[2^2\binom{n-1}{1} + 2^4\binom{n-1}{3} + \cdots + 2^n\binom{n-1}{n-1}\right].$$

By the Binomial Theorem,

$$\binom{n-1}{0} + \binom{n-1}{1}x + \binom{n-1}{2}x^2 + \binom{n-1}{3}x^3 + \cdots = (1+x)^{n-1}$$

for all real numbers x. Taking $x = 2$ and $x = -2$, we get

$$\binom{n-1}{0} + 2\binom{n-1}{1} + 2^2\binom{n-1}{2} + 2^3\binom{n-1}{3} + \cdots = 3^{n-1},$$

$$\binom{n-1}{0} - 2\binom{n-1}{1} + 2^2\binom{n-1}{2} - 2^3\binom{n-1}{3} + \cdots = (-1)^{n-1} = -1,$$

respectively. Subtracting the second equation from the first, we get

$$2^2\binom{n-1}{1} + 2^4\binom{n-1}{3} + \cdots = 3^{n-1} + 1.$$

Hence,

$$\sum_{k=0}^{n/2}\left[2^{2k} \cdot 2k\binom{n}{2k}\right] = n\sum_{k=1}^{n/2} 2^{2k}\binom{n-1}{2k-1}$$

$$= \boxed{n(3^{n-1} + 1)}.$$

12.19 First, we write the sum out:

$$\sum_{k=0}^{49}(-1)^k\binom{99}{2k} = \binom{99}{0} - \binom{99}{2} + \binom{99}{4} - \cdots - \binom{99}{98}.$$

By the Binomial Theorem,

$$\binom{99}{0} + \binom{99}{1}x + \binom{99}{2}x^2 + \binom{99}{3}x^3 + \cdots = (1+x)^{99}$$

for all x. To mimic the given sum, we want to take a value of x such that $x^2 = -1$. The values that satisfy this equation are the complex numbers i and $-i$. Substituting these values, we get

$$\binom{99}{0} + i\binom{99}{1} - \binom{99}{2} - i\binom{99}{3}x^3 + \cdots = (1+i)^{99},$$

$$\binom{99}{0} - i\binom{99}{1} - \binom{99}{2} + i\binom{99}{3}x^3 + \cdots = (1-i)^{99},$$

respectively. Adding these and dividing by 2, we get

$$\binom{99}{0} - \binom{99}{2} + \binom{99}{4} - \cdots = \frac{(1+i)^{99} + (1-i)^{99}}{2}.$$

Hence, the problem is finding $(1+i)^{99}$ and $(1-i)^{99}$.

Note that $(1+i)^2 = 1 + 2i - 1 = 2i$. Hence,

$$\begin{aligned}
(1+i)^{99} &= (1+i)^{98} \cdot (1+i) \\
&= [(1+i)^2]^{49} \cdot (1+i) \\
&= (2i)^{49} \cdot (1+i) \\
&= 2^{49} \cdot i^{49} \cdot (1+i) \\
&= 2^{49} \cdot i \cdot (1+i) \\
&= -2^{49} + 2^{49}i.
\end{aligned}$$

Similarly, $(1-i)^2 = 1 - 2i - 1 = -2i$. Hence,

$$\begin{aligned}
(1-i)^{99} &= (1-i)^{98} \cdot (1-i) \\
&= [(1-i)^2]^{49} \cdot (1-i) \\
&= (-2i)^{49} \cdot (1-i) \\
&= -2^{49} \cdot i^{49} \cdot (1-i) \\
&= -2^{49} \cdot i \cdot (1-i) \\
&= -2^{49} - 2^{49}i.
\end{aligned}$$

Therefore,

$$\begin{aligned}
\binom{99}{0} - \binom{99}{2} + \binom{99}{4} - \cdots &= \frac{(1+i)^{99} + (1-i)^{99}}{2} \\
&= \frac{-2^{49} + 2^{49}i - 2^{49} - 2^{49}i}{2} \\
&= \boxed{-2^{49}}.
\end{aligned}$$

12.20 Consider a dance class that has n men, n women, and one teacher. If only n people show up for a certain class (and the teacher might not!), then there are a total of $\binom{2n+1}{n}$ combinations of people that can be present.

We can also count the number of combinations as follows: Assemble the original n men and n women into n couples. Then among the n people who show up, there will be some people whose partners are also present and some people whose partners are absent. We count the number of combinations where there are i people whose partners are absent, for $0 \le i \le n$.

First, we choose the couples containing the i people with missing partners. There are a total of n couples, so we can choose these i couples in $\binom{n}{i}$ ways. Next, we want to choose one person from each couple to show up. This can be done in 2^i ways, so there are $2^i\binom{n}{i}$ ways to choose the i people with absent partners.

We now choose the couples who do show up. Let k be the number of couples who do show up. If the teacher shows up, then $2k + i + 1 = n$, so $k = (n - i - 1)/2$. If the teacher doesn't show up, then $2k + i = n$, so $k = (n - i)/2$. Either way, $k = \lfloor (n - i)/2 \rfloor$.

Above, we have already selected i people whose partners are absent, leaving $n - i$ potential couples to show up. Then the number of ways to choose the k couples who show up is $\binom{n-i}{k} = \binom{n-i}{\lfloor(n-i)/2\rfloor}$. Summing over $0 \le i \le n$, we get

$$\sum_{i=0}^{n} 2^i \binom{n}{i}\binom{n-i}{\lfloor (n-i)/2\rfloor} = \binom{2n+1}{n}.$$

12.21 We want the sum of every third coefficient of $(1 + x)^3$. Let $\omega = \frac{-1+\sqrt{3}i}{2}$ be a primitive cube root of unity, so that $\omega^3 = 1$. Note that $1 + \omega + \omega^2 = 0$, and more generally $1 + \omega^k + \omega^{2k} = 0$ for any k that is not a multiple of 3.

Then we apply the Binomial Theorem:

$$(1+1)^n = \binom{n}{0} + \binom{n}{1} + \binom{n}{2} + \cdots + \binom{n}{n},$$

$$(1+\omega)^n = \binom{n}{0} + \binom{n}{1}\omega + \binom{n}{2}\omega^2 + \cdots + \binom{n}{n}\omega^n,$$

$$(1+\omega^2)^n = \binom{n}{0} + \binom{n}{1}\omega^2 + \binom{n}{2}\omega^4 + \cdots + \binom{n}{n}\omega^{2n},$$

and if we add these together, all of the terms on the RHS with coefficients of the form $\binom{n}{k}$, where k is not a multiple of 3, will cancel out. Thus we have:

$$2^n + (1+\omega)^n + (1+\omega^2)^n = 3\left(\binom{n}{0} + \binom{n}{3} + \binom{n}{6} + \cdots\right).$$

To simplify the LHS of the last expression, note that $1 + \omega = -\omega^2$ and $1 + \omega^2 = -\omega$, therefore the LHS is equal to $2^n + (-\omega)^n + (-\omega^2)^n = 2^n + (-1)^n(\omega^n + \omega^{2n})$. We further note that $\omega^n + \omega^{2n} = -1$ if n is not a multiple of 3, and $\omega^n + \omega^{2n} = 2$ if n is a multiple of 3.

Therefore, we conclude that:

$$\binom{n}{0} + \binom{n}{3} + \binom{n}{6} + \cdots = \begin{cases} \dfrac{2^n + (-1)^{n+1}}{3} & \text{if } n \text{ is not a multiple of 3} \\ \dfrac{2^n + 2(-1)^n}{3} & \text{if } n \text{ is a multiple of 3} \end{cases}$$

12.22 For all parts, we'll define $S_n = \{1, 2, \ldots, n\}$, to make the solutions a bit more concise.

(a) There is only 1 way to partition S_n into 1 non-empty subset: that 1 subset has to be S_n itself. So $\left\{ {n \atop 1} \right\} = \boxed{1}$. Also, there is only 1 way to partition S_n into n non-empty disjoint subsets: each subset in the partition must have 1 element, so the only partition is $\{1\}, \{2\}, \dots, \{n\}$. Therefore, $\left\{ {n \atop n} \right\} = \boxed{1}$.

(b) To partition S_n into 2 non-empty disjoint subsets, we want $S_n = A \cup B$ with A, B nonempty and $A \cap B = \emptyset$. Each element of S_n can be placed into either A or B, so there are 2 choices for each element of S_n, and thus 2^n overall arrangements. We must then divide by 2, because we don't care about the order of A and B, and we must subtract 1, because $S_n, \emptyset$ is not a valid partition (both sets must be nonempty). Therefore, $\left\{ {n \atop 2} \right\} = \boxed{2^{n-1} - 1}$.

To partition S_n into $n - 1$ non-empty disjoint subsets, we must have 1 subset with 2 elements, and the rest with 1 element each. So we simply must choose which 2 elements of S_n are going to be in the 2-element subset, and therefore $\left\{ {n \atop n-1} \right\} = \boxed{\binom{n}{2}}$.

(c) The RHS counts partitions of S_{n+1} into k disjoint subsets. We will also count these partitions by the LHS, in two cases. If the subset $\{n + 1\}$ appears as a member of the partition, then the rest of the subsets form a valid partition of S_n with $k - 1$ sets, and there are $\left\{ {n \atop k-1} \right\}$ of these. Otherwise, $n + 1$ appears as an element in a larger subset of the partition. If we delete this element, we get a partition of S_n into k subsets. The element $n + 1$ could have been in any of the k subsets of this partition, so there are $k \left\{ {n \atop k} \right\}$ partitions of S_{n+1} with $n + 1$ in a subset of more than 1 element. Adding the two cases together establishes the identity.

(d) Multiply the desired identity by $k!$, so that we are trying to prove

$$k! \left\{ {n \atop k} \right\} = \sum_{j=0}^{k} (-1)^j \binom{k}{j} (k - j)^n.$$

The LHS counts the number of *ordered* partitions of S_n into k non-empty disjoint subsets. We will show that the RHS counts the same thing, using PIE, as follows. Write out the RHS without the summation notation, so that it is easier to see what's going on:

$$k^n - \binom{k}{1}(k - 1)^n + \binom{k}{2}(k - 2)^n - \cdots.$$

Imagine that there are k subsets (in order), and place each element of S_n into one of the subsets. The number of ways to do this is the first term, k^n. However, this may leave some of the subsets empty. The ith subset is empty if all of the elements are placed into one of the other $k - 1$ subsets, so there are $(k - 1)^n$ ways to do this for all of the elements of S_n, and there are $\binom{k}{1}$ ways to choose a subset to be left empty. This gives the second term. But this over-subtracts those arrangements in which two subsets are empty. There are $\binom{k}{2}$ choices of a pair of subsets, and $(k - 2)^n$ ways to place the n elements into the other $k - 2$ subsets, which gives the third term. But this overcounts the arrangements in which 3 subsets of empty... and so on.

Therefore, this expression is just the PIE expression for the number of ways to place the n elements into k distinguishable subsets, so that no subset is left empty. As discussed above, this is the same as $k! \left\{ {n \atop k} \right\}$, so we have established the formula.

CHAPTER 13

Events With States

Exercises for Section 13.2

13.2.1 There are two intermediate states—we'll call S the state of standing on a vertex that is one move away from A, and we'll call T the state of standing on a vertex that is one move away from B. Then we have the following state diagram, where the numbers indicate the number of moves from one state to the next:

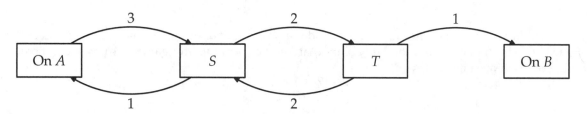

We have three different ways that we can get to B in 5 moves or less; for each of these ways, we multiply the number of choices in each step to get the total number of possibilities.

We can go directly to B via $ASTB$. This way has $3 \times 2 \times 1 = 6$ possibilities.

We can go to B via $ASASTB$. This way has $3 \times 1 \times 3 \times 2 \times 1 = 18$ possibilities.

We can go to B via $ASTSTB$. This way has $3 \times 2 \times 2 \times 2 \times 1 = 24$ possibilities.

Therefore, there are $6 + 18 + 24 = \boxed{48}$ paths to B in 5 steps or less.

13.2.2 Label the vertices of the cube A through H, as shown, and let the bug start at vertex A. From A, the bug can move to one of three vertices, and then from this second vertex, the bug can move to one of two vertices. Without loss of generality, assume that the bug goes from A to B to C. (We multiply the answer at the end by $3 \cdot 2 = 6$ to account for this assumption.) From C, the bug can go to either D or G.

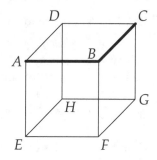

If the bug goes to D, then it must proceed to H, and then traverse around the bottom face in one of two directions. If the bug goes to G, then the only way the bug can visit every vertex is by passing through the vertices F, E, H, and D, in that order. Hence, the total number of paths (starting at A) that visit every vertex is $6 \cdot (2 + 1) = 18$.

Since there are three possible choices at each vertex, the total number of paths (starting at A) is 3^7. Therefore, the probability that the bug visits every vertex is $\dfrac{18}{3^7} = \boxed{\dfrac{2}{243}}$.

13.2.3 We set up a 4×4 state diagram, as we did in Problem 13.1:

Yankees win

Each step to the right corresponds to a win by the Red Sox and each step upwards corresponds to a win by the Yankees. For example, to compute the probability of reaching state (2,3) (which denotes the Red Sox winning 2 games and the Yankees winning 3 games), we look to the two possible previous states, namely states (1,3) and (2,2).

The probability of reaching state (1,3) is 17/36, and the probability of reaching state (2,2) is 2/9. In both states, four games have been played, and the probability that Red Sox win the fifth game is $4/6 = 2/3$. Therefore, the probability of reaching state (2,3) is

$$\frac{2}{3} \cdot \frac{17}{36} + \frac{1}{3} \cdot \frac{2}{9} = \frac{7}{18}.$$

The probability that the Red Sox win the series is the sum of the probabilities of the "Red Sox win" states, which is:

$$0 + \frac{1}{54} + \frac{85}{648} + \frac{227}{648} = \frac{324}{648} = \boxed{\frac{1}{2}}.$$

Seeing such a nice answer, we may wonder if there is a simpler solution. It turns out that there is a very clever solution. Suppose that the series is always played out to seven games, even if one of the teams wins four games in the interim. The probability that the Red Sox win game n is $(n-1)/6$, but the probability that the Yankees win game $8-n$ is $1 - (8-n-1)/6 = (6-8+n+1)/6 = (n-1)/6$. Hence, the series of seven games is symmetric with respect to both the Red Sox and Yankees, which means that both have a probability of 1/2 of winning the series.

13.2.4 We call a sequence of ants

$$A_1 \rightarrow A_2 \rightarrow A_3 \rightarrow \cdots \rightarrow A_d \rightarrow A_1$$

a *cycle*, where ant A_1 moves to A_2's spot, ant A_2 moves to A_3's spot, and so on, finishing with ant A_d moving to ant A_1's spot. The positive integer d is called the *length* of the cycle. (In particular, a cycle of length 2 is just two ants switching places.) If no two ants arrive at the same vertex, then the movement of the ants can be decomposed into one or more cycles, and we have the following cases.

Case 1 Two cycles of length 3.

A cycle of length 3 corresponds to a triangle, which must be a face of the octahedron. There are 8 faces, and once a face has been chosen, the other three vertices must form the other cycle of length 3. Note that this counts each pair of faces twice, so the number of ways of choosing a pair of faces is $8/2 = 4$. Then, each cycle of length 3 has two possible directions, so the number of permutations in this case is $4 \cdot 2 \cdot 2 = 16$.

Case 2 One cycle of length 4 and one cycle of length 2.

A cycle of length 2 corresponds to an edge of the octahedron, of which there are 12. Once the edge has been chosen, the other four vertices must form the cycle of length 4. The edges of this cycle are uniquely determined, but there are two possible directions, so the number of permutations in this case is $12 \cdot 2 = 24$.

Case 3 Three cycles of length 2.

As in Case 2, a cycle of length 2 corresponds to an edge of the octahedron, of which there are 12. We begin by choosing one of the 12 edges. This leaves four vertices, and there are two ways to divide them among two more edges. However, this counts each triple of cycles of length 2 three times, so the number of permutations in this case is $12 \cdot 2/3 = 8$.

Case 4 One cycle of length 6.

For clarity, we label the vertices:

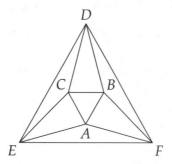

Consider a cycle of length 6 that begins with vertex A. One of the other five vertices must be the fourth vertex in this cycle. For example, we count that there are four cycles of length 6 that have B as the fourth vertex:

$$A \to C \to D \to B \to F \to E \to A,$$
$$A \to E \to C \to B \to D \to F \to A,$$
$$A \to E \to F \to B \to D \to C \to A,$$
$$A \to F \to D \to B \to C \to E \to A.$$

By symmetry, there also four cycles of length 6 that have C, E, and F as the fourth vertex. (The situation for these vertices is symmetric because they are all adjacent to A.)

We are left with counting the number of cycles of length 6 where the fourth vertex is D. The first half of this cycle must be of the form

$$A \to X \to Y \to D.$$

There are four vertices from which to choose X, and then a further two vertices from which to choose Y. Then the two vertices for the second half of the cycle are uniquely determined, but there are two ways to order them, so there are $4 \cdot 2 \cdot 2 = 16$ cycles of length 6 in which the fourth vertex is D. The number of permutations in this case is $4 \cdot 4 + 16 = 32$.

Hence, the total number of ways the ants can move so that no two ants arrive at the same vertex is $16 + 24 + 8 + 32 = 80$. Each ant has four possible vertices it can move to, so the total number of ways the ants can move is $4^6 = 4096$. Therefore, the probability that no two ants arrive at the same vertex is $80/4096 = \boxed{5/256}$.

Exercises for Section 13.3

13.3.1   Let p be the probability that Carol wins. Then for Carol to even get to her first roll, Alice must roll a number other than ⚁, and then Bob must roll a number other than ⚁. The probability of this occurring is $5/6 \cdot 5/6 = 25/36$. Then Carol wins if she rolls a ⚁, and the probability of this occurring is $1/6$. Otherwise, she does not roll a ⚁, and we are back to Alice rolling. Hence,

$$p = \frac{25}{36}\left(\frac{1}{6} + \frac{5}{6}p\right) \quad \Rightarrow \quad p = \boxed{\frac{25}{91}}.$$

13.3.2   Rather than one player taking all his swings and then the other player taking all his swings, we imagine that the players are alternating swings.

(a)   There are 3 possibilities for the result after each player has taken 1 swing.

- Doug could hit a home run and Ryan could strike out, in which case Doug wins. This occurs with probability $\frac{1}{6}$.

- Doug could hit a home run but Ryan could too, in which case we would be right back where we started (they'd be tied with 1 home run apiece, and they'd each get to swing again). This occurs with probability $\frac{1}{6}$.

- Doug could strike out, in which case he doesn't win (regardless of what Ryan does). This occurs with probability $\frac{2}{3}$.

If we let p denote the probability that Doug wins, then we have that $p = \frac{1}{6} + \frac{1}{6}p$. Solving for p gives us the answer $p = \boxed{\frac{1}{5}}$.

(b)   Again, there are 3 possibilities for the result after each player has taken 1 swing.

- They could both strike out, in which case they tie. This occurs with probability $\frac{1}{3}$.

- They could both hit a home run, in which case we get back to where we started (they'd be tied with 1 home run apiece, and they'd each get to swing again). This occurs with probability $\frac{1}{6}$.

- One of them hits a home run and the other one strikes out, and they don't finish tied.

Let q denote the probability that they finish tied. Then $q = \frac{1}{3} + \frac{1}{6}q$. Solving for q gives us the answer $q = \boxed{\frac{2}{5}}$.

13.3.3   Let μ be the expected number of points necessary. If Homer wins two consecutive points, then we will need 2 points for someone to win the game, and the same is true if Marge wins two consecutive points. This occurs with probability $\frac{9}{25} + \frac{4}{25} = \frac{13}{25}$. Otherwise, they each win a point, and we go back to deuce, and we will expect to need $2 + \mu$ points for someone to win the game. This occurs with probability $\frac{12}{25}$. Therefore, we have the equation

$$\mu = 2\left(\frac{13}{25}\right) + (2 + \mu)\left(\frac{12}{25}\right) = 2 + \frac{12}{25}\mu.$$

Solving gives $\mu = \boxed{\frac{50}{13}}$.

13.3.4   Let H and T denote a head and a tail, respectively, so a sequence of flips corresponds to a sequence of H's and T's. Then as the coin is flipped and the sequence of H's and T's is generated, the part that we are interested in is the current contiguous block of letters, whether it is a contiguous block of H's or a contiguous block of T's.

For example, suppose the sequence of flips begins THHTHHH. Then the significant part of this sequence consists of the last three H's. However, if the next flip is a T, then the current contiguous block would reset to a single T. With this in mind, we generate the following state diagram, where each state represents the current contiguous block of letters. Note that the process ends when either of the states HHHHH or TT is reached.

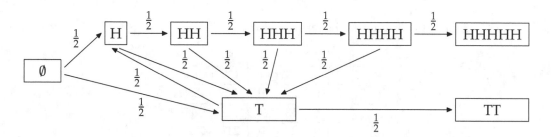

We can considerably simplify this diagram by consolidating the four intermediate "heads" states on the top row of the above diagram. Specifically, we consider our intermediate states to be series of flips that end in either T or HHHH. This produces the state diagram below:

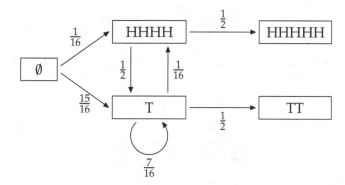

Note that if we are at state T, and we flip between 1 and 3 heads followed by a tail, we end up back in state T.

Let x be the probability of ending at HHHHH starting at state HHHH, and let y be the probability of ending at HHHHH starting at state T. Then we have the system of equations

$$x = \frac{1}{2} + \frac{1}{2}y,$$
$$y = \frac{1}{16}x + \frac{7}{16}y.$$

Solving for x and y, we get $x = 9/17$ and $y = 1/17$. Therefore, starting at state $\emptyset$, the probability that a run of 5 heads is encountered before a run of 2 tails is

$$\frac{1}{16}x + \frac{15}{16}y = \frac{24}{(16)(17)} = \boxed{\frac{3}{34}}.$$

13.3.5 Let p be the probability that in any individual game the person who goes first wins. The first player wins if the first flip is a head, which occurs with probability 1/2. Otherwise, the flip is a tail, and then it is the second player's turn, whose probability of losing is $1 - p$. Hence,

$$p = \frac{1}{2} + \frac{1}{2}(1 - p) \quad \Rightarrow \quad p = \frac{2}{3}.$$

Let a_n and b_n denote the probabilities that Alfred and Bonnie win the nth game, respectively. Since Alfred goes first in the first game, $a_1 = 2/3$ and $b_1 = 1/3$. For all $n \geq 2$, we have the recurrence relation

$$a_n = \frac{1}{3}a_{n-1} + \frac{2}{3}b_{n-1}.$$

Similarly,

$$b_n = \frac{2}{3}a_{n-1} + \frac{1}{3}b_{n-1}.$$

We can use these relations to generate all the terms up to b_6:

n	1	2	3	4	5	6
a_n	$\frac{2}{3}$	$\frac{4}{9}$	$\frac{14}{27}$	$\frac{40}{81}$	$\frac{122}{243}$	$\frac{364}{729}$
b_n	$\frac{1}{3}$	$\frac{5}{9}$	$\frac{13}{27}$	$\frac{41}{81}$	$\frac{121}{243}$	$\frac{365}{729}$

Hence, the probability that Alfred wins the sixth game is $\boxed{364/729}$.

We could have reached the answer more quickly by observing that

$$a_n - b_n = \left(\frac{1}{3}a_{n-1} + \frac{2}{3}b_{n-1}\right) - \left(\frac{2}{3}a_{n-1} + \frac{1}{3}b_{n-1}\right) = -\frac{1}{3}(a_{n-1} - b_{n-1})$$

for all $n \geq 2$, and $a_1 - b_1 = 1/3$. Hence, $a_n - b_n = -(-1/3)^n$ for all $n \geq 1$. But a_n and b_n are complementary probabilities, so $a_n + b_n = 1$. Therefore,

$$a_n = \frac{1 - (-1/3)^n}{2}.$$

In particular,

$$a_6 = \frac{1 - (-1/3)^6}{2} = \frac{364}{729}.$$

Exercises for Section 13.4

13.4.1   In all of these parts, we must show that, for every winning position, there exists a move that yields a losing position (or wins the game immediately), and that, for every losing position, all moves yield a winning position.

(a)   The losing positions are the multiples of 3. If the number of chips is 1 or 2 more than a multiple of 3, then the player can always take 1 or 2 chips, respectively, to move to a multiple of 3 (or to win the game if there are only 1 or 2 chips left). On the other hand, if the number of chips is a multiple of 3, then removing 1 or 2 chips will leave a non-multiple of 3, which is a winning position.

(b)   The losing positions are the multiples of 7. If the number of chips is between 1 and 6 more than a multiple of 7, then taking that "extra" number of chips will leave a multiple of 7 (or win the game if there are fewer than 7 chips left). If the number of chips is a multiple of 7, then removing any number of chips between 1 and 6 (inclusive) will leave a non-multiple of 7.

(c)   Experimenting with low numbers of chips will give the following:

Chips	1	2	3	4	5	6	7	8	9	10
Win/Lose	W	L	W	W	L	W	L	W	W	L

This suggests that positions that are 1, 3 or 4 (modulo 5) are winning positions, and positions that are 0 or 2 (modulo 5) are losing positions. Indeed, this is the case, as we see in the following chart:

Number of chips modulo 5	Move(s)
0 (losing)	Taking 1 chip leaves the winning position 4 mod 5
	Taking 4 chips leaves the winning position 1 mod 5
1 (winning)	Taking 1 chip leaves the losing position 0 mod 5
2 (losing)	Taking 1 chip leaves the winning position 1 mod 5
	Taking 4 chips leaves the winning position 3 mod 5
3 (winning)	Taking 1 chip leaves the losing position 2 mod 5
4 (winning)	Taking 4 chips leaves the losing position 0 mod 5

As we see from the chart, all moves from losing positions lead to winning positions, and there exists a move from every winning position to a losing position.

(d) This is actually the same as part (a); the losing positions are the multiples of 3. If the stack size is not a multiple of 3, then the player can take 1 or 2 chips to create a multiple of 3. On the other hand, if the stack size is a multiple of 3, then removing any power of 2 will create a stack size that is not a multiple of 3.

(e) The losing positions are any odd number (more than 1) of chips. Since all divisors of odd numbers are odd, a player with an odd stack will be forced to remove an odd number of chips, leaving an even stack size. From even-sized stacks, simply removing 1 chip will leave an odd-sized losing position (unless there are only 2 chips, in which case removing the 2 chips will win the game).

13.4.2 We work backwards from 1000. Note that $1000/9 = 111\frac{1}{9}$, so any integer greater than or equal to 112 is a winning position, since there exists a multiple of any of these that is at least 1000. (Throughout our solution, "multiple" means a multiple by 2 through 9.) Thus, any integer between 56 and 111 (inclusive) is losing, because all multiples of these integers are at least 112. Continuing backwards, any integer between 7 and 55 (inclusive) is winning, because for each there exists a multiple between 56 and 111. Then, the integers 4,5,6 are losing, because all multiples fall between 7 and 55. So 1 is winning, because Larry on his first turn can write 4 (or 5, or 6), forcing Sean to lose. Thus $\boxed{\text{Larry}}$ should win.

13.4.3 The immediate losing position is two piles of size 1; this is the only position in which a move is impossible. Therefore, any position with either pile of size 2 is winning: the player can remove the other pile and split the size-2 pile into two piles of size 1.

More generally, the losing positions are those with two piles each of odd size. The player is forced to split an odd pile, leaving an odd pile and an even pile. The other player can then remove the odd pile and split the even pile into two odd piles, producing a new losing position for the first player. (If the game starts with two even piles, simply remove one and split the other into two odd piles.) So the winning positions are those in which $\boxed{\text{at least one pile is even}}$.

13.4.4 We know that two equal piles is losing, and that three piles of sizes $(1, n, n+1)$ is losing for n even. We will show that, given any move by the first player, the second player can always leave one of these positions for the first player. This will show that the initial position of $(2, 4, 6)$ is losing.

If the first player takes all the chips from any pile, the second player can always then create two equal piles. So we will only list first-player moves that leave three piles. These moves, and the second player's responses, are shown in the table to the right.

As we see, every first-player move has a response that leaves a losing position. Therefore, the $\boxed{\text{second player}}$ should win.

Move	Response
(1,4,6)	(1,4,5)
(2,3,6)	(2,3,1)
(2,2,6)	(2,2,0)
(2,1,6)	(2,1,3)
(2,4,5)	(1,4,5)
(2,4,4)	(0,4,4)
(2,4,3)	(2,1,3)
(2,4,2)	(2,0,2)
(2,4,1)	(2,3,1)

13.4.5 The $\boxed{\text{first player}}$ can win by drawing a diagonal between two opposite vertices (that is, vertices that are 50 edges apart). This splits the 100-gon into two halves, and the first player can simply copy any move that the second player makes, but in the opposite half of the polygon. This ensures that the first player will always be able to move.

13.4.6

(a) The ┃first player┃ can win by removing 4 chips from each pile, leaving $(1,2)$. If the second player removes an entire pile, then the first player wins by removing the other pile; the only other possible move is to remove 1 chip from the larger pile, and then the first player wins by removing 1 chip from both piles.

(b) The smallest losing position is the $(1,2)$ position described above. Any other position of the form $(1,n)$ or $(2,n)$ is winning, by leaving the $(1,2)$ position for one's opponent.

We now look for losing positions with 3 chips. $(3,1)$, $(3,2)$ are winning as described above, and $(3,3)$ is an immediate win (just take 3 chips from both piles). $(3,4)$ is also winning since removing 2 chips from each pile leaves the $(1,2)$ losing position. But $(3,5)$ is losing: any move will leave a winning position. Also, any larger position in which the piles differ by 2 chips is a winning position: remove enough chips from both piles to leave $(3,5)$. Similarly, any larger position of the form $(3,n)$ or $(5,n)$ is winning: remove enough chips from the n-chip pile to leave $(3,5)$.

The next smallest losing position is the position $(4,7)$, where both piles contain a number of chips not in any previous losing position, and the difference in the number of chips is larger than any previously-considered difference. This leads to the winning positions $(4,n)$, $(7,n)$ and $(m,m+3)$ for any larger n or m.

These examples lead to a recursive method to determine the losing positions (x_n, y_n). We already have $(x_1, y_1) = (1,2)$, $(x_2, y_2) = (3,5)$, and $(x_3, y_3) = (4,7)$. We recursively define x_n to be the smallest positive integer that does not occur as x_i or y_i for any $1 \le i < n$, and then $y_n = x_n + n$. This gives the following chart of losing positions:

n	1	2	3	4	5	6	7	8	9	10
x_n	1	3	4	6	8	9	11	12	14	16
y_n	2	5	7	10	13	15	18	20	23	26

Note that every positive integer will appear as exactly one x_n or y_n. What is very remarkable (though we will not prove it here) is that

$$x_n = \left\lfloor \frac{1 + \sqrt{5}}{2} n \right\rfloor$$

for all positive integers n.

Review Problems

13.13 If Andrea ever flips a T, then she stops when she flips an H, at which point she ends with the sequence TH. Therefore, Andrea stops by flipping HH if and only if her first two flips are H's, and the probability of this occurring is ┃1/4┃.

13.14 There are four distinct types of cubes: corner cubes, edge cubes, face cubes (the cubes that are at the center of each face), and the center cube. These cubes are labeled C, E, and F, respectively, in the diagram at right. We have the following state diagram that shows the probabilities of moving from one cube to the next:

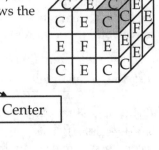

$$\text{Corner} \quad \text{Edge} \quad \text{Face} \quad \text{Center}$$

1    $\frac{1}{2}$ $\frac{1}{5}$

$\frac{1}{2}$ $\frac{4}{5}$

Let μ_C, μ_E, and μ_F denote the expected number of minutes to reach the cheese when the mouse starts from a corner, edge, and face cube, respectively. Then using the above state diagram, we have the system of equations:

$$\mu_C = \mu_E + 1,$$
$$\mu_E = \frac{1}{2}\mu_C + \frac{1}{2}\mu_F + 1,$$
$$\mu_F = \frac{4}{5}\mu_E + 1.$$

Substituting the third equation into the second equation, we get

$$\mu_E = \frac{1}{2}\mu_C + \frac{1}{2}\left(\frac{4}{5}\mu_E + 1\right) + 1 = \frac{1}{2}\mu_C + \frac{2}{5}\mu_E + \frac{3}{2},$$

so

$$\frac{3}{5}\mu_E = \frac{1}{2}\mu_C + \frac{3}{2}.$$

Substituting $\mu_E = \mu_C - 1$, we get

$$\frac{3}{5}(\mu_C - 1) = \frac{1}{2}\mu_C + \frac{3}{2},$$

so $\mu_C = \boxed{21}$.

13.15 For $1 \le n \le 2$, let a_n be the expected number of replacements needed when starting with n green beads and $4 - n$ red beads, until all the beads are red.

First we compute a_1. If the bag contains 1 green bead and 3 red beads, then the probability of drawing the green bead is $\frac{1}{4}$; if this occurs, then we are finished. The probability of drawing a red bead is $\frac{3}{4}$; if this occurs, there is still 1 green bead and 3 red beads. Therefore,

$$a_1 = \frac{1}{4} \cdot 1 + \frac{3}{4}(a_1 + 1) \quad \Rightarrow \quad a_1 = 4.$$

Now we compute a_2. If the bag contains 2 green beads and 2 red beads, then the probability of drawing a green bead is $\frac{1}{2}$; if this occurs, we will have 1 green bead and 3 red beads, which was done above. The probability of drawing a red bead is also $\frac{1}{2}$; if this occurs, we still have 2 green beads and 2 red beads. Therefore,

$$a_2 = \frac{1}{2}(a_1 + 1) + \frac{1}{2}(a_2 + 1) \quad \Rightarrow \quad a_2 = a_1 + 2 = \boxed{6}.$$

13.16 On any given point, Bart calls "Let" with probability $\frac{1}{3}$, Homer wins the point with probability $\frac{2}{3} \cdot \frac{3}{5} = \frac{2}{5}$, and Marge wins the point with probability $\frac{2}{3} \cdot \frac{2}{5} = \frac{4}{15}$. This results in the following state diagram:

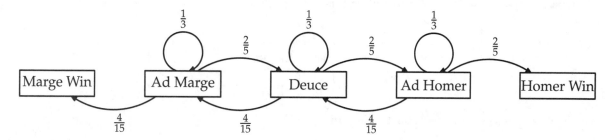

The loops above the intermediate states represent when Bart calls "Let."

Let d, h, and m denote the expected number of points remaining to play at Deuce, Ad Homer, and Ad Marge, respectively. Then we have the following system of equations:

$$m = 1 + \frac{1}{3}m + \frac{2}{5}d,$$

$$d = 1 + \frac{1}{3}d + \frac{2}{5}h + \frac{4}{15}m,$$

$$h = 1 + \frac{1}{3}h + \frac{4}{15}d.$$

We can multiply this system through by 15 to get rid of the fractions, and move all of the variables to one side:

$$10m - 6d = 15,$$

$$-4m + 10d - 6h = 15,$$

$$10h - 4d = 15.$$

Using the first and the third equations, we can substitute $m = (15 + 6d)/10$ and $h = (15 + 4d)/10$ into the second equation, giving:

$$-4((15 + 6d)/10) + 10d - 6((15 + 4d)/10) = 15,$$

which solves to give $d = \boxed{75/13}$.

13.17 Let a_n denote the expected number of visits to 0, given that the alien is at position n. We get the system of equations:

$$a_0 = a_1,$$

$$a_1 = \frac{1}{2}(a_0 + 1) + \frac{1}{2}a_2,$$

$$a_2 = \frac{1}{2}a_1 + \frac{1}{2}a_3,$$

$$a_3 = \frac{1}{2}a_2 + \frac{1}{2}a_4,$$

$$a_4 = \frac{1}{2}a_3.$$

Substituting the last equation into the one above it reduces the system to:

$$a_0 = a_1,$$

$$a_1 = \frac{1}{2}(a_0 + 1) + \frac{1}{2}a_2,$$

$$a_2 = \frac{1}{2}a_1 + \frac{1}{2}a_3,$$

$$a_3 = \frac{1}{2}a_2 + \frac{1}{4}a_3.$$

The last equation gives $a_3 = \frac{2}{3}a_2$, and substituting this reduces the system to:

$$a_0 = a_1,$$

$$a_1 = \frac{1}{2}(a_0 + 1) + \frac{1}{2}a_2,$$

$$a_2 = \frac{1}{2}a_1 + \frac{1}{3}a_2.$$

The last equation gives $a_2 = \frac{3}{4}a_1$, and substituting this give:

$$a_0 = a_1,$$

$$a_1 = \frac{1}{2}(a_0 + 1) + \frac{3}{8}a_1.$$

This last equation is $a_1 = \frac{7}{8}a_1 + \frac{1}{2}$, so $a_0 = a_1 = \boxed{4}$.

13.18 Note that the following solution is incorrect:

There are $\binom{7}{3} = 35$ paths to B. There are $\binom{6}{2} = 15$ paths to C. Therefore, the probability that a path to B passes through C is $\frac{15}{35} = \frac{3}{7}$.

This does not work because not all paths to B are equally likely. (If you made this error, go back and try the problem again, before reading the rest of the solution.)

Instead, we iteratively compute the probabilities of passing through each point. For all points except those on the bottom or right edges, the probability of passing through that point is $\frac{1}{2}$ times the probability of passing through the point immediately above (if there is one), plus $\frac{1}{2}$ times the probability of passing through the point immediately to the left (if there is one). The bottom and right edges are different, because once on that edge, our path must go directly to B.

We get the following chart of probabilities:

So the probability of passing through C is $\boxed{\dfrac{11}{32}}$. Note that we didn't need to compute the bottom row of the grid, but it is a nice check of our work.

13.19 Let's start by looking at a simpler version of the problem. (This is usually a good problem-solving strategy.) Suppose we play the game, but you're only allowed one strike. The only possible strategy is to decide ahead of time that you're going to play until you either lose or get n heads, where n is some fixed positive integer.

Using this strategy, we see that with probability $\left(\frac{1}{2}\right)^n$, you win $n(\$100)$, otherwise you win nothing. So the expected win is $\dfrac{\$100n}{2^n}$. We need to determine for what positive integer n this is maximized.

If either $n = 1$ or $n = 2$, this value is $\$50$. For $n \geq 2$, we can check pretty easily that

$$\frac{100(n+1)}{2^{n+1}} < \frac{100n}{2^n},$$

since

$$2^n(100(n+1)) \overset{?}{<} 2^{n+1}(100n)$$
$$\Leftrightarrow \quad 2^n(100) \overset{?}{<} 2^n(100n)$$
$$\Leftrightarrow \quad 1 < n.$$

So in terms of our expected winnings, it doesn't matter if we play to get 1 head or 2 heads; either way our expected win is $50.

Now we can look at the game when we're allowed 2 strikes. This time, the only strategy is to try to get n heads before the first strike, and then if we get a strike, to default to the 1-strike strategy that we just determined.

So now we have a $\left(\frac{1}{2}\right)^n$ probability of getting $100(n)$, and a $(1 - 1/2^n)$ probability of getting a strike. But in the latter case, we're in the 1-strike game, and we already know that the expected win is $50. So the expected win for a 2-strike n-head strategy is:

$$\frac{100n}{2^n} + \left(1 - \frac{1}{2^n}\right)50 = \frac{50(2^n - 1) + 100n}{2^n}.$$

Again, we wish to choose n so that this is maximized.

We can plug in some small values of n to get some idea:

n	1	2	3	4
$E(\text{Win})$	75	87.5	81.25	71.875

It looks like $n = 2$ produces the maximum, which is $87.50. To prove this, we can again compare n with $n + 1$ for $n > 1$:

$$\frac{50(2^n-1)+100n}{2^n} \overset{?}{>} \frac{50(2^{n+1}-1)+100(n+1)}{2^{n+1}}$$

$$\Leftrightarrow \quad 2^{n+1}(50(2^n - 1) + 100n) \overset{?}{>} 2^n(50(2^{n+1} - 1) + 100(n + 1))$$

$$\Leftrightarrow \quad 2^{n+1}(-50 + 100n) \overset{?}{>} 2^n(-50 + 100(n + 1))$$

$$\Leftrightarrow \quad 2^n(100n) \overset{?}{>} 2^n(150)$$

$$\Leftrightarrow \quad 100n \overset{?}{>} 150$$

This last inequality is true for all positive integers $n > 1$. So $n = 2$ indeed gives the best expected value for the 2-strike game.

Finally, we look at the original 3-strike problem. The expected win for an n-head strategy is:

$$\frac{100n}{2^n} + \left(1 - \frac{1}{2^n}\right)(87.50) = \frac{(87.50)(2^n - 1) + (100)n}{2^n}.$$

Above, the 87.50 term is the expected win in the 2-strike game.

Again, we can compute some small values of n:

n	1	2	3	4
$E(\text{Win})$	93.75	115.625	114.0625	107.03125

So again it appears that $n = 2$ is the best strategy. If we do the same calculation as we did in the 2-strike case, we will get the same expressions, except with 87.50 appearing everywhere that 50 did before. In particular, our last expression will be $100n > 187.50$, which is true for all integers $n > 1$.

In summary: our strategy is to try to get $200 in the pot by playing for two heads. If we get $200, we take it and quit. Otherwise, we lose and get nothing.

As a check, we can compute the probability of winning $200. We only lose if we fail to flip two consecutive heads in 3 attempts. On each attempt, the probability of failure is $\frac{3}{4}$. So the probability of failure on 3 attempts is $\left(\frac{3}{4}\right)^3 = \frac{27}{64}$, and hence the probability of winning $200 is $1 - 27/64 = 37/64$.

Thus, the expected win is $(37/64)(\$200) = \boxed{\$115.625}$.

13.20 This looks like a problem that can be handled using a typical block-walking argument, in which we assign to each vertex the number of paths that reach that vertex, but there is a twist: For each step, the set of possible directions is dependent upon the previous step.

To deal with this restriction, we encode each vertex with additional information. More precisely, to each vertex we assign an ordered triple of numbers, where the first, second and third numbers denote the number of paths that reach that vertex, whose last step is diagonal, to the right, and up, respectively.

To make this more clear, consider a vertex D, and the adjacent vertices A, B, C, whose triples have already been generated.

$A(a_1, a_2, a_3)$ • ——— • D

$B(b_1, b_2, b_3)$ • ——— • $C(c_1, c_2, c_3)$

For every path that reaches D, the previous vertex must have been B, A, or C, and the previous step was diagonal, to the right, or up, respectively.

There are $b_1 + b_2 + b_3$ paths that reach B, so this is also the first number at D.

There are $a_1 + a_2 + a_3$ paths that reach A. However, a_3 is the number of paths whose last step was up, so these paths cannot continue to D. Therefore, the second number at D is $a_1 + a_2$.

Similarly, there are $c_1 + c_2 + c_3$ paths that reach C, but c_2 is the number of paths whose last step was to the right, and these cannot continue to D, so the third number at D is $c_1 + c_3$.

Thus, the triple at D is $(b_1 + b_2 + b_3, a_1 + a_2, c_1 + c_3)$.

$A(a_1, a_2, a_3)$ • ——— • $D(b_1 + b_2 + b_3, a_1 + a_2, c_1 + c_3)$

$B(b_1, b_2, b_3)$ • ——— • $C(c_1, c_2, c_3)$

Starting with the triple $(0, 0, 0)$ at the origin, we can generate all the triples:

(0,0,1)	(1,0,4)	(4,1,7)	(8,5,11)	(15,13,18)	(27,28,28)
(0,0,1)	(1,0,3)	(3,1,4)	(5,4,6)	(9,9,9)	(15,18,13)
(0,0,1)	(1,0,2)	(2,1,2)	(3,3,3)	(5,6,4)	(8,11,5)
(0,0,1)	(1,0,1)	(1,1,1)	(2,2,1)	(3,4,1)	(4,7,1)
(0,0,1)	(1,0,0)	(1,1,0)	(1,2,0)	(1,3,0)	(1,4,0)
(0,0,0)	(0,1,0)	(0,1,0)	(0,1,0)	(0,1,0)	(0,1,0)

Hence, the total number of admissible paths from (0,0) to (5,5) is $27 + 28 + 28 = \boxed{83}$.

Challenge Problems

13.21 Let p_n denote the probability that after n moves, the center card is the queen. In particular, $p_0 = 1$, so assume that $n \geq 1$. After $n - 1$ moves, if the center card is the queen, then the queen always gets moved to one of the edge cards. If the center card is not the queen, then there is a probability of 1/2 that the queen becomes the center card. Hence,

$$p_n = \frac{1}{2}(1 - p_{n-1}) = \frac{1}{2} - \frac{1}{2}p_{n-1}.$$

We can solve this recursion as follows: shifting the index by 1, we get

$$p_{n-1} = \frac{1}{2} - \frac{1}{2}p_{n-2}.$$

Subtracting, we get

$$p_n - p_{n-1} = \frac{1}{2}p_{n-2} - \frac{1}{2}p_{n-1} \quad \Rightarrow \quad p_n = \frac{1}{2}p_{n-1} + \frac{1}{2}p_{n-2}.$$

The characteristic polynomial of this recursion is $c^2 - \frac{1}{2}c - \frac{1}{2} = (c - 1)(c + \frac{1}{2})$, so

$$p_n = \lambda_1 + \lambda_2\left(-\frac{1}{2}\right)^n$$

for some constants λ_1 and λ_2.

Since $p_0 = 1$ and $p_1 = \frac{1}{2}(1 - 1) = 0$, substituting $n = 0$ and $n = 1$ gives us the following system of equations:

$$1 = \lambda_1 + \lambda_2,$$

$$0 = \lambda_1 - \frac{1}{2}\lambda_2.$$

Solving, we get $\lambda_1 = 1/3$ and $\lambda_2 = 2/3$, so

$$p_n = \frac{1}{3} + \frac{2}{3}\left(-\frac{1}{2}\right)^n$$

for all $n \geq 0$. In particular,

$$p_{2004} = \frac{1}{3} + \frac{2}{3}\left(-\frac{1}{2}\right)^{2004} = \boxed{\frac{1}{3} + \frac{1}{3 \cdot 2^{2003}}}.$$

Note that this is extremely close to $\frac{1}{3}$, which makes intuitive sense: after 2004 moves, the cards are essentially "randomly" distributed, so the queen is (almost) equally likely to be in any of the three positions.

13.22 For $a \geq b \geq 0$, let $p(a, b)$ be the probability that the number b is displayed *at some point* when beginning with the number a. When the calculator originally displays a and the button is pressed, the next number displayed is randomly chosen from $\{0, 1, \ldots, a - 1\}$. However, only the numbers greater than or equal to b can possibly lead to the number b still being displayed, so

$$p(a, b) = \frac{p(a - 1, b) + p(a - 2, b) + \cdots + p(b, b)}{a}.$$

Let b be a fixed nonnegative integer. By definition, $p(b, b) = 1$. Also,

$$p(b + 1, b) = \frac{p(b, b)}{b + 1} = \frac{1}{b + 1},$$

and for $a \geq b + 2$,

$$\begin{aligned} p(a, b) &= \frac{p(a - 1, b) + p(a - 2, b) + \cdots + p(b, b)}{a} \\ &= \frac{p(a - 1, b) + [p(a - 2, b) + p(a - 3, b) + \cdots + p(b, b)]}{a} \\ &= \frac{p(a - 1, b) + (a - 1) \cdot \frac{p(a-2,b)+p(a-3,b)+\cdots+p(b,b)}{a-1}}{a} \\ &= \frac{p(a - 1, b) + (a - 1)p(a - 1, b)}{a} \\ &= p(a - 1, b). \end{aligned}$$

Hence, $p(a, b) = 1/(b + 1)$ for all $a \geq b + 1$. (Since this value is so nice, we might look for a simpler explanation, and indeed there is one. At some point, we must get one of the numbers in the set $\{0, 1, 2, \ldots, b\}$, and each of these numbers is equally likely to appear first. If any of the numbers other than b appears first, then b cannot appear at some later point. Therefore, the probability that it is b that appears first is $1/(b + 1)$.)

Since the sequence of numbers displayed is strictly decreasing, in order to hit all of 1000, 100, 10, and 1, we must first start at 2003 and hit 1000, then we must start at 1000 and hit 100, and so on. Therefore, the probability that the numbers 1, 10, 100, and 1000 all appear when starting with 2003 is

$$p(2003, 1000) \cdot p(1000, 100) \cdot p(100, 10) \cdot p(10, 1) = \frac{1}{1001} \cdot \frac{1}{101} \cdot \frac{1}{11} \cdot \frac{1}{2} = \boxed{\frac{1}{2,224,222}}.$$

13.23 For $0 \leq k \leq 6$, let p_k denote the probability that, when starting with k peas at the top, all six peas are on the top before all six are on the bottom.

By definition, $p_6 = 1$ and $p_0 = 0$. Now, suppose that 5 peas are at the top, and 1 is at the bottom. Then the probabilities that 0, 1, or 2 of the peas at the top sink are all 1/3, and the probability that the pea at the bottom floats up is 1/2. It follows that the probabilities that 6, 5, 4, and 3 peas are left at the top are 1/6, 1/3, 1/3, and 1/6, respectively, so

$$p_5 = \frac{1}{6}p_6 + \frac{1}{3}p_5 + \frac{1}{3}p_4 + \frac{1}{6}p_3.$$

Further relations can be computed similarly:

$$\begin{aligned} p_4 &= \frac{1}{9}p_6 + \frac{2}{9}p_5 + \frac{1}{3}p_4 + \frac{2}{9}p_3 + \frac{1}{9}p_2, \\ p_3 &= \frac{1}{9}p_5 + \frac{2}{9}p_4 + \frac{1}{3}p_3 + \frac{2}{9}p_2 + \frac{1}{9}p_1, \\ p_2 &= \frac{1}{9}p_4 + \frac{2}{9}p_3 + \frac{1}{3}p_2 + \frac{2}{9}p_1 + \frac{1}{9}p_0, \\ p_1 &= \frac{1}{6}p_3 + \frac{1}{3}p_2 + \frac{1}{3}p_1 + \frac{1}{6}p_0. \end{aligned}$$

We can simplify this system by taking advantage of symmetry. For example, the states corresponding to p_1 and p_5 are opposites, with the top and bottom reversed. This means that $p_1 = 1 - p_5$. Similarly, $p_2 = 1 - p_4$, and

$p_3 = 1/2$. Substituting, we get

$$p_5 = \frac{1}{6} + \frac{1}{3}p_5 + \frac{1}{3}p_4 + \frac{1}{12} \quad \Rightarrow \quad 8p_5 = 3 + 4p_4,$$

$$p_4 = \frac{1}{9} + \frac{2}{9}p_5 + \frac{1}{3}p_4 + \frac{1}{9} + \frac{1}{9}(1 - p_4) \quad \Rightarrow \quad 7p_4 = 3 + 2p_5.$$

Solving, we get $p_4 = \boxed{5/8}$.

13.24 For $0 \leq n \leq 28$, let a_n denote the expected number of flips until one of us runs out of money, when I start with n dollars and you start with $28 - n$ dollars. Then by definition, $a_0 = a_{28} = 0$, so let $1 \leq n \leq 27$. There is a probability of $1/2$ that I win a dollar, or lose a dollar, so

$$a_n = \frac{1}{2}(a_{n-1} + 1) + \frac{1}{2}(a_{n+1} + 1) \quad \Rightarrow \quad a_{n+1} = 2a_n - a_{n-1} - 2.$$

Shifting the index by 1, we get $a_n = 2a_{n-1} - a_{n-2} - 2$. Subtracting, we get

$$a_{n+1} = 3a_n - 3a_{n-1} + a_{n-2}.$$

The characteristic polynomial of this recursion is $c^3 - 3c^2 + 3c - 1 = (c - 1)^3$, so

$$a_n = \lambda_2 n^2 + \lambda_1 n + \lambda_0$$

for some constants λ_2, λ_1, and λ_0. In other words, a_n is a quadratic in n. Since $a_0 = a_{28} = 0$, a_n must be of the form

$$a_n = \lambda_2 n(n - 28).$$

We can then derive the value of λ_2 using the relation $a_{n+1} - 2a_n + a_{n-1} = -2$:

$$a_{n+1} - 2a_n + a_{n-1} = \lambda_2(n + 1)(n - 27) - 2\lambda_2 n(n - 28) + \lambda_2(n - 1)(n - 29) = 2\lambda_2 = -2,$$

so $\lambda_2 = -1$, and $a_n = -n(n - 28) = n(28 - n)$. In particular, $a_{14} = 14 \cdot 14 = \boxed{196}$.

There is an alternate solution. Write the system of equations:

$$2a_1 = a_2 + 2,$$
$$2a_2 = a_1 + a_3 + 2,$$
$$2a_3 = a_2 + a_4 + 2,$$
$$\vdots$$
$$2a_{26} = a_{25} + a_{27} + 2,$$
$$2a_{27} = a_{26} + 2.$$

Summing them all and cancelling like terms will give

$$a_1 + a_{27} = 54,$$

and since $a_1 = a_{27}$ by symmetry, we conclude that $a_1 = a_{27} = 27$. Then, we may recursively solve for the other a_i's:

$$a_2 = 2a_1 - 2 = 52,$$
$$a_3 = 2a_2 - a_1 - 2 = 75,$$
$$a_4 = 2a_3 - a_2 - 2 = 96,$$
$$\vdots$$

eventually getting $a_{14} = 196$.

13.25 Starting from a winning position, with at least one of A or B odd, we must show that it is always possible to make a move that either immediately wins the game, or leaves a losing position.

- If A and B are both odd, take a chip from one of the 2-chip piles. This lowers A by 1 and increases B by 1.

- If A is odd and B is even, take both chips from one of the 2-chip piles. This lowers A by 1 and leaves B unchanged.

- If A is even and B is odd, remove a 1-chip pile if one exists; otherwise remove a chip from an even pile with at least 4 chips. This lowers B by 1 and leaves A unchanged.

In all 3 cases, A and B are now even, leaving a losing position (or possibly immediately winning the game if both A and B are 0).

If a player is in a losing position, with A and B both even, we have the following possibilities:

- She takes a chip off an even pile with at least 4 chips. This reduces B by 1, and leaves A unchanged.

- She takes a chip off an odd pile with at least 5 chips. This increases B by 1, and leaves A unchanged.

- She takes a chip off a pile with 3 chips. This increases A by 1, and leaves B unchanged.

- She takes a chip off a pile with 2 chips. This changes both A and B by 1.

- She takes 2 chips from a pile of 2 chips. This decreases A by 1.

- She takes 1 chip from a pile with 1 chip. This decreases B by 1.

In all cases, she cannot leave A and B both even, so she must leave her opponent with a winning position.

13.26 If the number of 1's in each digit space is even, then any move must change the positions of the 1's in one of the piles, thus making at least one digit space have an odd number of 1's. So any move from a losing position must leave a winning position. (And since there must be more than one pile in any losing position, the player cannot win the game immediately.)

What's left to show is that in any winning position there is a move that either wins immediately or leaves a losing position. If there is only one pile remaining, then of course we just take that pile and win the game. Otherwise, if there is more than one pile, we find the left-most digit position that has an odd number of 1's, and we take from a pile that has a 1 in that digit position. We take chips so that we change that pile's digit in exactly those positions in which the piles collectively have an odd number of 1's. This is always possible, so we can always leave a losing position.

CHAPTER **14**

Generating Functions

Exercises for Section 14.2

14.2.1   The generating functions for Marilyn's, John's, and Bill's portion of the tip are $x + x^2 + x^3$, $x + x^2 + x^3$, and $x + x^2$, respectively, and their product is

$$(x + x^2 + x^3)(x + x^2 + x^3)(x + x^2) = x^3 + 3x^4 + 5x^5 + 5x^6 + 3x^7 + x^8.$$

Therefore, the number of ways they can leave a \$6 tip is the coefficient of x^6, which is $\boxed{5}$.

14.2.2   The generating functions for a and d are each $(1 + x + x^2 + x^3 + x^4)$. The generating function for b is $(1 + x^2 + x^4)$. The generating function for c is $(x + x^3)$. Therefore, the generating function for the possible values of $a + b + c + d$ is

$$(1 + x + x^2 + x^3 + x^4)^2(1 + x^2 + x^4)(x + x^3) = (1 + 2x + 3x^2 + 4x^3 + 5x^4 + 4x^5 + 3x^6 + 2x^7 + x^8)(x + 2x^3 + 2x^5 + x^7).$$

We only care about the coefficient of x^7 in this product, so rather than multiply the entire expression, we'll restrict ourselves to terms that can produce an x^7 term in the product:

$$(1 + 3x^2 + 5x^4 + 3x^6)(x + 2x^3 + 2x^5 + x^7) \quad \rightarrow \quad 20x^7,$$

so there are $\boxed{20}$ solutions.

14.2.3   The generating function for each friend is $(x^{-2} + x^{-1} + 1 + x + x^2)$, so the generating function for the combined amount that the four friends win is:
$$(x^{-2} + x^{-1} + 1 + x + x^2)^4.$$

We are looking for the constant term in this product (which is the coefficient of x^0). Note that

$$(x^{-2} + x^{-1} + 1 + x + x^2)^2 = (x^{-4} + 2x^{-3} + 3x^{-2} + 4x^{-1} + 5 + 4x + 3x^2 + 2x^3 + x^4),$$

so when we square this and look at just the constant term, we get:

$$1^2 + 2^2 + 3^2 + 4^2 + 5^2 + 4^2 + 3^2 + 2^2 + 1^2 = \boxed{85}.$$

We can also solve via a counting argument using casework, based on the number of individual friends who break even.

If they all break even, then of course they collectively break even. This can happen in 1 way.

If 3 of them break even, then they cannot collectively break even (since the fourth friend will either win or lose).

If 2 of them break even (and there are $\binom{4}{2} = 6$ choices for the two that break even), then one friend has to lose (2 choices) and the other has to win. There are also 2 choices for the amount lost and won. So this case can happen in $6 \times 2 \times 2 = 24$ ways.

If 1 of them breaks even (4 choices), then 1 has to win or lose \$2 (3 choices for the friend times 2 choices for winning or losing), and the other two have to lose or win \$1 each to compensate. This case can happen in $4 \times 3 \times 2 = 24$ ways.

If none of them break even, then two have to win ($\binom{4}{2} = 6$ choices). If they win an equal amount (2 choices), then the other two have to lose the same equal amount. If they win different amounts (2 choices), then the other two have to lose different amounts (another 2 choices). So this case can happen in $6 \times (2 + 2 \times 2) = 36$ ways.

This gives a total of $1 + 24 + 24 + 36 = 85$ possible ways to break even.

14.2.4 If the numbers on one die are $a_1, a_2, \ldots, a_6$, and the numbers on the other die are $b_1, b_2, \ldots, b_6$, then the generating function of the sum of the rolls is given by

$$(x^{a_1} + x^{a_2} + \cdots + x^{a_6})(x^{b_1} + x^{b_2} + \cdots + x^{b_6}).$$

In particular, the generating function for a pair of standard dice is

$$(x + x^2 + \cdots + x^6)(x + x^2 + \cdots + x^6).$$

Hence, the problem is to find all sets of positive integers a_i and b_i such that

$$(x^{a_1} + x^{a_2} + \cdots + x^{a_6})(x^{b_1} + x^{b_2} + \cdots + x^{b_6}) = (x + x^2 + \cdots + x^6)(x + x^2 + \cdots + x^6).$$

Let $f(x) = x^{a_1} + x^{a_2} + \cdots + x^{a_6}$ and $g(x) = x^{b_1} + x^{b_2} + \cdots + x^{b_6}$. First, note that $(x + x^2 + \cdots + x^6)(x + x^2 + \cdots + x^6)$ factors as

$$(x + x^2 + \cdots + x^6)(x + x^2 + \cdots + x^6) = x^2(x + 1)^2(x^2 - x + 1)^2(x^2 + x + 1)^2.$$

To see which factors should go to $f(x)$ and which factors should go to $g(x)$, we look at some of the properties these polynomials have.

Since the a_i and b_i are positive integers, taking $x = 0$, we get $f(0) = g(0) = 0$. Hence, one factor of x must go to $f(x)$, and the other factor of x must go to $g(x)$. Taking $x = 1$, we get $f(1) = 1^{a_1} + 1^{a_2} + \cdots + 1^{a_6} = 6$, $g(1) = 1^{b_1} + 1^{b_2} + \cdots + 1^{b_6} = 6$, and

$$x = 1,$$
$$x + 1 = 2,$$
$$x^2 - x + 1 = 1,$$
$$x^2 + x + 1 = 3.$$

Hence, to obtain a product of 6 when $x = 1$, each of $f(x)$ and $g(x)$ must contain a factor of $x + 1$ and $x^2 + x + 1$. So far, we have that $f(x)$ and $g(x)$ are of the form

$$f(x) = x(x + 1)(x^2 + x + 1) \cdots ,$$
$$g(x) = x(x + 1)(x^2 + x + 1) \cdots .$$

The only part left is to the assign the two factors of $x^2 - x + 1$. If one factor goes to $f(x)$ and the other factor goes to $g(x)$, then $f(x) = g(x) = x(x + 1)(x^2 + x + 1)(x^2 - x + 1) = x + x^2 + x^3 + x^4 + x^5 + x^6$, which corresponds to a pair of standard dice. The only other possibility is that both factors of $x^2 - x + 1$ go to one polynomial, say $f(x)$, and we get

$$f(x) = x(x + 1)(x^2 + x + 1)(x^2 - x + 1)^2$$
$$= x + x^3 + x^4 + x^5 + x^6 + x^8,$$
$$g(x) = x(x + 1)(x^2 + x + 1)$$
$$= x + 2x^2 + 2x^3 + x^4$$
$$= x + x^2 + x^2 + x^3 + x^3 + x^4.$$

Hence, a die labeled with the numbers 1, 3, 4, 5, 6, and 8 and a die labeled with the numbers 1, 2, 2, 3, 3, and 4 produce the same distribution of sums as a pair of standard dice, and this is the only possible pair of unfair dice whose sides are positive integers.

Exercises for Section 14.3

14.3.1 There is a total of 15 choices of toppings: Joe can have ketchup, mustard, relish, onions, or sauerkraut on his first hot dog, and the same for his second hot dog, and the same for his third hot dog. Joe must choose 6 of these toppings. Hence, the number of different ways that Joe can choose toppings is $\binom{15}{6}$.

14.3.2 The generating function for each boy is $(1 + x^2)$ and the generating function for each girl is $(1 + x^3)$. So the generating function for the whole group is
$$(1 + x^2)^6(1 + x^3)^8.$$

We want the coefficient of x^{20} in this function. The x^{20} term is equal to:

$$\left(\binom{6}{1}x^2\right)\left(\binom{8}{6}x^{18}\right) + \left(\binom{6}{4}x^8\right)\left(\binom{8}{4}x^{12}\right),$$

so the coefficient is $\binom{6}{1}\binom{8}{6} + \binom{6}{4}\binom{8}{4} = (6)(28) + (15)(70) = \boxed{1218}$.

14.3.3 The generating function for each of the first 29 people is $(1 + x)$, and the generating function for the last person is $(1 + x^2 + x^5)$, so the combined generating function is

$$(1 + x)^{29}(1 + x^2 + x^5).$$

We want the coefficient of the x^{22} term of this product, which is the sum of the coefficients of the x^{22}, x^{20}, and x^{17} terms of $(1 + x)^{29}$. Thus, the answer is

$$\boxed{\binom{29}{22} + \binom{29}{20} + \binom{29}{17} = 63,471,720}.$$

14.3.4 The generating function for the number of "yes" votes from the Chief Justice is $(1 + x^3)$, and the corresponding generating function for each Associate Justice is $(1 + x)$. So the overall generating function for the number of "yes" votes is
$$(1 + x)^{12}(1 + x^3).$$

We want the coefficient of the x^8 term, which is the sum of the coefficients of the x^8 and x^5 terms of $(1 + x)^{12}$. Therefore, the answer is

$$\binom{12}{8} + \binom{12}{5} = \boxed{1287}.$$

14.3.5 Consider the identity

$$(1 + x)^m(1 + x)^n = (1 + x)^{m+n}.$$

The coefficient of x^r must be the same on both sides, and we see that this coefficient in the RHS is $\binom{m+n}{r}$.

When the LHS is expanded, we see that each term of degree r is the product of a term of degree k in $(1 + x)^m$ and a term of degree $r - k$ in $(1 + x)^n$, for some $0 \le k \le r$. The coefficient of x^k in $(1 + x)^m$ is $\binom{m}{k}$, and the coefficient of x^{r-k} in $(1 + x)^n$ is $\binom{n}{r-k}$. Summing over $0 \le k \le r$, we derive Vandermonde's identity:

$$\sum_{k=0}^{r} \binom{m}{k}\binom{n}{r-k} = \binom{m+n}{r}.$$

Exercises for Section 14.4

14.4.1 Let $y = x^m$, so

$$\frac{1}{(1 - x^m)^n} = \frac{1}{(1 - y)^n}.$$

We know that

$$\frac{1}{(1 - y)^n} = \sum_{i=0}^{\infty} \binom{n + i - 1}{n - 1} y^i = \sum_{i=0}^{\infty} \binom{n + i - 1}{n - 1} x^{mi}.$$

To find the coefficient of x^k, we set $k = mi$, so $i = k/m$. Then

$$\binom{n + i - 1}{n - 1} = \binom{n + k/m - 1}{n - 1}.$$

Note that such an index i exists if and only if k is a multiple of m. So to summarize, the coefficient of x^k is

$$\binom{n + k/m - 1}{n - 1}$$

if k is a multiple of m, and zero otherwise.

14.4.2   The generating function for each of the kids who will take only an odd number of candies is

$$x + x^3 + x^5 + \cdots = x(1 + x^2 + x^4 + \cdots) = \frac{x}{1 - x^2}.$$

The generating function for the kid who will take any number of candies is

$$1 + x + x^2 + \cdots = \frac{1}{1 - x}.$$

The generating function for the kid who will take 0 or 1 candies is $1 + x$, and the generating function for the kid who will take 0 or 5 candies is $1 + x^5$. Hence, the generating function for all five kids is

$$\left(\frac{x}{1 - x^2}\right)^2 \cdot \frac{1}{1 - x} \cdot (1 + x) \cdot (1 + x^5) = \frac{x^2(1 + x)(1 + x^5)}{(1 - x^2)^2(1 - x)}$$

$$= \frac{x^2(1 + x)(1 + x^5)}{(1 + x)^2(1 - x)^2(1 - x)}$$

$$= \frac{x^2(1 + x^5)}{(1 + x)(1 - x)^3}.$$

We can factor $1 + x^5 = (1 + x)(1 - x + x^2 - x^3 + x^4)$, so our generating function is:

$$
\frac{x^2(1 + x^5)}{(1 + x)(1 - x)^3} = \frac{x^2(1 + x)(1 - x + x^2 - x^3 + x^4)}{(1 + x)(1 - x)^3}
$$

$$
= \frac{x^2(1 - x + x^2 - x^3 + x^4)}{(1 - x)^3}
$$

$$
= \frac{x^2}{(1 - x)^3} - \frac{x^3}{(1 - x)^3} + \frac{x^4}{(1 - x)^3} - \frac{x^5}{(1 - x)^3} + \frac{x^6}{(1 - x)^3}.
$$

The coefficient of x^{100} in $\frac{x^2}{(1-x)^3}$ is the coefficient of x^{98} in $\frac{1}{(1-x)^3}$, which is $\binom{100}{2}$. Similarly, the coefficients of x^{100} in $\frac{x^3}{(1-x)^3}$, $\frac{x^4}{(1-x)^3}$, $\frac{x^5}{(1-x)^3}$, and $\frac{x^6}{(1-x)^3}$ are $\binom{99}{2}$, $\binom{98}{2}$, $\binom{97}{2}$, and $\binom{96}{2}$, respectively.

Hence, the number of different ways of distributing the 100 candies is

$$
\binom{100}{2} - \binom{99}{2} + \binom{98}{2} - \binom{97}{2} + \binom{96}{2} = 4950 - 4851 + 4753 - 4656 + 4560 = \boxed{4756}.
$$

14.4.3 The text shows how to generate a distribution of 100 candies from a division of 101 candies into 3 piles. We want to show that the reverse is possible.

Let the middle kid receive a candies. Let the first young kid receive b_1 candies, and let the first old kid receive c_1 candies, where b_1 is 0 or 1 and c_1 is odd. Similarly, let the second young kid receive b_2 candies, and let the second old kid receive c_2 candies, where b_2 is 0 or 1 and c_2 is odd.

Take the a candies from the middle kid, add one candy, and put the $a + 1$ candies in the first pile. Then, take the b_1 candies from the first young kid and the c_1 candies from the first old kid, and put the $b_1 + c_1$ candies in the second pile. Finally, take the b_2 candies from the second young kid and the c_2 candies from the second old kid, and put the $b_2 + c_2$ candies in the third pile. Since $a + 1 + b_1 + c_1 + b_2 + c_2 = 101$, this gives us a division of 101 candies in 3 piles.

Reversing these operations as described in the text gets us back to the original distribution of the 100 candies to the 5 kids. This establishes the 1-1 correspondence.

14.4.4 The generating function for each of the children is $1 + x + x^2 + \cdots + x^6$, and the generating function of each of the adults is $1 + x + x^2 + \cdots + x^{10}$, so the generating function of the four children and three adults is

$$
(1 + x + x^2 + \cdots + x^6)^4(1 + x + x^2 + \cdots + x^{10})^3
$$

$$
= \left(\frac{1 - x^7}{1 - x}\right)^4 \left(\frac{1 - x^{11}}{1 - x}\right)^3
$$

$$
= \frac{(1 - x^7)^4(1 - x^{11})^3}{(1 - x)^7}
$$

$$
= (1 - x^7)^4(1 - x^{11})^3\left[\binom{6}{6} + \binom{7}{6}x + \binom{8}{6}x^2 + \binom{9}{6}x^3 + \cdots\right].
$$

We want to find the coefficient of x^{20} in this expression. It would be very complicated to expand it completely, but we can simplify the calculations as follows. Note that

$$
(1 - x^7)^4 = 1 - 4x^7 + 6x^{14} - 4x^{21} + x^{28}.
$$

The terms $-4x^{21}$ and x^{28} are irrelevant for our purpose, since they cannot affect the coefficient of x^{20}. Similarly,

$$
(1 - x^{11})^3 = 1 - 3x^{11} + 3x^{22} - x^{33},
$$

and we can ignore the terms $3x^{22}$ and $-x^{33}$. Hence, we want the x^{20} coefficient of

$$(1 - 4x^7 + 6x^{14})(1 - 3x^{11})\left[\binom{6}{6} + \binom{7}{6}x + \binom{8}{6}x^2 + \binom{9}{6}x^3 + \cdots\right]$$

$$= (1 - 4x^7 - 3x^{11} + 6x^{14} + 12x^{18} - 18x^{25})\left[\binom{6}{6} + \binom{7}{6}x + \binom{8}{6}x^2 + \binom{9}{6}x^3 + \cdots\right].$$

To obtain a term of degree 20, the term 1 must be multiplied by $\binom{26}{6}x^{20}$. Similarly, the term $-4x^7$ must be multiplied by $\binom{19}{6}x^{13}$, and so on. (We may ignore the term $-18x^{25}$ since its power of x is too large to contribute to x^{20}.) Hence, the coefficient of x^{20} is

$$\binom{26}{6} - 4\binom{19}{6} - 3\binom{15}{6} + 6\binom{12}{6} + 12\binom{8}{6}$$

$$= 230{,}230 - 4(27{,}132) - 3(5{,}005) + 6(924) + 12(28)$$

$$= \boxed{112{,}567}.$$

14.4.5 The generating function for the sum of Tina's two numbers is

$$x(x^2 + x^3 + x^4 + x^5) + x^2(x^3 + x^4 + x^5) + x^3(x^4 + x^5) + x^4 \cdot x^5$$

$$= x^3 + x^4 + 2x^5 + 2x^6 + 2x^7 + x^8 + x^9.$$

For $3 \le k \le 9$, if Tina gets a sum of k, then for Sergio's number to be greater, it must be a number from $k + 1$ through 10, for a total of $10 - k$ possibilities. Hence, summing over $3 \le k \le 9$, we find that the total number of outcomes in which Tina's sum is smaller than Sergio's number is $1 \cdot 7 + 1 \cdot 6 + 2 \cdot 5 + 2 \cdot 4 + 2 \cdot 3 + 1 \cdot 2 + 1 \cdot 1 = 40$.

The total number of possible outcomes is $\binom{5}{2} \cdot 10 = 100$, so the desired probability is $40/100 = \boxed{2/5}$.

Exercises for Section 14.5

14.5.1 The generating function for the pennies is

$$(1 + x + x^2 + \cdots) = \frac{1}{1 - x}.$$

Similarly, the generating function for the nickels is

$$(1 + x^5 + x^{10} + \cdots) = \frac{1}{1 - x^5},$$

and the generating function for the dimes is

$$(1 + x^{10} + x^{20} + \cdots) = \frac{1}{1 - x^{10}}.$$

Therefore, the desired generating function is $\boxed{\dfrac{1}{(1 - x)(1 - x^5)(1 - x^{10})}}.$

14.5.2 We take the generating function for partitions:

$$\frac{1}{(1 - x)(1 - x^2)(1 - x^3) \cdots},$$

and delete the terms in the denominator that correspond to odd parts. Therefore, the desired generating function is:

$$\frac{1}{(1-x^2)(1-x^4)(1-x^6)\cdots} = \prod_{k=1}^{\infty} \frac{1}{1-x^{2k}}.$$

14.5.3 The generating function for the number of partitions of n in which no part appears more than twice is:

$$f(x) = (1 + x + x^2)(1 + x^2 + x^4)(1 + x^3 + x^6)\cdots = \frac{1-x^3}{1-x} \cdot \frac{1-x^6}{1-x^2} \cdot \frac{1-x^9}{1-x^3} \cdots,$$

and the generating function for the number of partitions of n in which no multiple of 3 appears is:

$$g(x) = \frac{1}{1-x} \cdot \frac{1}{1-x^2} \cdot \frac{1}{1-x^4} \cdot \frac{1}{1-x^5} \cdot \frac{1}{1-x^7} \cdots.$$

Note that every factor of the form $1 - x^k$ appears as a denominator of $f(x)$, but that for those values of k that are a multiple of 3, the factor $1 - x^k$ will get canceled with the corresponding factor in the numerator of $f(x)$. Therefore, after canceling, we see that $f(x) = g(x)$, and therefore the corresponding numbers of partitions of n are equal.

14.5.4 Let c_n be the coefficient of x^n in $f(x)$. Then $f(x)(1 - x - x^2 - x^3 - x^4 - x^5 - x^6) = 1$, which implies that $c_0 = 1$ and for all $n > 0$,

$$c_n - c_{n-1} - c_{n-2} - c_{n-3} - c_{n-4} - c_{n-5} - c_{n-6} = 0,$$

where we say that $c_m = 0$ for all $m < 0$. This gives a recursive definition:

$$c_n = c_{n-1} + c_{n-2} + \cdots + c_{n-6}.$$

Each term in the sequence c_n depends on the previous 6 terms. This suggests a die, since rolling a die has the 6 possible outcomes ⚀ through ⚅. We conclude that c_n counts the number of ways to roll any number of distinguishable dice to get a sum of n, since if the first die is ⚀, ⚁, ..., ⚅, then the number of ways to roll additional dice to sum to $n - 1, n - 2, \ldots, n - 6$, respectively, is $c_{n-1}, c_{n-2}, \ldots, c_{n-6}$, respectively.

Thus $f(x)$ is the generating function for the number of ways to roll any number of distinguishable dice to sum to n.

14.5.5 If the three sides of a triangle with perimeter n have integer lengths a, b, c, with $0 < a \leq b \leq c$, then we must have $a + b + c = n$. So (a, b, c) is a partition of n into 3 parts. Recall from Problem 4.19 that the number of partitions of n into 3 parts is equal to the number of partitions of n in which the largest part is 3. We established this using a Ferrers diagram: if we have 3 rows of dots of lengths c, b, and a (reading top-to-bottom), then the columns give us a partition of n into 3's, 2's, and 1's, and the first column (of 3 dots) guarantees that there will be at least one 3.

But we cannot take every such partition; we also need to satisfy the Triangle Inequality, meaning that we must have $a + b > c$. If i, j, k are the number of 3's, 2's, and 1's, respectively, in our corresponding partition of n with largest part 3, then we see that $i = a$, $j = b - a$, and $k = c - b$. We can rewrite these as $b = i + j$ and $c = i + j + k$, which converts the Triangle Inequality to $i + (i + j) > i + j + k$, or $i > k$. In other words, our partition of n with largest part 3 must have more 3's than 1's.

We now show a 1-1 correspondence:

$$\begin{Bmatrix} \text{partitions of } n \text{ with largest part 3} \\ \text{with more 3's than 1's} \end{Bmatrix} \leftrightarrow \begin{Bmatrix} \text{partitions of } n \text{ using only 2's, 3's,} \\ \text{and 4's, with at least one 3} \end{Bmatrix}.$$

If we have a partition in the left set above, we can add all of the 1's to 3's, creating 4's. There will also be at least one 3 left over, as there are more 3's than 1's to start with. Conversely, if we have a partition in the right set, we split a 1 off from each 4 term. This will leave a partition with 1's, 2's, and 3's, which has fewer 1's than 3's: each 1 will have come from a 4 in the original partition, which is now a 3 in the new partition, but there was at least one "extra" 3 in the original partition which is still a 3 in the new partition as well. (We leave it to you to check that these two procedures are the reverses of each other, thus giving a 1-1 correspondence.)

Finally, we can write the generating function for this last set of partitions shown on the right above. We have partitions consisting of 2's, 3's, and 4's, with at least one 3. The generating function is:

$$(1 + x^2 + x^4 + \cdots)(x^3 + x^6 + \cdots)(1 + x^4 + x^8 + \cdots) = \boxed{\frac{x^3}{(1 - x^2)(1 - x^3)(1 - x^4)}}.$$

Review Problems

14.19

(a) Since

$$\frac{1}{1 - x} = 1 + x + x^2 + \cdots + x^{10} + \cdots,$$

the coefficient of x^{10} is $\boxed{1}$.

(b) Since

$$\frac{1}{1 - x^2} = 1 + x^2 + x^4 + \cdots + x^{10} + \cdots,$$

the coefficient of x^{10} is $\boxed{1}$.

(c) Since

$$\frac{1}{(1 - x)^2} = \binom{1}{1} + \binom{2}{1}x + \binom{3}{1}x^2 + \cdots + \binom{11}{1}x^{10} + \cdots,$$

the coefficient of x^{10} is $\binom{11}{1} = \boxed{11}$.

(d) Since

$$(1 + x^5)^5 = \binom{5}{0} + \binom{5}{1}x^5 + \binom{5}{2}x^{10} + \cdots + \binom{5}{5}x^{25},$$

the coefficient of x^{10} is $\binom{5}{2} = \boxed{10}$.

(e) We can write

$$(1 + x + x^2 + \cdots + x^6)^6 = \left(\frac{1 - x^7}{1 - x}\right)^6$$

$$= \frac{(1 - x^7)^6}{(1 - x)^6}$$

$$= (1 - x^7)^6 \left[\binom{5}{5} + \binom{6}{5}x + \binom{7}{5}x^2 + \cdots\right]$$

$$= (1 - 6x^7 + 15x^{14} - \cdots) \left[\binom{5}{5} + \binom{6}{5}x + \binom{7}{5}x^2 + \cdots\right].$$

To obtain a term of degree 10, the term 1 must be multiplied by $\binom{15}{5}x^{10}$, and the term $-6x^7$ must be multiplied by $\binom{8}{5}x^3$. The term $15x^{14}$ and other terms of higher degree do not affect the coefficient of x^{10}, so the coefficient of x^{10} is

$$\binom{15}{5} - 6\binom{8}{5} = 3003 - 6 \cdot 56 = \boxed{2667}.$$

(f) Let $y = x^2$. Then

$$\frac{1}{(1-x^2)^3} = \frac{1}{(1-y)^3}$$

$$= \binom{2}{2} + \binom{3}{2}y + \binom{4}{2}y^2 + \cdots + \binom{7}{2}y^5 + \cdots$$

$$= \binom{2}{2} + \binom{3}{2}x^2 + \binom{4}{2}x^4 + \cdots + \binom{7}{2}x^{10} + \cdots .$$

Hence, the coefficient of x^{10} is $\binom{7}{2} = \boxed{21}$.

14.20 The generating function for the number of ways to place coins in each bowl is

$$x + x^2 + x^3 + \cdots = \frac{x}{1-x}.$$

Therefore, the generating function for the number of ways to place the coins in all three bowls is

$$\left(\frac{x}{1-x}\right)^3 = \frac{x^3}{(1-x)^3}.$$

We want the coefficient of x^{25} of this function, which is the coefficient of x^{22} in $\dfrac{1}{(1-x)^3}$. This coefficient is $\binom{24}{2} = \boxed{276}$.

14.21 The first child must get at least two toys, so his generating function is $\dfrac{x^2}{1-x}$. The generating function for each of the other 3 children is $\dfrac{1}{1-x}$. So the combined generating function is $\dfrac{x^2}{(1-x)^4}$. We want the coefficient of x^8 of this function, which is also the coefficient of x^6 of $\dfrac{1}{(1-x)^4}$. This coefficient is $\binom{9}{3} = \boxed{84}$.

14.22 The generating function for each type of penny is $(1 + x + x^2 + \cdots)$, and the generating function for each type of nickel is $(1 + x^5 + x^{10} + x^{15} + \cdots)$. Since there are 3 types of pennies and 2 types of nickels, the combined generating function is

$$\boxed{(1 + x + x^2 + x^3 + \cdots)^3(1 + x^5 + x^{10} + x^{15} + \cdots)^2} = \boxed{\frac{1}{(1-x)^3(1-x^5)^2}}.$$

14.23 The generating function for each of Sara and me is

$$x + x^3 + x^5 + \cdots = x(1 + x^2 + x^4 + \cdots) = \frac{x}{1-x^2}.$$

The generating function for Krishna is

$$1 + x^3 + x^6 + \cdots = \frac{1}{1-x^3}.$$

The generating function for Shyster is

$$1 + x^{-1} + x^{-2} = \frac{1 + x + x^2}{x^2}.$$

Hence, the generating function for the whole group is

$$\left(\frac{x}{1-x^2}\right)^2 \cdot \frac{1}{1-x^3} \cdot \frac{1+x+x^2}{x^2} = \frac{x^2(1+x+x^2)}{(1-x^2)^2(1-x^3)x^2}$$

$$= \frac{1+x+x^2}{(1-x^2)^2(1-x^3)}$$

$$= \frac{1+x+x^2}{(1-x^2)^2(1-x)(1+x+x^2)}$$

$$= \frac{1}{(1-x^2)^2(1-x)}.$$

To simplify the denominator, we can multiply top and bottom by $1+x$ to get

$$\frac{1}{(1-x^2)^2(1-x)} = \frac{1+x}{(1-x^2)^2(1-x)(1+x)}$$

$$= \frac{1+x}{(1-x^2)^3}$$

$$= \frac{1}{(1-x^2)^3} + \frac{x}{(1-x^2)^3}.$$

Then

$$\frac{1}{(1-x^2)^3} = \binom{2}{2} + \binom{3}{2}x^2 + \binom{4}{2}x^4 + \cdots + \binom{17}{2}x^{30} + \cdots,$$

so the coefficient of x^{30} is $\binom{17}{2}$, and

$$\frac{x}{(1-x^2)^3} = x\left[\binom{2}{2} + \binom{3}{2}x^2 + \binom{4}{2}x^4 + \cdots\right].$$

All the terms have odd degree, so the coefficient of x^{30} is 0. Hence, the total number of ways of paying the bill is $\binom{17}{2} = \boxed{136}$. (A simple answer might mean a simple counting explanation. Can you come up with one?)

14.24 The generating function for the ten indistinguishable candies is $1 + x + x^2 + \cdots + x^{10}$, and the generating function for the 21 different candies is $(1+x)^{21}$, so we seek the coefficient of x^{10} of the generating function

$$(1 + x + x^2 + \cdots + x^{10})(1+x)^{21} = (1 + x + x^2 + \cdots + x^{10})\left[\binom{21}{0} + \binom{21}{1}x + \binom{21}{2}x^2 + \cdots\right].$$

To obtain a term of degree 10, the term 1 must be multiplied with $\binom{21}{10}x^{10}$, the term x must be multiplied with $\binom{21}{9}x^9$, and so on. Therefore, the coefficient of x^{10} is

$$\binom{21}{10} + \binom{21}{9} + \binom{21}{8} + \binom{21}{7} + \binom{21}{6} + \binom{21}{5} + \binom{21}{4} + \binom{21}{3} + \binom{21}{2} + \binom{21}{1} + \binom{21}{0}$$

$$= 352{,}716 + 293{,}930 + 203{,}490 + 116{,}280 + 54{,}264 + 20{,}349 + 5985 + 1330 + 210 + 21 + 1$$

$$= \boxed{1{,}048{,}576}.$$

A more clever finish would be to notice that $\binom{21}{10} + \cdots + \binom{21}{0} = \boxed{2^{20}}$.

14.25 The generating function for Superman is

$$x + x^3 + x^5 + \cdots = x(1 + x^2 + x^4 + \cdots) = \frac{x}{1-x^2}.$$

The generating function for Batman is

$$1 + x + x^2 + \cdots + x^{40} = \frac{1 - x^{41}}{1 - x}.$$

The generating function for Mighty Mouse is $1 + x + x^2$. Hence, the generating function for all three superheroes is

$$\frac{x}{1 - x^2} \cdot \frac{1 - x^{41}}{1 - x} \cdot (1 + x + x^2) = \frac{x(1 + x + x^2)(1 - x^{41})}{(1 - x^2)(1 - x)}$$

$$= \frac{x(1 + x)(1 + x + x^2)(1 - x^{41})}{(1 - x^2)(1 - x)(1 + x)}$$

$$= \frac{(x + 2x^2 + 2x^3 + x^4)(1 - x^{41})}{(1 - x^2)^2}$$

$$= (x + 2x^2 + 2x^3 + x^4 - x^{42} - 2x^{43} - 2x^{44} - x^{45})\left[\binom{1}{1} + \binom{2}{1}x^2 + \binom{3}{1}x^4 + \cdots\right].$$

(a) We want to find the coefficient of x^{37} in the expression above. All the terms in the second factor have even degree, so to obtain a term with degree x^{37}, we only need to consider the terms in the first factor whose degrees are odd and at most 37. The term x must be multiplied by $\binom{19}{1}x^{36}$, and the term $2x^3$ must be multiplied by $\binom{18}{1}x^{34}$. Hence, the coefficient of x^{37} is $\binom{19}{1} + 2\binom{18}{1} = \boxed{55}$.

(b) We want to find the coefficient of x^{87} in the expression above. All the terms in the second factor have even degree, so to obtain a term with degree x^{87}, we only need to consider the terms in the first factor whose degrees are odd. The term x must be multiplied by $\binom{44}{1}x^{86}$, and so on. Hence, the coefficient of x^{87} is

$$\binom{44}{1} + 2\binom{43}{1} - 2\binom{23}{1} - \binom{22}{1} = 44 + 2 \cdot 43 - 2 \cdot 23 - 22 = \boxed{62}.$$

14.26 The generating function for each y_i is

$$x + x^2 + \cdots + x^{12} = x(1 + x + \cdots + x^{11}) = x \cdot \frac{1 - x^{12}}{1 - x},$$

so the generating function for the sum $y_1 + y_2 + y_3 + y_4$ is

$$\left(x \cdot \frac{1 - x^{12}}{1 - x}\right)^4 = x^4 \cdot \frac{(1 - x^{12})^4}{(1 - x)^4}$$

$$= x^4(1 - 4x^{12} + 6x^{24} - 4x^{36} + x^{48})\left[\binom{3}{3} + \binom{4}{3}x + \binom{5}{3}x^2 + \cdots\right].$$

We seek the coefficient of x^{30}. Because of the factor of x^4, the coefficient of x^{30} in this expression is the same as the coefficient of x^{26} in

$$(1 - 4x^{12} + 6x^{24} - 4x^{36} + x^{48})\left[\binom{3}{3} + \binom{4}{3}x + \binom{5}{3}x^2 + \cdots\right].$$

To obtain a term of degree 26, the term 1 must be multiplied by $\binom{29}{3}x^{26}$, the term $-4x^{12}$ must be multiplied by $\binom{17}{3}x^{14}$, and the term $6x^{24}$ must be multiplied by $\binom{5}{3}x^2$. Hence, the coefficient of x^{26} is

$$\binom{29}{3} - 4\binom{17}{3} + 6\binom{5}{3} = 3654 - 4 \cdot 680 + 6 \cdot 10 = \boxed{994}.$$

14.27 Let $a = y + z$. Then

$$(x + y + z)^{2006} + (x - y - z)^{2006} = (x + a)^{2006} + (x - a)^{2006}$$

$$= \left[x^{2006} + \binom{2006}{1} x^{2005} a + \binom{2006}{2} x^{2004} a^2 + \cdots + a^{2006} \right]$$

$$+ \left[x^{2006} - \binom{2006}{1} x^{2005} a + \binom{2006}{2} x^{2004} a^2 - \cdots + a^{2006} \right]$$

$$= 2x^{2006} + 2 \binom{2006}{2} x^{2004} a^2 + \cdots + 2a^{2006}$$

$$= 2x^{2006} + 2 \binom{2006}{2} x^{2004} (y + z)^2 + 2 \binom{2006}{4} x^{2002} (y + z)^4 + \cdots + 2(y + z)^{2006}.$$

In this sum, each term has the form

$$t_k = 2 \binom{2006}{2k} x^{2006-2k} (y + z)^{2k},$$

where $0 \le k \le 1003$. If we were to expand t_k for each k, then no term in t_k could be equal to another term in a different t_j, since each term of t_k shares a unique number as the degree of x, namely $2006 - 2k$.

Expanding t_k, we obtain

$$t_k = 2 \binom{2006}{2k} x^{2006-2k} \left[y^{2k} + \binom{2k}{1} y^{2k-1} z + \binom{2k}{2} y^{2k-2} z^2 + \cdots + z^{2k} \right],$$

which contains $2k + 1$ terms.

Therefore, the number of terms in the sum, when expanded and simplified, is

$$\sum_{k=0}^{1003} (2k + 1) = 2 \sum_{k=0}^{1003} k + \sum_{k=0}^{1003} 1$$

$$= 2 \cdot \frac{1003 \cdot 1004}{2} + 1004$$

$$= \boxed{1{,}008{,}016}.$$

Challenge Problems

14.28 We have the identity

$$\frac{1}{(1 - x)^2} = \sum_{k=0}^{\infty} \binom{k + 1}{1} x^k = \sum_{k=0}^{\infty} (k + 1) x^k.$$

Multiplying both sides by x, we get

$$\frac{x}{(1 - x)^2} = \sum_{k=0}^{\infty} (k + 1) x^{k+1} = \sum_{k=0}^{\infty} k x^k.$$

In particular, for $x = 1/3$,

$$\sum_{k=0}^{\infty} k \left(\frac{1}{3} \right)^k = \frac{1/3}{(1 - 1/3)^2} = \boxed{\frac{3}{4}}.$$

14.29 Factor $(1 + x + x^2 + x^3)$ as $(1 + x^2)(1 + x)$, so that $Q(n,k)$ is the coefficient of x^k in $(1 + x^2)^n(1 + x)^n$. We can write this in terms of generating functions as:

$$\sum_{k=0}^{\infty} Q(n,k)x^k = (1 + x^2)^n(1 + x)^n$$

$$= \left(\sum_{j=0}^{n} \binom{n}{j}x^{2j}\right)\left(\sum_{i=0}^{n} \binom{n}{i}x^{i}\right)$$

$$= \sum_{j=0}^{n}\sum_{i=0}^{n} \binom{n}{j}\binom{n}{i}x^{2j+i}.$$

We can now see that to get an x^k term in this last sum, we must have $2j + i = k$, so $i = k - 2j$. The sum of these coefficients will be:

$$Q(n,k) = \sum_{j=0}^{n} \binom{n}{j}\binom{n}{k - 2j},$$

and to finish, note that if $j > k$, then $k - 2j < 0$, so we can delete the terms with $j > k$ and write

$$Q(n,k) = \sum_{j=0}^{k} \binom{n}{j}\binom{n}{k - 2j}.$$

Note that this generating function solution can be reinterpreted to give a counting solution. The function $(1 + x + x^2 + x^3)^n$ is the generating function for how many ways a group of n people can pay a bill if each person gives 0, 1, 2, or 3 dollars. Thus, the coefficient of x^k is the number of ways the people can pay a total of k dollars.

We pay our bill by first choosing j people to pay \$2, then choosing $k - 2j$ people to pay \$1. Some people will be chosen both times, and end up paying \$3. Some people do not get chosen and pay nothing. In fact, as we sum over all possible j, we count every possible way of making payment exactly once, as for any given arrangement of paying, we can determine the j people who get selected to pay \$2 and the $k - 2j$ who get selected to pay \$1. Hence,

$$\sum_{j=0}^{k} \binom{n}{j}\binom{n}{k - 2j}$$

must be the coefficient of x^k in the expansion of $(1 + x + x^2 + x^3)^n$.

14.30

(a) We prove the result by induction on n. For the base case $n = 1$, we have:

$$(x + y)^{-1} = \frac{1}{x + y} = \frac{1/x}{1 + y/x}$$

$$= \frac{1}{x}\left(1 - \frac{y}{x} + \left(\frac{y}{x}\right)^2 - \cdots\right)$$

$$= \frac{1}{x} - \frac{y}{x^2} + \frac{y^2}{x^3} - \cdots$$

$$= x^{-1} - x^{-2}y + x^{-3}y^2 - \cdots.$$

The coefficient of $x^{-(1+k)}y^k$ is $(-1)^k = (-1)^k\binom{k}{k} = (-1)^k\binom{1+k-1}{k}$, establishing the base case of the induction.

Now assume that the result is true for some positive integer n. We compute $(x + y)^{-(n+1)}$ as follows:

$$(x + y)^{-(n+1)} = (x + y)^{-1}(x + y)^{-n}$$

$$= \left(x^{-1} - x^{-2}y + x^{-3}y^2 - \cdots\right)\left(\binom{n-1}{0}x^{-n} - \binom{n}{1}x^{-(n+1)}y + \binom{n+1}{2}x^{-(n+2)}y^2 - \cdots\right)$$

$$= \left(\sum_{i=0}^{\infty}(-1)^i x^{-(i+1)}y^i\right)\left(\sum_{j=0}^{\infty}(-1)^j\binom{n+j-1}{j}x^{-(n+j)}y^j\right).$$

The $x^{-(n+k+1)}y^k$ term of this product arises from terms of the sums with $i + j = k$. Therefore,

$$a_k = \sum_{i+j=k}(-1)^i(-1)^j\binom{n+j-1}{j}$$

$$= \sum_{j=0}^{k}(-1)^k\binom{n+j-1}{j}$$

$$= \left(\sum_{j=0}^{k}\binom{n+j-1}{j}\right)(-1)^k.$$

We can apply the Hockey Stick identity to the sum of binomial coefficients in the last line above:

$$\sum_{j=0}^{k}\binom{n+j-1}{j} = \sum_{j=0}^{k}\binom{n+j-1}{n-1} = \binom{n+k}{n} = \binom{(n+1)+k-1}{k}.$$

Therefore, we conclude that

$$a_k = (-1)^k\binom{(n+1)+k-1}{k},$$

completing the induction.

We could also have used the identity

$$\frac{1}{(1-x)^n} = \binom{n-1}{n-1} + \binom{n}{n-1}x + \binom{n+1}{n-1}x^2 + \cdots.$$

Then

$$(x + y)^{-n} = \frac{1}{(x+y)^n}$$

$$= \frac{1}{x^n} \cdot \frac{1}{(1 + y/x)^n}$$

$$= \frac{1}{x^n} \cdot \frac{1}{[1 - (-y/x)]^n}$$

$$= \frac{1}{x^n}\left[\binom{n-1}{n-1} + \binom{n}{n-1}\left(-\frac{y}{x}\right) + \binom{n+1}{n-1}\left(-\frac{y}{x}\right)^2 + \cdots\right]$$

$$= \frac{1}{x^n}\left[\binom{n-1}{n-1} - \binom{n}{n-1}\frac{y}{x} + \binom{n+1}{n-1}\frac{y^2}{x^2} + \cdots\right]$$

$$= \binom{n-1}{n-1}x^{-n} - \binom{n}{n-1}x^{-(n+1)}y + \binom{n+1}{n-1}x^{-(n+2)}y^2 + \cdots.$$

Thus,

$$a_k = (-1)^k\binom{n+k-1}{n-1} = (-1)^k\binom{n+k-1}{k}.$$

(b)   We think about how we normally compute binomial coefficients. If n and k are both positive, we write:

$$\binom{n}{k} = \frac{n!}{k!(n-k)!} = \frac{n(n-1)(n-2)\cdots(n-k+1)}{k!}.$$

The numerator is the product of k consecutive integers, the largest of which is n, and the denominator is $k!$. Let's simply do the same procedure with $-n$: put the product of k consecutive integers, the largest of which is $-n$, in the numerator, and put $k!$ in the denominator:

$$\binom{-n}{k} = \frac{(-n)(-n-1)(-n-2)\cdots(-n-k+1)}{k!}.$$

There are k negative terms in the numerator, so we can factor $(-1)^k$ out and simplify:

$$\binom{-n}{k} = (-1)^k \frac{(n)(n+1)(n+2)\cdots(n+k-1)}{k!}$$

$$= (-1)^k \frac{(n+k-1)!}{k!(n-1)!}$$

$$= (-1)^k \binom{n+k-1}{k}$$

$$= a_k.$$

14.31   The generating function for the nonnegative integers is

$$1 + t + t^2 + \cdots = \frac{1}{1-t},$$

and the generating function for the nonnegative integers of the form $3y$ is

$$1 + t^3 + t^6 + t^9 + \cdots = \frac{1}{1-t^3},$$

so the generating function for the nonnegative integers of the form $x + 3y$ is

$$\frac{1}{1-t} \cdot \frac{1}{1-t^3} = \frac{1}{(1-t)(1-t^3)}.$$

In particular, the number of solutions of $x + 3y = 2k - 1$ is the coefficient of t^{2k-1}.

In general, for $1 \le m \le k$, the mth equation in the system is given by

$$(2m-1)x + (2m+1)y = 2k - (2m-1).$$

The generating function for the values of the LHS of the above equation is:

$$(1 + t^{2m-1} + t^{2(2m-1)} + \cdots)(1 + t^{2m+1} + t^{2(2m+1)} + \cdots) = \frac{1}{1-t^{2m-1}} \cdot \frac{1}{1-t^{2m+1}}$$

$$= \frac{1}{(1-t^{2m-1})(1-t^{2m+1})},$$

and the number of solutions is the coefficient of $t^{2k-(2m-1)}$. This means that as m varies, the degree of the term whose coefficient we seek varies as well.

We can set all the degrees to be equal as follows: the coefficient of $t^{2k-(2m-1)}$ in

$$\frac{1}{(1-t^{2m-1})(1-t^{2m+1})}$$

is equal to the coefficient of t^{2k-1} in

$$\frac{t^{2m-2}}{(1-t^{2m-1})(1-t^{2m+1})}.$$

Hence, since no ordered pair (x, y) can be the solution to more than one of the equations, we can sum the generating functions for the number of solutions to each equation, and conclude that the total number of solutions is equal to the coefficient of t^{2k-1} in

$$\sum_{m=1}^{k} \frac{t^{2m-2}}{(1-t^{2m-1})(1-t^{2m+1})}.$$

Let S_k denote this sum. We compute S_k for small values of k:

$$S_1 = \frac{1}{(1-t)(1-t^3)},$$

$$\begin{aligned} S_2 &= \frac{1}{(1-t)(1-t^3)} + \frac{t^2}{(1-t^3)(1-t^5)} \\ &= \frac{1-t^5+t^2(1-t)}{(1-t)(1-t^3)(1-t^5)} \\ &= \frac{1+t^2-t^3-t^5}{(1-t)(1-t^3)(1-t^5)} \\ &= \frac{(1-t^3)(1+t^2)}{(1-t)(1-t^3)(1-t^5)} \\ &= \frac{1+t^2}{(1-t)(1-t^5)}, \end{aligned}$$

$$\begin{aligned} S_3 &= \frac{1+t^2}{(1-t)(1-t^5)} + \frac{t^4}{(1-t^5)(1-t^7)} \\ &= \frac{(1+t^2)(1-t^7)}{(1-t)(1-t^5)(1-t^7)} + \frac{t^4(1-t)}{(1-t)(1-t^5)(1-t^7)} \\ &= \frac{1+t^2+t^4-t^5-t^7-t^9}{(1-t)(1-t^5)(1-t^7)} \\ &= \frac{(1+t^2+t^4)(1-t^5)}{(1-t)(1-t^5)(1-t^7)} \\ &= \frac{1+t^2+t^4}{(1-t)(1-t^7)}. \end{aligned}$$

Based on these values, we guess that

$$S_k = \frac{1+t^2+t^4+\cdots+t^{2(k-1)}}{(1-t)(1-t^{2k+1})}.$$

Since $1+t^2+t^4+\cdots+t^{2(k-1)} = (1-t^{2k})/(1-t^2)$, we can rewrite this formula as

$$S_k = \frac{1-t^{2k}}{(1-t)(1-t^2)(1-t^{2k+1})}.$$

We now prove it by induction.

It is easy to verify that our formula is correct for $k = 1$, which establishes the base case. Now assume that our formula is correct for some positive integer l, so that

$$S_l = \frac{1-t^{2l}}{(1-t)(1-t^2)(1-t^{2l+1})}.$$

Then

$$S_{l+1} = S_l + \frac{t^{2l}}{(1 - t^{2l+1})(1 - t^{2l+3})}$$

$$= \frac{1 - t^{2l}}{(1 - t)(1 - t^2)(1 - t^{2l+1})} + \frac{t^{2l}}{(1 - t^{2l+1})(1 - t^{2l+3})}$$

$$= \frac{(1 - t^{2l})(1 - t^{2l+3})}{(1 - t)(1 - t^2)(1 - t^{2l+1})(1 - t^{2l+3})} + \frac{t^{2l}(1 - t)(1 - t^2)}{(1 - t)(1 - t^2)(1 - t^{2l+1})(1 - t^{2l+3})}$$

$$= \frac{(1 - t^{2l})(1 - t^{2l+3}) + t^{2l}(1 - t)(1 - t^2)}{(1 - t)(1 - t^2)(1 - t^{2l+1})(1 - t^{2l+3})}$$

$$= \frac{1 - t^{2l} - t^{2l+3} + t^{4l+3} + t^{2l} - t^{2l+1} - t^{2l+2} + t^{2l+3}}{(1 - t)(1 - t^2)(1 - t^{2l+1})(1 - t^{2l+3})}$$

$$= \frac{1 - t^{2l+1} - t^{2l+2} + t^{4l+3}}{(1 - t)(1 - t^2)(1 - t^{2l+1})(1 - t^{2l+3})}$$

$$= \frac{(1 - t^{2l+1})(1 - t^{2l+2})}{(1 - t)(1 - t^2)(1 - t^{2l+1})(1 - t^{2l+3})}$$

$$= \frac{1 - t^{2l+2}}{(1 - t)(1 - t^2)(1 - t^{2l+3})}.$$

Hence, our formula holds for $k = l + 1$, and by induction, it holds for all positive integers k.

To find the coefficient of t^{2k-1} in

$$\frac{1 - t^{2k}}{(1 - t)(1 - t^2)(1 - t^{2k+1})},$$

we use the same techniques as in previous problems. We have:

$$\frac{1 - t^{2k}}{(1 - t)(1 - t^2)(1 - t^{2k+1})} = \frac{(1 - t^{2k})(1 + t)}{(1 - t)(1 - t^2)(1 - t^{2k+1})(1 + t)}$$

$$= \frac{(1 - t^{2k})(1 + t)}{(1 - t^2)^2(1 - t^{2k+1})}$$

$$= (1 - t^{2k})(1 + t) \cdot \frac{1}{(1 - t^2)^2} \cdot \frac{1}{1 - t^{2k+1}}$$

$$= (1 + t - t^{2k} - t^{2k+1})\left[1 + \binom{2}{1}t^2 + \binom{3}{1}t^4 + \cdots\right](1 + t^{2k+1} + t^{2(2k+1)} + \cdots).$$

Look at the factor $1 + t^{2k+1} + t^{2(2k+1)} + \cdots$. The terms t^{2k+1}, $t^{2(2k+1)}$, and so on all have degree greater than $2k - 1$, so they cannot affect the coefficient of t^{2k-1}, so they can be dropped. Similarly, the terms $-t^{2k}$ and $-t^{2k+1}$ in the first factor can also be dropped, leaving us with

$$(1 + t)\left[1 + \binom{2}{1}t^2 + \binom{3}{1}t^4 + \cdots\right].$$

Now, each term in the second factor has even degree, and we seek the coefficient of t^{2k-1}, which has odd degree. Hence, the only way to obtain a term with degree $2k - 1$ is to multiply the t in the first factor with the term of degree $2k - 2$ in the second factor. Every term in the second factor is of the form $(i + 1)t^{2i}$, so setting $i = k - 1$, we find that the coefficient is $i + 1 = k$, as desired.

14.32

(a) What is the coefficient of x^n in $(C(x))^2$? Recalling that

$$C(x) = C_0 + C_1 x + C_2 x^2 + \cdots,$$

we see that if we multiply $C(x) \times C(x)$ out, the coefficient of x^n is

$$C_0 C_n + C_1 C_{n-1} + \cdots + C_n C_0.$$

Does this look familiar? It should—it's the recurrence relation for the Catalan numbers! The above sum is equal to C_{n+1}. So the coefficient of x^n in $(C(x))^2$ is C_{n+1}. However, in our generating function for the Catalan numbers, we have the coefficient of x^{n+1} equal to C_{n+1}, so we need to multiply $(C(x))^2$ by x.

Finally, since the resulting polynomial has no constant term, but $C_0 = 1$, we add 1 to get that

$$C(x) = x(C(x))^2 + 1.$$

(b) Move everything in $C(x) = x(C(x))^2 + 1$ to one side:

$$0 = x(C(x))^2 - C(x) + 1,$$

We can view this as a quadratic function in terms of $C(x)$. Then the quadratic formula gives us

$$C(x) = \frac{1 \pm \sqrt{1 - 4x}}{2x}.$$

How do we know whether we want the $\pm$ to be $+$ or $-$? Actually, we don't know, but we can check that in fact the $-$ works and the $+$ doesn't, as we'll see in the next problem.

(c) In order to get a handle on the function

$$\frac{1 - \sqrt{1 - 4x}}{2x},$$

we need to remember that we can use the Binomial Theorem even with non-integer exponents. In particular,

$$(1 + y)^r = 1 + \binom{r}{1} y + \binom{r}{2} y^2 + \binom{r}{3} y^3 + \cdots,$$

where

$$\binom{r}{k} = \frac{r(r-1)(r-2)\cdots(r-k+1)}{k!}.$$

So in our case, the coefficient of x^n in $C(x)$ is equal to the coefficient of x^{n+1} in $(1 - 4x)^{\frac{1}{2}}$, divided by -2. This coefficient is thus

$$-\frac{1}{2} \binom{\frac{1}{2}}{n+1} (-4)^{n+1} = -\frac{1}{2} \frac{\frac{1}{2}(-\frac{1}{2})(-\frac{3}{2}) \cdots (-\frac{2n-1}{2})}{(n+1)!} (-4)^{n+1}.$$

This is a bit ugly but can be simplified with not too much effort. To start, let's collect the $n + 1$ 2's from the denominators of the factors in the numerator, and divide them into the 4's:

$$-\frac{1}{2} \frac{(1)(-1)(-3) \cdots (-(2n-1))}{(n+1)!} (-2)^{n+1}.$$

Next, notice that there are $n + 1$ minus signs that cancel with the minus sign inside $(-2)^{n+1}$, giving:

$$\frac{1}{2} \frac{(1)(3)(5) \cdots (2n-1)}{(n+1)!} 2^{n+1} = \frac{1(3)(5) \cdots (2n-1)}{(n+1)!} 2^n.$$

Multiply numerator and denominator by $n!$, and distribute the 2^n factors amongst the terms of $n!$, so we have:

$$\frac{1(3)(5)\cdots(2n-1)}{(n+1)!}\frac{(2)(4)(6)\cdots(2n)}{n!}.$$

The numerator of the entire expression is now $(2n)!$, so the expression is

$$\frac{(2n)!}{(n+1)!n!}=\frac{1}{n+1}\frac{(2n)!}{n!n!}=\frac{1}{n+1}\binom{2n}{n},$$

our closed-form formula for the Catalan numbers.

CHAPTER 15

Graph Theory

Exercises for Section 15.3

15.3.1 Let E denote the number of edges, and for any nonnegative integer n, let V_n denote the number of vertices with degree n. Each such vertex contributes n to the number of edges, so

$$V_1 + 2V_2 + 3V_3 + \cdots = 2E.$$

The coefficient of E is 2 because each edge is counted twice, once for each of its endpoints.

Reducing this equation modulo 2, we get

$$V_1 + V_3 + V_5 + \cdots \equiv 0 \pmod 2.$$

But $V_1 + V_3 + V_5 + \cdots$ is precisely the number of vertices of odd degree. Hence, this number is even.

15.3.2 Let the graph have n vertices. For the sake of contradiction, suppose that every vertex has a different degree.

The degree of each vertex must be a nonnegative integer from 0 to $n - 1$, and there are exactly n such numbers, so if every vertex has a different degree, then there must be a vertex with every degree from 0 to $n - 1$. However, a vertex with degree 0 is not connected to any other vertices, and a vertex with degree $n - 1$ must be connected to all other vertices, so two such vertices cannot co-exist within the same graph, giving a contradiction.

Therefore, there must be two vertices that have the same degree.

15.3.3 Consider the airline network as a graph. The only vertices of odd degree are New York and San Diego. Let G be the subgraph of all cities that it is possible to fly to from San Diego (including San Diego itself). If New York is not in G, then G has only 1 vertex of odd degree, which is not possible since every graph must have an even number of vertices of odd degree. Therefore, New York must be in G, so it is possible to fly between New York and San Diego.

15.3.4 Consider the train system of Graphdom as a graph, where each city is a vertex and a direct train line is an edge. Let V and W be any two vertices. If there is an edge between V and W, then there's no problem. Otherwise, let S and T be the set of vertices that are adjacent to V and W, respectively, so that both S and T contain exactly 6 vertices. Then V cannot be in T, nor can W be in S. But we count vertices: V, W, the vertices in S, and the vertices in T give us 14 vertices, and there are only 13 vertices in the graph. Hence, S and T must have a vertex U in common, and we can travel by train from V via U to W.

15.3.5

(a) Consider a graph where each vertex corresponds to a line segment, and there is an edge between two vertices if the two corresponding line segments intersect. Then in this graph, there are 7 vertices, and each vertex has degree 3. But then the number of edges would be $7 \cdot 3/2$, which is not an integer. Therefore, such a graph cannot exist, which means it is impossible to draw 7 such line segments.

(b)   It is possible to draw 6 such line segments, as shown in the figure below:

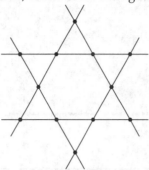

15.3.6   Choose one person, say A. First, we claim that A knows everyone, except possibly for two people. Suppose that there are three people that A does not know, say B, C, and D. Then the quadruple $\{A, B, C, D\}$ violates the given condition, so the number of people that A does not know is at most 2.

If A knows everyone, then we are done. If A does not know some person, then call this person B. Let C and D be two people other than A or B. Then in the quadruple $\{A, B, C, D\}$, the person who knows everyone else in the quadruple cannot be A or B, so it must either be C or D; in particular, C and D always know each other. This tells us two things. First, since C and D were chosen arbitrarily, every pair of people, not including A or B, knows each other. Second, one of C or D must know both A and B. Therefore, one of C or D knows everyone.

15.3.7   Suppose that every pair of vertices in G has an odd number of neighbors in common. We will show that this leads to a contradiction.

Let V be a vertex in G and let $W_1, W_2, \ldots, W_k$ be its neighbors. Consider the subgraph G' of G consisting just of the W_i's together with any edges between them. We are assuming that V and each W_i have an odd number of neighbors in common; this means that the degree of W_i in G' is odd. Thus every vertex in G' has odd degree, which means that k is even (otherwise, G' would have an odd number of vertices of odd degree, which cannot happen). So every vertex in G has even degree.

Consider the set
$$S = \{(i, X) \mid 1 \leq i \leq k \text{ and } X \text{ is a neighbor of } W_i\}.$$

Each W_i has an even number of neighbors, so S has an even number of elements. Also, pairs of the form (i, V) appear k times (once for each $1 \leq i \leq k$), and pairs of the form (i, W_j) each appear an odd number of times, so the total number of such pairs is even (since there are an even number of W_j's). The remaining elements of S are

$$T = \{(i, X) \mid 1 \leq i \leq k \text{ and } X \notin \{V, W_1, \ldots, W_k\} \text{ is a neighbor of } W_i\},$$

and T has an even number of elements. On the other hand, there are an odd number of such vertices X (since G has an even number of vertices, and we've thrown away V and $W_1, \ldots, W_k$), and each one appears an odd number of times in T, since X and V have an odd number of neighbors in common. Thus T has an odd number of elements, giving a contradiction.

Thus G must have a pair of vertices with an even number of neighbors in common.

Exercises for Section 15.4

15.4.1   We know that a tree with n vertices must have between 2 and $n - 1$ leaves (inclusive). Therefore a tree with 3 vertices must have 2 leaves, a tree with 4 vertices can have 2 or 3 leaves, and a tree with 5 vertices can have 2, 3, or 4 leaves. We can indeed draw one tree with 3 vertices, two trees with four vertices, and three trees with five vertices, as shown in the diagram below.

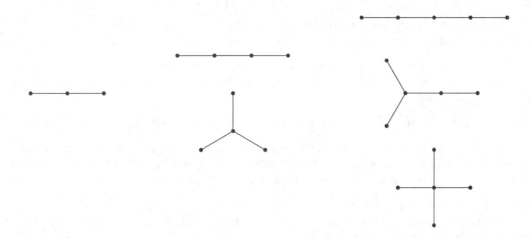

15.4.2 Choose a pair of vertices, say A and B, that are not connected by an edge. (If every pair of vertices is connected by an edge, then any four vertices form a 4-cycle.) Let S and T be the set of vertices that are adjacent to A and B, respectively, so A is not in T and B is not in S.

Since every vertex has degree at least 40, $\#(S) \geq 40$ and $\#(T) \geq 40$. Furthermore, $\#(S \cup T) \leq 78$, since neither A nor B belong to $S \cup T$. Therefore, by PIE,

$$\#(S \cap T) = \#(S) + \#(T) - \#(S \cup T) \geq 40 + 40 - 78 = 2.$$

In other words, sets S and T must have at least two vertices in common. Let these vertices be C and D. Then vertices A, C, B, and D form a 4-cycle.

15.4.3 We prove a stronger result: A minimal path between A and B cannot visit the same vertex twice.

Let p be a path between A and B. Suppose that p visits some vertex twice, say V. Then we can delete from p the portion of the path between the two times that V is visited. This produces a shorter path between A and B. So any minimal path cannot visit any vertex twice. It follows that no edge can be repeated.

15.4.4 First, we show that we can assume that paths p and q don't overlap.

If they do overlap, then let V' be the last vertex that paths p and q have in common when traversing the path p from V to A. Subsequently, let p' be the portion of the path p going from V' to A, and let q' be the portion of the path q going from V' to B.

Then by construction, p' cannot overlap with any part of q, so it does not overlap with q'. Thus, we can proceed in the proof by using paths p' and q' instead of p and q. (It is as if we chose vertex V' originally, instead of vertex V.)

Now we show that we can assume that paths p and q do not include the edge e between A and B, supposing such an edge exists. Since paths p and q do not overlap, both paths cannot include e, which means that at most one of these paths includes e. With loss of generality, let path p include edge e.

Since p is a minimal path from V to A, e must be the last edge in p. Let p' be the portion of the path going from V to B. Then going from V to B along p', and then back to V by going along q in reverse creates a cycle. Let c denote this cycle.

Since path p has even length, path p' has odd length. Also, path q has even length, which means that cycle c has odd length. However, this contradicts the fact that G has cycles of odd length. Therefore, the edge e cannot exist.

15.4.5 Let G be a connected, bipartite graph. Since G is bipartite, the vertices of G can be partitioned into two sets S and T, such that every edge of G connects a vertex in S to a vertex in T.

For the sake of contradiction, suppose that G contains a cycle of odd length. Let the vertices in this odd cycle be $v_1, v_2, \ldots, v_n, v_1$, where n is odd. Without loss of generality, let v_1 be in S. Since v_1 is connected to v_2 by an edge, v_2 must be in T. Similarly, since v_2 is connected to v_3 by an edge, v_3 must be in S, and so on.

Subsequently, all the vertices with an odd index must be in S, and all the vertices with an even index must be in T. Since n is odd, v_n is in S, which means v_1 is in T. However, v_1 is in S, which is a contradiction. Therefore, G cannot contain any odd cycles.

15.4.6 First, we prove that if the graph G contains no odd cycles, then G is bipartite.

Let $G_1, G_2, \ldots, G_c$ be the connected components of G. Since G does not contain any odd cycles, neither does any of its connected components. Therefore, each connected component G_i is bipartite, meaning that the vertices in G_i can be partitioned into two sets S_i and T_i, such that every edge of G_i connects a vertex in S_i to a vertex in T_i.

Now, let $S = S_1 \cup S_2 \cup \cdots \cup S_c$ and $T = T_1 \cup T_2 \cup \cdots \cup T_c$, so sets S and T partition the vertices of G. Furthermore, each edge in G belongs to some connected component G_i, and each edge in G_i connects a vertex in S_i to a vertex in T_i. Hence, every edge in G connects a vertex in S to a vertex in T. Therefore, G is bipartite.

Next, we prove that if G is bipartite, then G contains no odd cycles.

Since G is bipartite, the vertices of G can be partitioned into two sets S and T such that every edge of G connects a vertex in S to a vertex in T. For the sake of contradiction, suppose that G contains a cycle of odd length. Then this odd cycle must belong to one of the connected components G_i.

Let S_i be the set of vertices in both S and G_i, and let T_i be the set of vertices in both T and G_i, so the sets S_i and T_i partition the vertices of G_i. Furthermore, since G_i is a connected component, every edge in G_i connects a vertex in S_i to a vertex in T_i. Hence, the graph G_i is bipartite, which means that it cannot contain an odd cycle, a contradiction. Therefore, G has no odd cycles.

15.4.7 Let V be the vertex of maximum degree in the graph, and let d be this degree. Let S be the set of vertices that are adjacent to V, so $\#(S) = d$. Finally, let T be the set of vertices other than those in S, so $\#(T) = 10 - d$.

Note that no two vertices in S can be connected by an edge (because such an edge would create a triangle), so every edge of the graph has at least one endpoint in T. Every vertex in T has degree at most d (by definition of d), so the the number of edges in the graph is at most

$$d(10 - d) = 10d - d^2 = 25 - (d^2 - 10d + 25) = 25 - (d - 5)^2 \leq \boxed{25}.$$

Now, we construct such a graph with 25 edges. Let S be a set with 5 vertices, and let T be a set with 5 vertices. Connect every vertex in S to every vertex in T by an edge. Then this graph contains $5 \cdot 5 = 25$ edges, and is by definition bipartite, so it cannot contain any odd cycles, and in particular it does not contain any triangles.

Exercises for Section 15.5

15.5.1 This graph is actually the graph K_5, which we showed in Problem 15.13 is $\boxed{\text{not planar}}$.

15.5.2 Label the vertices with the numbers 1 through 6, as shown below. If we delete the edge connecting vertices 2 and 3, and the edge connecting vertices 5 and 6, then we obtain the same bipartite graph examined in Problem 15.15, as shown below.

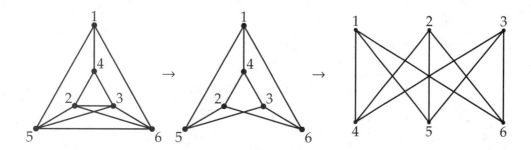

If the original graph was planar, then we could draw a planar representation, delete the two edges, and obtain a planar representation of our bipartite graph. But we know that this bipartite graph is not planar, from Problem 15.15, so the original graph is $\boxed{\text{not planar}}$.

15.5.3 Suppose K_n was planar for some $n \geq 5$. Then we could draw a planar representation of K_n and delete $n - 5$ of the vertices and all of the edges connected to at least one of these $n - 5$ vertices. This would produce a planar representation of K_5, which we know does not exist. Therefore, K_n is not planar for $n \geq 5$.

15.5.4 Let G be a planar graph, and suppose that every vertex in G has degree at least 6. If G is not connected, then consider just one connected component of G, so that we may assume that G is connected. Then $2E \geq 6V$, since every edge has two endpoints, so $V \leq E/3$. Also, since G is connected, planar, and has more than one edge, we have $F \leq 2E/3$.

Then

$$V - E + F \leq \frac{E}{3} - E + \frac{2E}{3} = 0,$$

but $V - E + F = 2$ for every connected planar graph, giving a contradiction. Therefore, G must contain a vertex with degree less than 6.

15.5.5

(a) If a knight is on a white square, then it can only move to a black square, and vice versa. Therefore, every edge in the graph connects a white square to a black square. Hence, the graph is bipartite, with the two underlying sets being the set of white squares and the set of black squares.

(b) First, label the squares of the 4×4 checkerboard with the numbers 1 through 16, as shown. The figure on the right depicts a subgraph of the graph in the problem, where each vertex is identified by the label of the corresponding square. (In other words, we obtain the graph on the right by removing certain edges from the graph in the problem.)

1	2	3	4
5	6	7	8
9	10	11	12
13	14	15	16

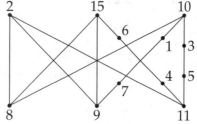

If we "remove" the vertices labeled 1, 3, 4, 5, 6, and 7, then we obtain a graph that is the same as $K_{3,3}$, the bipartite graph from Problem 15.15. (We call it $K_{3,3}$ because it has 3 vertices in each half of the graph, and it is "complete" in the sense that it has every possible edge between the two halves.) We can then argue as follows: If the graph in the problem was planar, then we could draw it in the plane and remove the unnecessary edges and the six vertices listed above, to obtain a planar representation of $K_{3,3}$. However, we know that $K_{3,3}$ is not planar, so the graph in the problem is $\boxed{\text{not planar}}$.

15.5.6

(a) Since every vertex has degree d and every edge has two endpoints, $2E = dV$, so $V = 2E/d$. Similarly, since every face has b boundary edges and every edge borders two faces, $2E = bF$, so $F = 2E/b$. Therefore,

$$2 = V - E + F = \frac{2E}{d} - E + \frac{2E}{b} = \frac{(2b + 2d - bd)E}{bd},$$

so

$$E = \frac{2bd}{2b + 2d - bd},$$

which means

$$V = \frac{2E}{d} = \frac{4b}{2b + 2d - bd}$$

and

$$F = \frac{2E}{b} = \frac{4d}{2b + 2d - bd}.$$

(b) Since E is positive, $2b + 2d - bd > 0$, so

$$(d - 2)(b - 2) = bd - 2b - 2d + 4 < 4.$$

(c) Since $d \geq 3$ and $b \geq 3$, $(d - 2)(b - 2)$ is a positive integer. By part (b), $(d - 2)(b - 2)$ is less than 4, so $(d - 2)(b - 2)$ is equal to 1, 2, or 3.

   If $(d - 2)(b - 2) = 1$, then $d - 2 = b - 2 = 1$, so $d = b = 3$. These parameters are satisfied by the following graph.

   If $(d - 2)(b - 2) = 2$, then $d - 2 = 1$ and $b - 2 = 2$, or $d - 2 = 2$ and $b - 2 = 1$, which leads to the solutions $(d, b) = (3, 4)$ and $(4, 3)$, respectively. These parameters are satisfied by the following graphs.

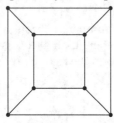
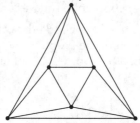

   If $(d - 2)(b - 2) = 3$, then $d - 2 = 1$ and $b - 2 = 3$, or $d - 2 = 3$ and $b - 2 = 1$, which leads to the solutions $(d, b) = (3, 5)$ and $(5, 3)$, respectively. These parameters are satisfied by the following graphs.

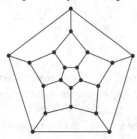
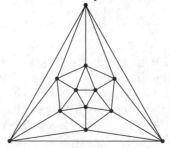

Exercises for Section 15.6

15.6.1

(a) There are 8 vertices of degree 3. A connected graph has an Eulerian path if and only if the number of vertices of odd degree is at most 2, so this graph does not have an Eulerian path, nor does it have an Eulerian cycle.

(b) Label the squares of the 4×4 checkerboard with the numbers 1 through 16, as below:

1	2	3	4
5	6	7	8
9	10	11	12
13	14	15	16

We say that numbers i and j are *adjacent* if a knight on square i can move to square j. Note that 1 is adjacent only to 7 and 10, and 16 is also adjacent only to 7 and 10. Therefore, if square 1 is not the first square nor the last square on the Hamiltonian path, then its neighbors on the path must be squares 7 and 10. But the same is true for square 16, which means that one of squares 1 or 16 must be the first square or the last square. Without loss of generality, assume that square 1 is the first square in the Hamiltonian path.

Furthermore, if square 1 is the first square, then either square 7 or 10 must be the second square, square 16 must be the third square, and then square 7 or 10 (whichever was not the second square) must be the fourth square. Without loss of generality, assume that square 10 is the second square and square 7 is the fourth square.

Note that 4 is adjacent only to 6 and 11, and 13 is also adjacent only to 6 and 11. Therefore, by the same argument, one of the squares 4 or 13 must be the last square. Without loss of generality, assume that square 4 is the last square in the Hamiltonian path.

Furthermore, if square 4 is the last square, then either square 6 or 11 must be the second-last square, square 13 must be the third-last square, and then square 6 or 11 (whichever was not the second-last square) must be the fourth-last square. Without loss of generality, assume that square 11 is the second-last square and square 6 is the fourth-last square.

With squares 1, 4, 6, 7, 10, 11, 13, and 16 already used up, the following graph shows the remaining edges that can be used in a Hamiltonian path:

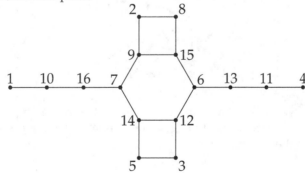

The graph illustrates that if the Hamiltonian path passes through any of the squares 2, 8, 9, or 15, then it cannot pass through any of the squares 3, 5, 12, or 14, and vice versa. Therefore, there is no Hamiltonian path.

15.6.2 We prove the result using strong induction.

First, we prove the result for the base case $n = 1$. Let G be a graph with 2 vertices of odd degree. We must show that there is a path that includes all the edges. But this is an Eulerian path, which we know exists. Therefore, the result is true for $n = 1$.

Now, assume that the result is true for all positive integers $n = 1, 2, \ldots, k - 1$, for some positive integer $k \geq 2$. Let G be a graph with $2k$ vertices of odd degree.

Let V_1 and V_2 be two vertices of odd degree in G, and let p be a simple path from V_1 to V_2. If we delete every edge in p, then we are left with a graph G' with $2k - 2$ vertices of odd degree. The remaining graph G' may not be connected, so let the connected components of G' be $G_1, G_2, \ldots, G_c$. For $1 \leq i \leq c$, let $2n_i$ be the number of vertices of odd degree in G_i, so $2n_1 + 2n_2 + \cdots + 2n_c = 2k - 2$.

First, we deal with the case that some n_i is equal to 0. If n_i is equal to 0, then the connected component G_i has an Eulerian cycle. Furthermore, since the graph G was connected, the path p and graph G_i must have some vertex in common, say V. We can "absorb" the graph G_i into path p as follows: Start at the first vertex of p and go along p until you hit V. Then go along the Eulerian cycle of G_i that begins and ends at V, and then traverse the the rest of p. This new path is still simple. We can absorb any graph G_i where $n_i = 0$ in this way, and so we can assume that $n_i \geq 1$ for all i.

Since $2n_1 + 2n_2 + \cdots + 2n_c = 2k - 2$, we have $2n_i < 2k$ for all i, so by the inductive hypothesis, G_i can be decomposed into n_i disjoint paths that include all of the edges of G_i. Thus, G' can be decomposed into $n_1 + n_2 + \cdots + n_c = (2k - 2)/2 = k - 1$ disjoint paths that include all of the edges of G'. Then including p, the original graph G can be decomposed into $(k - 1) + 1 = k$ disjoint paths that include all of the edges of G.

Therefore, the result is true for $n = k$, and by induction, for all positive integers n.

15.6.3 There are many possible Hamiltonian paths: one example is shown at right. The path shown at right cannot be extended to a Hamiltonian cycle, because the two ends of the path are not adjacent.

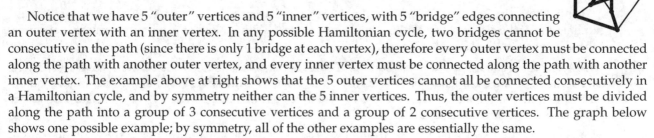

Notice that we have 5 "outer" vertices and 5 "inner" vertices, with 5 "bridge" edges connecting an outer vertex with an inner vertex. In any possible Hamiltonian cycle, two bridges cannot be consecutive in the path (since there is only 1 bridge at each vertex), therefore every outer vertex must be connected along the path with another outer vertex, and every inner vertex must be connected along the path with another inner vertex. The example above at right shows that the 5 outer vertices cannot all be connected consecutively in a Hamiltonian cycle, and by symmetry neither can the 5 inner vertices. Thus, the outer vertices must be divided along the path into a group of 3 consecutive vertices and a group of 2 consecutive vertices. The graph below shows one possible example; by symmetry, all of the other examples are essentially the same.

But from here, there is no way to complete the cycle: in particular, the top inner point, which is not yet connected to the path, must be connected to both of the lower inner points, but this would create a cycle with 5 points that can not link up with the rest of the path:

Thus there is no Hamiltonian cycle.

15.6.4 We prove the result by induction on n.

First, we prove the result for the base case. For $n = 2$, we have the Hamiltonian cycle (0,0), (0,1), (1,1), (1,0), (0,0).

Now, assume that the result is true for some positive integer $n = k \geq 2$. Let $v_1, v_2, \ldots, v_{2^k}, v_1$ be a Hamiltonian cycle on a k-dimensional cube.

For $1 \leq i \leq 2^k$, let a_i be the point that is obtained when the coordinate of 0 is added to the end of v_i (so for example, the point (1, 0, 0, 1) would become (1, 0, 0, 1, 0)), and let b_i be the point that is obtained when the coordinate of 1 is added to the end of v_i. We claim that the sequence of points

$$a_1, \quad a_2, \quad a_3, \quad \ldots, \quad a_{2^k}, \quad b_{2^k}, \quad b_{2^k-1}, \quad \ldots, \quad b_1, \quad a_1$$

is a Hamiltonian cycle on a $(k + 1)$-dimensional cube.

First, we show that any two adjacent points in this sequence differ in exactly one coordinate. Let $1 \leq i \leq 2^k - 1$. Then a_i and a_{i+1} differ in exactly one coordinate, because they are obtained by adding a 0 to the end of v_i and v_{i+1}, respectively, and v_i and v_{i+1} differ in exactly one coordinate. Similarly, b_{i+1} and b_i differ in exactly one coordinate, because they are obtained by adding a 1 to the end of v_{i+1} and v_i, respectively.

Finally, a_{2^k} and b_{2^k} differ in exactly one coordinate, because they are obtained by adding a 0 and a 1 to v_{2^k}, respectively, and a_1 and b_1 differ in exactly one coordinate, because they are obtained by adding a 0 and a 1 to v_1, respectively. Therefore, any two adjacent points in this sequence differ in exactly one coordinate, which means it is a cycle on a $(k + 1)$-dimensional cube.

To prove that it is a Hamiltonian cycle, we must show that every point in the $(k + 1)$-dimensional cube appears exactly once in our sequence. Let p be a point in the $(k + 1)$-dimensional cube, and let q be the point obtained when the last coordinate of p is deleted. Then q is in the k-dimensional cube, so $q = v_i$ for some $1 \leq i \leq 2^k$. Then p is equal to a_i or b_i, depending on whether the last coordinate of p is 0 or 1, respectively, and each a_i and b_i appears exactly once in our sequence. Hence, our sequence is a Hamiltonian cycle on a $(k + 1)$-dimensional cube.

In other words, the result is true for $n = k + 1$, so by induction, it is true for all positive integers $n \geq 2$.

Review Problems

15.20

(a) $\boxed{\text{Yes}}$. The problem is equivalent to determining if there is a graph with 50 vertices, such that each vertex has degree 3. It is not difficult to construct such a graph. For example, arrange the 50 vertices in a circle. Then connect each vertex to its two neighbors, and to the vertex that is diametrically opposite.

(b) $\boxed{\text{No}}$. The problem is equivalent to determining if there is a graph with 35 vertices, such that each vertex has degree 3. In such a graph, the number of edges would be $3 \cdot 35/2$, which is not an integer. Therefore, no such graph exists.

15.21 We rephrase the problem in graph-theoretic terms. Let G be a graph with 17 vertices. There is an edge between every pair of vertices, and each edge is colored either red (if the people are friends), yellow (if they are enemies), or blue (if they don't know each other). We must show that there is a monochromatic triangle (that is, we must show that there are three vertices such that all of the edges connecting these three vertices have the same color).

Choose one vertex, say v. This vertex is connected to 16 other vertices. By the Pigeonhole Principle, at least 6 of these vertices are connected to v with edges of the same color, say blue. Let these 6 vertices be $w_1, w_2, \ldots, w_6$. If any pair of these six vertices are connected by a blue edge, then we are done.

Otherwise, every pair of these six vertices is connected by a red edge or yellow edge. Then by Problem 15.4, there is either a red triangle or a yellow triangle among these six vertices, as desired.

15.22   Recasting the problem in terms of graph theory, we are given a graph with 6 vertices (the students) and 7 edges (the games). The other condition on this graph is that given any 3 vertices, there must be at least 1 edge between some 2 of them. Now we can try to prove the two statements in terms of our graph.

(a)   *There exists a vertex with degree at least 3.* There doesn't seem to be a clear way to attack this directly. But the statement that we are trying to prove is equivalent to the statement "It is impossible for every vertex to have degree less than 3." This we *can* attack directly: if every vertex had degree at most 2, then the graph would have at most $6(2)/2 = 6$ edges. But we are given that the graph has 7 edges, so this is impossible. Therefore, there must exist a vertex with degree at least 3.

(b)   *There exists a subgraph that is a triangle.* This should remind you of Problem 15.4. Indeed, Problem 15.4 proves this immediately, as we know from Problem 15.4 that our graph either must have a triangle or it must have 3 vertices with no edges between them. But the latter is impossible—the conditions of our problem specifically prohibit it. Therefore, there must be a triangle.

15.23   To construct a path of length 2 (which has three vertices), we choose the middle vertex, say v_i. Then there are d_i choices for the first vertex, and d_i choices for the third vertex, for a total of d_i^2 total choices. (Note that the first and third vertices could be the same—this would give us a path with a "u-turn.") Hence, summing over all vertices, we find that there are $\boxed{d_1^2 + d_2^2 + \cdots + d_n^2}$ paths of length 2.

15.24   There exists a path from A to B with length $d(A, B)$, and a path from B to C with length $d(B, C)$. Combining these paths produce a path from A to C with length $d(A, B) + d(B, C)$, which means the minimal path from A to C cannot be any longer than this one. Hence, $d(A, C) \le d(A, B) + d(B, C)$.

15.25   Let V be the number of vertices. Every vertex has degree four, and every edge has two endpoints, so $2E = 4V$, or $E = 2V$. Also, $F = 10$, so

$$V - E + F = V - 2V + 10 = 2,$$

which means $V = \boxed{8}$.

15.26   Let P be the number of faces bordered by 5 edges, and let H be the number of faces bordered by 6 edges. Then the number of faces is $F = P + H$, and the number of edges is $E = (5P + 6H)/2$. (We divide by 2 because every edge borders 2 faces.) We are given that every vertex has degree 3, so the number of vertices is $V = 2E/3 = (5P + 6H)/3$. Then by Euler's formula,

$$2 = V - E + F = \frac{5P + 6H}{3} - \frac{5P + 6H}{2} + P + H = \frac{P}{6}.$$

Therefore, $P = \boxed{12}$.

15.27   We rephrase the problem in graph-theoretic terms: let G be a graph with n vertices, such that every vertex has degree at least 1. For any subset of vertices, the number of edges among these vertices is never exactly two. Prove that there is a vertex that is connected to every other vertex.

We use the extremal principle, by focusing on the most "extreme" vertex. Specifically, let V be the vertex of maximum degree in the graph, and let d be its degree. If $d = 1$, then every vertex in G has degree 1. If there is only one edge in the graph, then there are only two vertices, and the condition in the problem is satisfied. Otherwise, take any two edges. Since every vertex in G has degree 1, these two edges cannot have any endpoints in common, so the set of four vertices that are the endpoints of these two edges violates the condition that no subset of vertices has 2 edges among them. So we have $d \ge 2$.

Let S be the set of vertices that are adjacent to V, so $d = \#(S)$, and let $S' = S \cup \{V\}$. Let A and B be 2 arbitrary vertices in S. The number of edges connecting vertices V, A, and B is not exactly two, so vertices A and B must also be connected by an edge. Since vertices A and B were chosen arbitrarily, any pair of vertices in S are connected by an edge. Furthermore, since the maximum degree of a vertex in G is d, each vertex in S' can only be connected to the other d vertices in S'. In other words, the vertices in S' form a copy of K_{d+1}, the complete graph with $d + 1$ vertices, and are a connected component of G.

If there is another vertex C in G but not in S', then since the degree of C is at least 1, C must be connected to some other vertex D also not in S'. But then if A and B are any two vertices in S', then the set $\{A, B, C, D\}$ has exactly 2 edges (the edge between A and B and the edge between C and D), contradicting an assumption of the problem. So S' must be the only connected component of G, which means that $G = K_{d+1}$.

The conclusion is that not only does there exist a person who is friends with everybody else, but that in fact *everybody* is friends with everybody else.

15.28 Let G be the graph with vertices corresponding to the squares on the checkerboard and edges corresponding to all possible knight moves. Then a knight can travel around the checkerboard, making every possible move exactly once, if and only if the graph G has an Eulerian path. To see if G has an Eulerian path, we must count the number of vertices of odd degree. The vertex V shown at right has degree 3. Furthermore, by rotating and reflecting the checkerboard, we find that there are (at least) eight vertices of degree 3. Therefore, the graph does not have an Eulerian path.

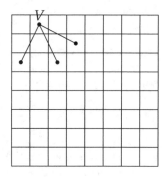

Challenge Problems

15.29 Consider the ham radio club as a graph, where each vertex corresponds to a member, and a pair of vertices is connected by an edge if the corresponding members are friends. Then the degree of every vertex is between 52 and 77 inclusive, so there are 26 different possible degrees. To show that there are four members with the same number of friends, we must show that there are four vertices with the same degree.

Suppose that there are at most three vertices of each possible degree. Since $3 \cdot 26 = 78$, each degree from 52 to 77 inclusive must occur exactly three times. There are 13 odd numbers from 52 to 77 inclusive, which means the number of vertices of odd degree is $3 \cdot 13 = 39$, which is an odd number. However, the number of vertices of odd degree must be even, giving a contradiction. Therefore, there are four vertices with the same degree.

15.30 Define a *conflict* to be a pair of enemies within the same group. There are only a finite number of ways to split the people into two groups, so consider the split that minimizes the total number of conflicts. We claim that in this minimal split, each person has at most one enemy in his or her group.

For the sake of contradiction, suppose that some person has at least two enemies in his group. Let the two groups be S and T, and let A be a person with at least two enemies in his group. Without loss of generality, assume that A is in group S. Now suppose that A is moved to group T. There are a number of cases to consider. If A only has two enemies, then they are both in S, so the total number of conflicts decreases by 2. Otherwise, A has three enemies. If A's third enemy is also in S, then the total number of conflicts decreases by 3. Otherwise, A's third enemy is in T, and the total number of conflicts decreases by 1.

In every case, the total number of conflicts must decrease. However, this contradicts the fact that we initially chose the split with the smallest number of conflicts. Therefore, in this particular split, each person has at most one enemy in his or her group.

15.31 We construct a graph G, where each vertex corresponds to a citizen, and we draw an edge between two vertices if the two corresponding citizens *do not* know each other. The condition of the problem states that any subset of n vertices in G must have fewer than n edges. In particular, this means that G has no cycles, because a cycle of length n would give a subset of n vertices with at least n edges.

Since G has no cycles, in particular it has no odd cycles, so it is bipartite. Thus we can partition the vertices of G into two sets A and B, so that every edge in G is between a vertex in A and a vertex in B. This means that if there are two citizens that do not know each other, then one is in A and one is in B. Hence, everyone in A knows everyone else in A, and everyone in B knows everyone else in B, as desired.

15.32 Let b be the boy who danced with the most number of girls. Since no boy dances with every girl, there is a girl, say g', that b did not dance with. Since every girl danced with at least one boy, there is a boy, say b', that g'

danced with.

There must be at least one girl, say g, that b danced with but that b' did not dance with (otherwise, b' would have danced with more girls than b). Then the boys b and b' and girls g and g' satisfy the given conditions.

15.33 Let $v_1, v_2, \ldots, v_n$ be an arbitrary ordering of the vertices, and set $v_{n+1} = v_1$. We say that there is a *gap* between consecutive vertices v_i and v_{i+1} if there is no edge connecting them. Consider the ordering that has the smallest number of gaps. (Since there are only a finite number of orderings, one of them has to have the smallest.) We claim that the number of gaps is 0.

For the sake of contradiction, suppose that there is a gap. Without loss of generality, assume that this gap is at the end, between v_n and $v_{n+1} = v_1$, so there is no edge between v_1 and v_n. We will show that it is possible to rearrange the vertices to make this gap disappear. In particular, we are looking for a vertex v_i with $2 \leq i \leq n - 2$ such that v_i is connected to v_n and v_{i+1} is connected to v_1. This will allow us to reorder the vertices as:

$$v_1, v_2, \ldots, v_{i-1}, v_i, v_n, v_{n-1}, v_{n-2}, \ldots, v_{i+1}, v_1.$$

In doing so, we break up the consecutive pairs (v_i, v_{i+1}) and (v_n, v_1), and form the consecutive pairs (v_i, v_n) and (v_{i+1}, v_1). We know that there is no edge connecting v_n and v_1, and we will have an edge between v_i and v_n and an edge between v_1 and v_{i+1}. Hence, by reordering the vertices, we will have reduced the number of gaps by at least one.

So it remains to find i with $2 \leq i \leq n - 2$ such that v_i is connected to v_n and v_{i+1} is connected to v_1. Define the sets

$$S = \{2 \leq i \leq n - 2 \mid v_i \text{ is connected to } v_n\},$$
$$T = \{2 \leq i \leq n - 2 \mid v_{i+1} \text{ is connected to } v_1\}.$$

Since every vertex has degree at least $n/2$, we see that $\#S \geq \frac{n}{2} - 1$ and $\#T \geq \frac{n}{2} - 1$. But $S \cup T \subseteq \{2, 3, \ldots, n - 2\}$, hence $\#(S \cup T) \leq n - 3$. Thus,

$$\#(S \cap T) = \#S + \#T - \#(S \cup T) \geq \left(\frac{n}{2} - 1\right) + \left(\frac{n}{2} - 1\right) - (n - 3) = 1,$$

so there must be some i in both S and T. This gives us the vertices v_i and v_{i+1} that we need to rearrange the sequence as described above to reduce the number of gaps. But we chose the ordering with the smallest number of gaps, which gives us our contradiction.

Hence, there is an ordering of the vertices that has no gaps, which produces a Hamiltonian cycle.

15.34 Each domino can be considered as an edge of the graph at right. For example, the 3-4 domino is the edge connecting vertices 3 and 4, and the double-six domino is the loop connecting vertex 6 to itself. Furthermore, two dominoes can be adjacent if and only if their corresponding edges share a vertex. Hence, an arrangement of the 28 dominoes in a circle corresponds to an Eulerian cycle in this graph.

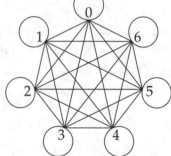

Each vertex in the graph has even degree, namely 8. Therefore, there is an Eulerian cycle, which means that it is possible to arrange the 28 dominoes in a circle such that neighboring dominoes have the same number of dots.

15.35 First, we rephrase the problem in graph theoretic terms. Consider the complete graph K_n, where each edge is colored either red or blue. We wish to show that for each vertex V, there is a color (either red or blue) such that every other vertex can be reached from V by traveling along at most 2 edges of that color. We prove this result by using induction on n.

The result is trivial for the base case $n = 2$, so assume that the result is true for some positive integer $n = t \geq 2$. Consider a graph K_{t+1}, where each edge is colored red or blue.

Let V be one of the $t + 1$ vertices. Then choose a vertex W other than V, and consider the complete graph on the t vertices other than W, including V. By the inductive hypothesis, there is a color (either red or blue) such that every vertex other than V and W can be reached from V by traveling along at most 2 edges of that color. Without loss of generality, let this color be blue. If the edge between V and W is also blue, then we are done, so assume that the edge between V and W is red.

Let S be the set of vertices that are connected to V by a blue edge. If any edge connecting W to a vertex in S is blue, then again we are done, since we then have a blue path of length 2 from V to W via the vertex in S. So assume that every edge connecting W to a vertex in S is red.

But now every vertex in the graph can be reached from V by a red path of length at most 2: W and all the other vertices not in S are connected directly to V by a red edge, and all of the vertices in S can be reached by a red path of length 2 from V, via W.

Therefore, V has the desired property. Since the vertex V was chosen arbitrarily, every vertex in the graph has the desired property. Therefore, the result is true for $n = t + 1$, and by induction, the result is true for all positive integers n.

CHAPTER **16**

_____Challenge Problems

Challenge Problems

16.1 The plane with 3 engines crashes if 2 or 3 engines fail, and the probability of this occurring is

$$\binom{3}{2}p^2(1-p) + \binom{3}{3}p^3 = 3p^2 - 2p^3.$$

The plane with 5 engines crashes if 3, 4, or 5 engines fail, and the probability of this occurring is

$$\binom{5}{3}p^3(1-p)^2 + \binom{5}{4}p^4(1-p) + \binom{5}{5}p^5 = 10p^3 - 15p^4 + 6p^5.$$

So the two probabilities are equal if and only if

$$3p^2 - 2p^3 = 10p^3 - 15p^4 + 6p^5$$
$$\Leftrightarrow \quad 6p^5 - 15p^4 + 12p^3 - 3p^2 = 0$$
$$\Leftrightarrow \quad 3p^2(p-1)^2(2p-1) = 0.$$

Hence, the two probabilities are equal if and only if $p = \boxed{0, 1, \text{ or } 1/2}$.

See if you can think of an intuitive reason why this answer should be true. In particular, if we had an airplane with 2007 engines, it would crash with the same frequency as a plane with 3 engines if and only if $p = 0, 1$, or $1/2$. Why?

16.2 Since $2004/6 = 334$, the values of n than can produce a roll of 2004 are $334 \leq n \leq 2004$. There is a 1-1 correspondence between rolls that sum to 2004 and rolls that sum to $7n - 2004$, given by replacing each individual die roll of r with $7 - r$. Therefore, the possible values of X are the elements of the set

$$\{7n - 2004 \mid 334 \leq n \leq 2004\} = \{334 + 7k \mid 0 \leq k \leq 1670\}.$$

16.3 Let the first box contain b_1 and w_1 black and white marbles, respectively, and let the second box contain b_2 and w_2 black and white marbles, respectively. Let $s_1 = b_1 + w_1$ and $s_2 = b_2 + w_2$. Then $b_1 + w_1 + b_2 + w_2 = s_1 + s_2 = 25$, and the probability that both randomly chosen marbles are black is

$$\frac{b_1}{b_1 + w_1} \cdot \frac{b_2}{b_2 + w_2} = \frac{27}{50} \quad \Rightarrow \quad 50b_1b_2 = 27(b_1 + w_1)(b_2 + w_2) = 27s_1s_2.$$

Without loss of generality, assume that $s_1 < s_2$. We see that 50 must divide $27s_1s_2$. Since 27 is relatively prime to 50, we have that 50 must divide s_1s_2. In particular, one of s_1 and s_2 must be divisible by 5. Since $s_1 + s_2 = 25$, either $(s_1, s_2) = (5, 20)$ or $(s_1, s_2) = (10, 15)$.

Case 1. $s_1 = 5$ and $s_2 = 20$.

In this case, $50b_1b_2 = 27 \cdot 5 \cdot 20$, so $b_1b_2 = 54$. Since $b_1 \leq s_1 = 5$, we can test every value from 1 to 5 for b_1, and find that the only solution is $b_1 = 3$ and $b_2 = 18$. Then $w_1 = s_1 - b_1 = 2$, and $w_2 = s_2 - b_2 = 2$, so the probability of drawing two white marbles is

$$\frac{w_1}{s_1} \cdot \frac{w_2}{s_2} = \frac{2}{5} \cdot \frac{2}{20} = \frac{1}{25}.$$

Case 2. $s_1 = 10$ and $s_2 = 15$.

In this case, $50b_1b_2 = 27 \cdot 10 \cdot 15$, so $b_1b_2 = 81$. Since $b_1 \leq s_1 = 10$ and $b_2 \leq s_2 = 15$, the only solution is $b_1 = b_2 = 9$. Then $w_1 = s_1 - b_1 = 1$, and $w_2 = s_2 - b_2 = 6$, so the probability of drawing two white marbles is

$$\frac{w_1}{s_1} \cdot \frac{w_2}{s_2} = \frac{1}{10} \cdot \frac{6}{15} = \frac{1}{25}.$$

In either case, the probability of drawing two white marbles is $\boxed{1/25}$.

16.4 $\boxed{\text{Yes}}$. Suppose that we want the dice to be equally likely to sum to 1, 2, 3, ..., 12. Then each sum must be the outcome of $36/12 = 3$ possible rolls. This suggests letting one die have 3 faces with one number and 3 faces with another number, and having the other die have six different numbers, each of which sums with a number on the first die to give a different result.

Specifically, let the numbers on one die be 0, 0, 0, 1, 1, and 1, and let the numbers on the other die be 1, 3, 5, 7, 9, and 11. Then there are exactly three rolls that produce each sum of 1, 2, 3, ..., 12, so each sum is equally likely.

16.5 At any given moment, let N denote the number of cards in the suit with the maximum number of cards. We claim that if we follow the given instructions, then the number of suits that we guess correctly will be at least N.

For example, suppose that the suit with the maximum number of cards is spades, so for the next card, we guess spades. If the next card is not spades, then there are still N spades left in the deck. If the next card is spades, then we have correctly guessed the suit, and the quantity N may decrease by 1, or it may stay the same. (It will stay the same if there were N cards of another suit in the deck.) Hence, the quantity N decreases only if we correctly guess the suit. At the end, when there are no more cards, N is equal to 0. Hence, we must have correctly guessed the suit at least N times.

To finish off the problem, by the Pigeonhole Principle, in a deck of 52 cards, there must be 13 cards in some suit. Therefore, we guess correctly at least 13 times.

16.6 First, we make a table that shows the distribution of people in the first few minutes:

time (minutes)	Room 1	Room 2	Room 3	Room 4
0	1000	0	0	0
1	999	1	0	0
2	998	2	0	0
3	997	2	1	0
4	996	2	2	0
5	995	2	2	1
6	994	2	2	2

We see that after n minutes, there are $1000 - n$ people left in the first room. Furthermore, if n is odd, then there are people in the next $(n + 1)/2$ rooms, and if n is even, then there are people in the next $n/2$ rooms. (This is true as long as there are at least 2 people in the first room to feed the remaining rooms.)

So, after one hour (or 60 minutes), there are people in $1 + 60/2 = \boxed{31}$ different rooms.

16.7   Suppose that the board is composed of all points in the set

$$\{(a, b, c) \mid 0 \le a, b, c \le 3\}.$$

Winning sets come in 3 types:

Case 1 4 points on a line perpendicular to one of the coordinate planes.

These are sets of the form $\{(a, b, 0), (a, b, 1), (a, b, 2), (a, b, 3)\}$ for some fixed $0 \le a, b \le 3$, which are on segments perpendicular to the xy-plane, and the similar sets of segments perpendicular to the xz-plane and the yz-plane. Since there are $4 \times 4 = 16$ choices for a and b, there are 16 such winning sets forming segments perpendicular to the xy-plane, and the same number for each of the other two planes, giving 48 total winning sets in this case.

Case 2 4 points on a line parallel to a coordinate plane, not included in Case 1.

These are segments that form a diagonal of a plane in which we fix one of the coordinates. For example, the set $\{(2, 3, 0), (2, 2, 1), (2, 1, 2), (2, 0, 3)\}$ is a diagonal in the $x = 2$ plane. There are 3 choices for which coordinate to fix, then 4 choices for the value at which the chosen coordinate is fixed, then 2 choices for a diagonal. This gives $3 \times 4 \times 2 = 24$ total winning sets in this case.

Case 3 4 points on a line not parallel to any coordinate plane.

These are the "space diagonals" of the cube. There are 4 of them, one for each pair of opposite corners.

Thus, there are $48 + 24 + 4 = \boxed{76}$ winning sets.

There is a very clever way to arrive at this solution via a 1-1 correspondence. Imagine that our $4 \times 4 \times 4$ cube sits inside a larger $6 \times 6 \times 6$ cube. Then every winning line on the $4 \times 4 \times 4$ can be extended by 1 unit in each direction so that it intersects the $6 \times 6 \times 6$ cube. This gives a 1-1 correspondence:

$$\{\text{Winning lines on the } 4 \times 4 \times 4 \text{ cube}\} \quad \leftrightarrow \quad \{\text{Pairs of points on the outside of the } 6 \times 6 \times 6 \text{ cube}\}.$$

Thus, the number of winning lines is equal to the half of the number of points on the outside of the $6 \times 6 \times 6$ cube, which is $\frac{6^3 - 4^3}{2} = 76$.

16.8   The generating function for Alice's sum is $(x + x^2 + x^3 + x^4)^2$. Let the numbers in Betty's first bag be $n_1, n_2, n_3,$ and n_4, and let the numbers in her second bag be $m_1, m_2, m_3,$ and m_4. Then the generating function for Betty's sum is $(x^{n_1} + x^{n_2} + x^{n_3} + x^{n_4})(x^{m_1} + x^{m_2} + x^{m_3} + x^{m_4})$. So for the two distributions to be equal, we want

$$\begin{aligned}
(x^{n_1} + x^{n_2} + x^{n_3} + x^{n_4})(x^{m_1} + x^{m_2} + x^{m_3} + x^{m_4}) &= (x + x^2 + x^3 + x^4)^2 \\
&= x^2(1 + x + x^2 + x^3)^2 \\
&= x^2(1 + x)^2(1 + x^2)^2.
\end{aligned}$$

Let $f(x) = x^{n_1} + x^{n_2} + x^{n_3} + x^{n_4}$ and $g(x) = x^{m_1} + x^{m_2} + x^{m_3} + x^{m_4}$. Since the n_i and m_i are positive integers, both $f(x)$ and $g(x)$ must be divisible by x. Also, taking $x = 1$, we get $f(1) = 1^{n_1} + 1^{n_2} + 1^{n_3} + 1^{n_4} = 4$ and $g(1) = 1^{m_1} + 1^{m_2} + 1^{m_3} + 1^{m_4} = 4$. Taking $x = 1$ in the factors above, we get

$$1 + x = 2,$$
$$1 + x^2 = 2.$$

So, to satisfy $f(1) = g(1) = 4$, either both factors of $1 + x$ go to one polynomial and both factors of $1 + x^2$ go to the other polynomial, or each gets one factor of $1 + x$ and $1 + x^2$. In the former case, the polynomials are

$$x(1 + x)^2 = x(1 + 2x + x^2) = x + 2x^2 + x^3 = x + x^2 + x^2 + x^3, \quad \text{and}$$
$$x(1 + x^2)^2 = x(1 + 2x^2 + x^4) = x + 2x^3 + x^5 = x + x^3 + x^3 + x^5,$$

and in the latter case, both polynomials are $x(1 + x)(1 + x^2) = x + x^2 + x^3 + x^4$. This second case recovers Alice's numbers, so Betty's numbers are 1, 2, 2, and 3 in one bag, and 1, 3, 3, and 5 in the other bag.

16.9 For a positive integer n, let S_n denote the set of ordered sums of 1s and 2s that sum to n. We list S_n and $f(n)$ for the first few values of n.

n	S_n	$f(n)$
1	1	1
2	$2, 1 + 1$	2
3	$2 + 1, 1 + 2, 1 + 1 + 1$	3
4	$2 + 2, 2 + 1 + 1, 1 + 2 + 1, 1 + 1 + 2, 1 + 1 + 1 + 1$	5

The sums in S_n can be divided into two categories: those that end with 1, and those that end with 2. The sums in S_n that end with 1 can be generated by adding a 1 to the sums in S_{n-1}. The sums in S_n that end with 2 can be generated by adding a 2 to the sums in S_{n-2}. Thus, $f(n) = f(n - 1) + f(n - 2)$. This is the same as the Fibonacci relation. Furthermore, $f(1) = 1 = F_2$ and $f(2) = 2 = F_3$, so it follows that $f(n) = F_{n+1}$ for all $n \geq 1$.

Now, let T_n denote the set of ordered sums of integers greater than 1 that sum to n. We list T_n and $g(n)$ for the first few values of n.

n	T_n	$g(n)$
1	$\emptyset$	0
2	2	1
3	3	1
4	$4, 2 + 2$	2
5	$5, 3 + 2, 2 + 3$	3
6	$6, 4 + 2, 3 + 3, 2 + 4, 2 + 2 + 2$	5

Each sum in T_n can be obtained by adding a number (that is at least 2) to a sum that appears earlier in the table. For example, the sums $4 + 2$ and $2 + 2 + 2$ in T_6 can be obtained by adding 2 to the sums 4 and $2 + 2$ in T_4. The exception is the sum n itself. Hence,

$$g(n) = g(n - 2) + g(n - 3) + \cdots + g(3) + g(2) + 1.$$

Shifting the index by 1, we get

$$\begin{aligned} g(n + 1) &= g(n - 1) + g(n - 2) + \cdots + g(3) + g(2) + 1 \\ &= g(n - 1) + [g(n - 2) + \cdots + g(3) + g(2) + 1] \\ &= g(n - 1) + g(n). \end{aligned}$$

This is again the Fibonacci relation. Furthermore, $g(2) = 1 = F_1$ and $g(3) = 1 = F_2$, so it follows that $g(n) = F_{n-1}$ for all $n \geq 1$.

Therefore, $f(k) = g(k + 2) = F_{k+1}$ for all positive integers k.

16.10 More generally, let p be the probability of getting heads, and let q be the probability of getting tails, so in this case, $p = 2/3$ and $q = 1/3$. Then the probability of getting k heads out of 50 tosses is $\binom{50}{50-k}p^k q^{50-k}$, so the probability of getting an even number of heads is

$$\binom{50}{0}p^{50} + \binom{50}{2}p^{48}q^2 + \binom{50}{4}p^{46}q^4 + \cdots + \binom{50}{50}q^{50}.$$

By the Binomial theorem,

$$\binom{50}{0}p^{50} + \binom{50}{1}p^{49}q + \binom{50}{2}p^{48}q^2 + \cdots + \binom{50}{50}q^{50} = (p+q)^{50},$$

$$\binom{50}{0}p^{50} - \binom{50}{1}p^{49}q + \binom{50}{2}p^{48}q^2 - \cdots + \binom{50}{50}q^{50} = (p-q)^{50}.$$

Adding and dividing by 2, we get

$$\binom{50}{0}p^{50} + \binom{50}{2}p^{48}q^2 + \binom{50}{4}p^{46}q^4 + \cdots + \binom{50}{50}q^{50} = \frac{(p+q)^{50} + (p-q)^{50}}{2}.$$

Therefore, in our problem, the probability of getting an even number of heads is

$$\frac{(2/3 + 1/3)^{50} + (2/3 - 1/3)^{50}}{2} = \boxed{\frac{1}{2}\left(1 + \frac{1}{3^{50}}\right)}.$$

16.11 We can use casework based on the number of elements in the set.

If the set has only 1 element, then we can choose any of the 15 elements (since none are less than 1). Thus there are $\binom{15}{1}$ possible sets.

If the set has 2 elements, then we must choose 2 non-consecutive elements from $\{2, 3, \ldots, 15\}$. We can think of this as a distribution problem, where we must distribute the 12 non-chosen elements into 3 groups: those less than the first chosen element, those between the two elements, and those greater than the last chosen element. The middle group must be positive, since the two chosen elements must be non-consecutive. Thus, the number of ways to choose the 2 elements is equal to the number of solutions to $a + b + c = 12$, where a, c are nonnegative integers and b is a positive integer. Solutions to this are equivalent to solutions to $a' + b + c' = 14$, where a', b, c' are all positive. This is the same as inserting 2 dividers into 13 slots, so there are $\binom{13}{2}$ solutions, and hence $\binom{13}{2}$ such sets.

If the set has 3 elements, then we must choose 3 non-consecutive elements from $\{3, 4, \ldots, 15\}$. Again, we can think of this as a distribution problem, distributing the 10 non-chosen elements into 4 groups. This corresponds to solutions to $a + b + c + d = 10$, where b, c are positive and a, d are nonnegative; this in turn corresponds to solutions to $a' + b + c + d' = 12$, where all the variable are positive. This equation has $\binom{11}{3}$ solutions.

Similarly, the number of sets with 4 elements is $\binom{9}{4}$, and the number of sets with 5 elements is $\binom{7}{5}$, using the same reasoning. There can be no sets with 6 or more elements: it is impossible to select 6 non-consecutive elements from $\{7, 8, \ldots, 15\}$.

Thus, the total number of sets is

$$\binom{15}{1} + \binom{13}{2} + \binom{11}{3} + \binom{9}{4} + \binom{7}{5} = 15 + 78 + 165 + 126 + 21 = \boxed{405}.$$

More generally, the number of subsets of $\{1, 2, \ldots, n\}$ with the desired property is

$$\binom{n}{1} + \binom{n-2}{2} + \binom{n-4}{3} + \cdots.$$

16.12 Let p_n be the probability that in a tournament of Pushover with 2^{n+1} competitors, players 1 and 2^n face each other in the last round.

Before computing p_n, we compute another probability: Let q_n be the probability that in a tournament of Pushover with 2^{n+1} competitors, players 1 and $2^n + 1$ face each other in the last round. Note that when the 2^{n+1} competitors stand in a circle, players 1 and $2^n + 1$ are diametrically opposite.

If $n = 0$, then $2^n + 1 = 2$, and players 1 and 2 are the only players in the tournament, so $q_0 = 1$. Now consider a tournament of Pushover with 2^{n+1} competitors, where $n \geq 1$. Take players 1 and $2^n + 1$, and call them players A and B instead. Then for players A and B to face each other in the last round, each must win his respective game of Pushover, which occurs with probability $1/2 \cdot 1/2 = 1/4$. Furthermore, if both players A and B win their games, then no matter how the referee pairs off the players, players A and B will still be diametrically opposite, taking the place of players 1 and $2^{n-1} + 1$ in a tournament with 2^n competitors. Therefore, $q_n = q_{n-1}/4$. Since $q_0 = 1$, we see that $q_n = 1/4^n$ for all $n \geq 0$.

Now we return to the original problem of computing p_n. To compute p_1, consider a tournament of Pushover with 4 competitors. If the referee pairs up players 1 and 2, then one of them must win and they cannot face each other in the final round. However, if the referee pairs up players 4 and 1, and players 2 and 3, and if both players 1 and 2 win, then they will face each other in the final round. Therefore, $p_1 = 1/2 \cdot 1/2 \cdot 1/2 = 1/8$.

Now consider a tournament of Pushover with 2^{n+1} competitors, where $n \geq 2$. This time, take player 1 and 2^n, and call them players A and B. As before, for players A and B to face each other in the last round, each must win his respective game of Pushover, which occurs with probability $1/2 \cdot 1/2 = 1/4$. If the referee pairs players 1 and 2 together, and so on, then players A and B will take the place of players 1 and 2^{n-1} in a tournament with 2^n competitors, reducing to the probability of p_{n-1}. But if the referee pairs players 2^{n+1} and 1 together, and so on, then players A and B will be diametrically opposite, reducing to the probability of q_{n-1}. Hence,

$$p_n = \frac{1}{2} \cdot \frac{1}{4} p_{n-1} + \frac{1}{2} \cdot \frac{1}{4} q_{n-1} = \frac{1}{8} p_{n-1} + \frac{1}{2 \cdot 4^n}.$$

We can solve this recursion, or we may test the first few values:

$$p_1 = \frac{1}{8},$$
$$p_2 = \frac{1}{8} p_1 + \frac{1}{2 \cdot 4^2} = \frac{3}{64} = \frac{2^2 - 1}{8^2},$$
$$p_3 = \frac{1}{8} p_2 + \frac{1}{2 \cdot 4^3} = \frac{7}{512} = \frac{2^3 - 1}{8^3},$$
$$p_4 = \frac{1}{8} p_3 + \frac{1}{2 \cdot 4^4} = \frac{15}{4096} = \frac{2^4 - 1}{8^4}.$$

It looks like $p_n = (2^n - 1)/8^n$, which we prove by induction. This formula is correct in the base case $n = 1$, so assume that it is true for some positive integer $n = k$, so

$$p_k = \frac{2^k - 1}{8^k}.$$

Then

$$p_{k+1} = \frac{1}{8} p_k + \frac{1}{2 \cdot 4^{k+1}} = \frac{1}{8} \cdot \frac{2^k - 1}{8^k} + \frac{1}{8 \cdot 4^k} = \frac{2^k - 1}{8^{k+1}} + \frac{2^k}{8^{k+1}} = \frac{2^{k+1} - 1}{8^{k+1}}.$$

Hence, the formula is correct for $n = k + 1$, and by induction, it is correct for all positive integers n. Therefore, the desired probability is

$$\boxed{p_n = \frac{2^n - 1}{8^n}}.$$

16.13 Let the pirates, in order from shortest to tallest, be P_1, P_2, P_3, P_4, and P_5.

Consider the situation where there are only two pirates left, P_4 and P_5. Then pirate P_4 can distribute the coins in any way he wants to, since his vote constitutes at least half the votes, so in this situation, pirate P_4 would give himself all 500 gold coins and give pirate P_5 nothing.

Next, consider the situation where there are only three pirates left, P_3, P_4 and P_5. Pirate P_3 must secure at least two votes, including his own vote. Pirate P_3 can secure pirate P_5's vote by giving him only one gold coin, because if P_5 does not vote for P_3's plan, then P_3 walks the plank, and it will be down to pirates P_4 and P_5, in which case P_5 gets nothing. (And P_3 could only secure P_4's vote by giving him all the gold coins.) Therefore, P_3's best plan is to give 499 coins to himself and one coin to P_5.

Next, consider the situation where there are only four pirates left, P_2, P_3, P_4 and P_5. Pirate P_2 must secure at least two votes, including his own vote. Pirate P_2 can secure pirate P_4's vote by giving him only one gold coin, because if P_4 does not vote for P_2's plan, then P_2 walks the plank, and it will be down to pirates P_3, P_4 and P_5, in which case P_4 gets nothing. Therefore, P_2's best plan is to give 499 coins to himself and one coin to P_4.

Finally, consider the situation with all five pirates. Pirate P_1 must secure at least three votes, including his own vote. Pirate P_1 can secure pirate P_3's and P_5's vote by giving each only one gold coin, because if P_3 and P_5 do not vote for P_1's plan, then P_1 walks the plank, and it will be down to pirates P_2, P_3, P_4 and P_5, in which case P_3 and P_5 get nothing. Therefore, P_1's best plan is to give 498 coins to himself, one coin to P_3, and one coin to P_5.

Therefore, the shortest pirate P_1 should receive $\boxed{498}$ coins.

16.14 Since the first student knows how to solve at least one problem and can choose any problem he likes, the first student can successfully present a solution with probability 1. Let $1 \le k \le n - 1$. By the time the $(k + 1)^{\text{st}}$ student selects his problem, k problems have already been solved, so he has $n - k$ problems to choose from.

Suppose this student knows how to solve r problems. If $r \ge k + 1$, then at least one of the problems he knows how to solve has not been taken yet, so he can successfully present a solution with probability 1. If $r \le k$, then we compute the probability that he *cannot* successfully present a solution.

If he cannot successfully present a solution, then all r problems he knows how to solve must be a subset of the k problems that have already been taken, and this occurs in $\binom{k}{r}$ ways. The set of r problems the student knows how to solve can be chosen in $\binom{n}{r}$ ways, so the probability that he cannot successfully present a solution is $\binom{k}{r}/\binom{n}{r}$. Therefore, the probability that he can successfully present a solution is $1 - \binom{k}{r}/\binom{n}{r}$.

The probability that r is equal to any of the values $1, 2, \ldots, n$ is $1/n$, so the probability that the $(k + 1)^{\text{st}}$ student can successfully present a solution is

$$\frac{1}{n}\sum_{r=1}^{k}\left(1 - \frac{\binom{k}{r}}{\binom{n}{r}}\right) + \frac{1}{n}\sum_{r=k+1}^{n}1 = \frac{k}{n} - \frac{1}{n}\sum_{r=1}^{k}\frac{\binom{k}{r}}{\binom{n}{r}} + \frac{n-k}{n} = 1 - \frac{1}{n}\sum_{r=1}^{k}\frac{\binom{k}{r}}{\binom{n}{r}}.$$

To make this expression easier to sum, we modify it as follows:

$$\frac{\binom{k}{r}}{\binom{n}{r}} = \frac{\frac{k!}{r!(k-r)!}}{\frac{n!}{r!(n-r)!}} = \frac{k!(n-r)!}{n!(k-r)!}$$

$$= \frac{k!}{n!}\cdot\frac{(n-r)!}{(k-r)!}\cdot\frac{(n-k)!}{(n-k)!}$$

$$= \frac{k!(n-k)!}{n!}\cdot\frac{(n-r)!}{(n-k)!(k-r)!}$$

$$= \frac{\binom{n-r}{n-k}}{\binom{n}{k}}.$$

Hence,

$$1 - \frac{1}{n}\sum_{r=1}^{k}\frac{\binom{k}{r}}{\binom{n}{r}} = 1 - \frac{1}{n}\sum_{r=1}^{k}\frac{\binom{n-r}{n-k}}{\binom{n}{k}} = 1 - \frac{1}{n\binom{n}{k}}\sum_{r=1}^{k}\binom{n-r}{n-k}.$$

By the Hockey Stick identity,

$$\sum_{r=1}^{k}\binom{n-r}{n-k} = \binom{n}{n-k+1},$$

so

$$1 - \frac{1}{n\binom{n}{k}}\sum_{r=1}^{k}\binom{n-r}{n-k} = 1 - \frac{\binom{n}{n-k+1}}{n\binom{n}{k}}$$

$$= 1 - \frac{\frac{n!}{(n-k+1)!(k-1)!}}{n\cdot\frac{n!}{k!(n-k)!}}$$

$$= 1 - \frac{k!(n-k)!}{n(k-1)!(n-k+1)!}$$

$$= 1 - \frac{k}{n(n-k+1)}$$

$$= \frac{n(n-k+1)-k}{n(n-k+1)}$$

$$= \frac{n^2 - kn + n - k}{n(n-k+1)}$$

$$= \frac{n(n-k)+(n-k)}{n(n-k+1)}$$

$$= \frac{(n+1)(n-k)}{n(n-k+1)}.$$

Therefore, the probability that every student can successfully present a solution is

$$\prod_{k=1}^{n-1}\frac{(n+1)(n-k)}{n(n-k+1)} = \frac{(n+1)^{n-1}}{n^{n-1}}\prod_{k=1}^{n-1}\frac{n-k}{n-k+1}$$

$$= \frac{(n+1)^{n-1}}{n^{n-1}}\cdot\frac{n-1}{n}\cdot\frac{n-2}{n-1}\cdots\frac{2}{3}\cdot\frac{1}{2}$$

$$= \boxed{\frac{(n+1)^{n-1}}{n^n}}.$$

16.15 Let n be the number of players. Let us call a player *weak* if he is one of the ten lowest scoring players, and *strong* otherwise, so there are $n - 10$ strong players.

Collectively, there are $\binom{10}{2} = 45$ points up for grabs over all games played between weak players. Since half of the points for each player came from games against weak players, it means that among all games played between a weak player and a strong player, an additional 45 points were won collectively by weak players.

However, there are a total of $10(n - 10)$ points up for grabs over all games played between a weak player and a strong player, so $10(n - 10) - 45$ points were won collectively among these games by strong players. Collectively, there are $\binom{n-10}{2} = \dfrac{(n-10)(n-11)}{2}$ points up for grabs over all games played between strong players. Hence,

$$10(n-10) - 45 = \frac{(n-10)(n-11)}{2}$$
$$\Leftrightarrow \qquad 10n - 145 = \frac{n^2 - 21n + 110}{2}$$
$$\Leftrightarrow \qquad 20n - 290 = n^2 - 21n + 110$$
$$\Leftrightarrow \qquad n^2 - 41n + 400 = 0$$
$$\Leftrightarrow \qquad (n-16)(n-25) = 0,$$

so n must be 16 or 25.

However, a tournament with 16 people is impossible. If there were such a tournament, then there would be 10 weak players and 6 strong players. Collectively, the weak players win 90 points, so some weak player must win at least $90/10 = 9$ points. Hence, every strong player must win at least 9 points, so collectively the strong players win at least $6 \cdot 9 = 54$ points. However, according to our reasoning above, they collectively score only $2 \cdot \binom{6}{2} = 30$ points, which is a contradiction.

Therefore, there are $\boxed{25}$ players in the tournament. (We leave it as an exercise to show that such a tournament is possible.)

16.16 If you choose n balls, then the probability that each ball lands in a different slot is

$$p_n = 1 \cdot \frac{59}{60} \cdot \frac{58}{60} \cdots \frac{61-n}{60},$$

and your expected winnings, in dollars, is np_n.

To maximize this expression, we compare np_n and $(n+1)p_{n+1}$:

$$np_n < (n+1)p_{n+1}$$
$$\Leftrightarrow \qquad \frac{n}{n+1} < \frac{p_{n+1}}{p_n}$$
$$\Leftrightarrow \qquad \frac{n}{n+1} < \frac{1 \cdot \frac{59}{60} \cdot \frac{58}{60} \cdots \frac{61-n}{60} \cdot \frac{60-n}{60}}{1 \cdot \frac{59}{60} \cdot \frac{58}{60} \cdots \frac{61-n}{60}}$$
$$\Leftrightarrow \qquad \frac{n}{n+1} < \frac{60-n}{60}$$
$$\Leftrightarrow \qquad 60n < 60 + 59n - n^2$$
$$\Leftrightarrow \qquad n^2 + n < 60.$$

This inequality is satisfied for $n \leq 7$, but not $n \geq 8$. In other words, np_n is increasing from $n = 1$ to 8, but decreasing from 8 onwards, so the expected winnings are maximized for $\boxed{8}$ balls.

16.17 To each student, we assign a 10-tuple of 0's and 1's, where the ith element is 1 if the student is a member of the ith club, and 0 otherwise. For example, if a student was a member of clubs 1, 2, and 10, then the corresponding 10-tuple would be $(1, 1, 0, 0, 0, 0, 0, 0, 0, 1)$. According to the first condition, no two 10-tuples are alike.

To get started on the problem, let's consider three example 10-tuples:

$$x = (1, 1, 0, 1, 1, 0, 1, 0, 0, 0),$$
$$y = (0, 1, 1, 1, 0, 1, 1, 1, 0, 1),$$
$$z = (1, 0, 1, 0, 1, 1, 0, 1, 0, 1).$$

Note that these three 10-tuples violate the second condition, because for every $1 \le i \le 10$, the number of 1's that appear in the ith place among x, y, and z is either 0 or 2. (To satisfy the second condition, the number of 1's that appear in the ith place must be 1 or 3 for some i.)

Another way to express this is to say that $x + y + z = (0, 0, \ldots, 0)$, where addition is element-wise, and reduced modulo 2. Note that this is equivalent to saying that $x = y + z$, $y = x + z$, and $z = x + y$. We use this observation as follows.

First, there are a total of $2^{10} = 1024$ possible 10-tuples. Choose a student who belongs to some club, and let his 10-tuple be v, so v is not all 0's. (If no such student exists, then the college can have at most 1 student.) Then the set of all possible 10-tuples can be divided into pairs $\{x, y\}$, where $x + y = v$. (Note that this relation between x and y is symmetric.) One of these pairs is going to be $\{v, v_0\}$, where v_0 is the 10-tuple containing all 0's (which corresponds to the student who does not belong to any clubs), so the remaining $1024 - 2 = 1022$ 10-tuples can be divided into $1022/2 = 511$ pairs as follows:

$$\{v_1, v_1'\}, \quad \{v_2, v_2'\}, \quad \ldots, \quad \{v_{511}, v_{511}'\}.$$

For each i, at most one of v_i and v_i' can appear among the 10-tuples of the students, because $v_i + v_i' = v$, so the presence of both v_i and v_i' would violate the second condition. Therefore, counting v and v_0, the number of students at the college can be at most $2 + 511 = 513$. (We can include both v and v_0, because in the condition $x + y = v$, we assume that x, y, and v are distinct.)

We can construct an admissible set of 513 10-tuples, by taking v_0 and all the 10-tuples where the first element is 1. This gives a total of $1 + 2^9 = 513$ 10-tuples. Clearly, the first condition is satisfied. To check that the second condition is satisfied, we must verify that the equation $x + y + z = (0, 0, \ldots, 0)$ never holds, where x, y, and z are distinct. If one of x, y, and z is v_0, then the other two must be equal, so we may dismiss this case. Hence, the first element in each of x, y, and z is 1, which means the first element in $x + y + z$ is 1, so in particular, $x + y + z$ cannot be equal to $(0, 0, \ldots, 0)$, so the second condition is satisfied.

Therefore, the maximum number of students at the college is $\boxed{513}$.

16.18 The coefficients $\binom{n}{0}$, $\binom{n+1}{1}$, etc. in the sum should remind you of the Hockey Stick identity. So let's look for a block-walking argument on Pascal's Triangle similar to the block-walking proof of the Hockey Stick identity.

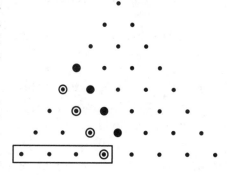

Consider the example where $n = 3$. At right is a picture of Pascal's Triangle with the points corresponding to $\binom{3}{0}$, $\binom{4}{1}$, $\binom{5}{2}$, and $\binom{6}{3}$ shown as large dark circles. Note that every path to the left side of Row 7 (boxed at right) must pass through one of the dark points, and also must pass through one of the circled points corresponding to $\binom{4}{0}$, $\binom{5}{1}$, $\binom{6}{2}$, and $\binom{7}{3}$.

We count paths to the left half of Row 7 based on which of the circled points gets passed through *first*. For example, a path to Row 7 that passes through the $\binom{4}{0}$ point before any of the other circled points must pass through $\binom{3}{0}$, take a step down and to the left, then take any 3 steps down to Row 7. Thus, there are $2^3\binom{3}{0}$ of these paths. Similarly, a path to Row 7 that passes through $\binom{5}{1}$ before any of the other circled points must pass through $\binom{4}{1}$, take a step down and to the left, and then take any 2 steps down to Row 7, so there are $2^2\binom{4}{1}$ of these paths. Similarly, there are $2^1\binom{5}{2}$ paths that have the $\binom{6}{2}$ point as the first circled point, and $2^0\binom{6}{3}$ paths that have the $\binom{7}{3}$ point as the first circled point.

Adding these up, we see that there are a total of

$$2^3\binom{3}{0} + 2^2\binom{4}{1} + 2^1\binom{5}{2} + 2^0\binom{6}{3}$$

paths to the left side of Row 7. But we know that there are $2^7/2 = 2^6$ total paths to this half-row, therefore

$$2^3\binom{3}{0} + 2^2\binom{4}{1} + 2^1\binom{5}{2} + 2^0\binom{6}{3} = 2^6,$$

and dividing by 2^3 gives our identity

$$\sum_{k=0}^{3}\binom{3+k}{k}\left(\frac{1}{2}\right)^k = 2^3.$$

This argument generalizes to arbitrary n. We count the number of paths to the left half of Row $2n + 1$, based on which of the points $\binom{n+1}{0}, \binom{n+2}{1}, \ldots, \binom{2n+1}{n}$ the path passes through first. To first pass through $\binom{n+1+k}{k}$, the path must go through $\binom{n+k}{k}$, take a step down and to the left, and then take any $n - k$ steps down to Row $2n + 1$. Thus, there are $2^{n-k}\binom{n+k}{k}$ such paths, and summing all paths to the left half of Row $2n + 1$, we get

$$\sum_{k=0}^{n} 2^{n-k}\binom{n+k}{k} = 2^{2n}.$$

Dividing both sides by 2^n gives us our desired identity.

16.19 Number the coins 1 through 8 around the circle. For $1 \le i \le 8$, let c_i be the number of times that we flip coins i and $i+1$ (where coin #9 as the same coin #1, so that c_8 is the number of times that we flip the pair consisting of coins #8 and #1). Note that the c_i are all nonnegative integers and that $c_1 + c_2 + \cdots + c_8 = 6$.

First, we consider the case where all of the odd numbered coins end up tails. If we can count the number of sequences flips that lead to this case, then we can simply double our count to get the final answer.

Note that once the parity (odd or even) of one c_i is determined, then the parities of all the c_i are determined. For example, if c_1 is odd, then since coin #2 must end up heads, we must have c_2 odd as well. But then coin #3 must end up tails, so c_3 must be even, and so on. We see that we must have one of the following two cases:

Case 1 c_1, c_2, c_5, c_6 are odd and c_3, c_4, c_7, c_8 are even.

Case 2 c_1, c_2, c_5, c_6 are even and c_3, c_4, c_7, c_8 are odd.

It is clear that these two cases give the same number of solutions to $c_1 + \cdots + c_8 = 6$, so let's focus on case (1). Since c_1, c_2, c_5, c_6 are all positive, we only have two possibilities.

Case 1.1 One of c_1, c_2, c_5, c_6 is 3, the rest are 1, and $c_3 = c_4 = c_7 = c_8 = 0$.

There are 4 choices for which flip is done 3 times. Then, we can arrange the flips into a sequence in $6!/3! = 120$ ways (we divide by 3! since the same flip gets done 3 times). So there are $4 \times 120 = 480$ sequences in this case.

Case 1.2 $c_1 = c_2 = c_5 = c_6 = 1$, one of c_3, c_4, c_7, c_8 is 2, and the rest are 0.

The are 4 choices for which flip is done twice. Then, we can arrange the flips into a sequence in $6!/2! = 360$ ways (we divide by 2! since the same flip gets done twice). So there $4 \times 360 = 1440$ sequences in this case.

This gives a total of $480 + 1440 = 1920$ sequences of flips in case (1), and hence $2(1920) = 3840$ sequences of flips which leave the odd-numbered coins as tails. The same number of sequences of flips leave the even-numbered coins as tails, so the final answer is $2(3840) = \boxed{7680}$.

16.20 These sorts of problems—where every other card gets removed from a stack—are often easier to analyze for powers of 2. So instead of a stack of 2000 cards, we will first consider a stack of $2^{11} = 2048$ cards, hoping that this case is easier to analyze and that our analysis can be extended to the original 2000-card problem.

Let the labels on our 2048-card stack, from top to bottom, be $x_1, x_2, \ldots, x_{2048}$. After one pass through the stack, the cards lying on the table are $x_1, x_3, \ldots, x_{2047}$ (in other words, all the odd-indexed cards), and the cards remaining in the stack, from top to bottom, are $x_2, x_4, \ldots, x_{2048}$ (in other words, all the even-indexed cards).

After another pass through the stack, the cards $x_2, x_6, \ldots, x_{2046}$ are placed on the table, and the cards remaining in the stack, from top to bottom, are $x_4, x_8, \ldots, x_{2048}$. If we continue this process, we see that the last two cards placed on the table are x_{1024} and x_{2048}.

Now let's try to use our analysis of the 2048-card stack to solve the problem for the 2000-card stack. The first 48 cards of the 2048-card stack that get placed on the table are $x_1, x_3, \ldots, x_{95}$. After these 48 cards have been removed from the stack, the 2000 cards remaining in the stack, from top to bottom, are

$$x_{97}, \quad x_{98}, \quad x_{99}, \quad \ldots, \quad x_{2047}, \quad x_{2048}, \quad x_2, \quad x_4, \quad x_6, \quad \ldots, \quad x_{96}.$$

Suppose that we continue the given procedure with this stack of 2000 cards, and from these we obtain the cards $1, 2, 3, \ldots, 1999, 2000$, as described in the problem statement. Because we are just continuing the procedure started with the 2048-card stack, the next-to-last card placed to the right is x_{1024}. Thus, $x_{1024} = 1999$. The cards above this card in the stack of 2000 cards are $x_{97}, x_{98}, \ldots, x_{1023}$, and the number of these cards is $1023 - 97 + 1 = \boxed{927}$.

www.artofproblemsolving.com

The Art of Problem Solving (AoPS) is:

- # Books

  For over 28 years, the classic *Art of Problem Solving* books have been used by students as a resource for the American Mathematics Competitions and other national and local math events.

  > *Every school should have this in their math library.*
  > – Paul Zeitz, past coach of the U.S. International Mathematical Olympiad team

  The Art of Problem Solving Introduction and Intermediate texts, together with our *Prealgebra*, *Precalculus*, and *Calculus* texts, form a complete curriculum for outstanding math students in grades 6-12.

  > *The new book [Introduction to Counting & Probability] is great. I have started to use it in my classes on a regular basis. I can see the improvement in my kids over just a short period.*
  > – Jeff Boyd, 4-time MATHCOUNTS National Competition winning coach

- # Classes

  The Art of Problem Solving offers online classes on topics such as number theory, counting, geometry, algebra, and more at beginning, intermediate, and Olympiad levels.

  > *All the children were very engaged. It's the best use of technology I have ever seen.*
  > – Mary Fay-Zenk, coach of National Champion California MATHCOUNTS teams

- # Forum

  As of March 2022, the Art of Problem Solving Forum has over 860,000 members who have posted over 17,000,000 messages on our discussion board. Members can also participate in any of our free "Math Jams."

  > *I'd just like to thank the coordinators of this site for taking the time to set it up. . . I think this is a great site, and I bet just about anyone else here would say the same. . .*
  > – AoPS Community Member

- # Resources

  We have links to summer programs, book resources, problem sources, national and local competitions, scholarship listings, a math wiki, and a LaTeX tutorial.

  > *I'd like to commend you on your wonderful site. It's informative, welcoming, and supportive of the math community. I wish it had been around when I was growing up.*
  > – AoPS Community Member

- # . . . and more!

Membership is **FREE**! Come join the Art of Problem Solving community today!